VIIIA
		IIIA	IVA	VA	VIA	VIIA	2 **He** Helium 4.00
		5 **B** Boron 10.81	6 **C** Carbon 12.01	7 **N** Nitrogen 14.01	8 **O** Oxygen 16.00	9 **F** Fluorine 19.00	10 **Ne** Neon 20.18
IB	**IIB**	13 **Al** Aluminum 26.98	14 **Si** Silicon 28.09	15 **P** Phosphorus 30.97	16 **S** Sulfur 32.06	17 **Cl** Chlorine 35.45	18 **Ar** Argon 39.95
29 **Cu** Copper 63.55	30 **Zn** Zinc 65.38	31 **Ga** Gallium 69.72	32 **Ge** Germanium 72.59	33 **As** Arsenic 74.92	34 **Se** Selenium 78.96	35 **Br** Bromine 79.90	36 **Kr** Krypton 83.80
47 **Ag** Silver 107.87	48 **Cd** Cadmium 112.40	49 **In** Indium 114.82	50 **Sn** Tin 118.69	51 **Sb** Antimony 121.75	52 **Te** Tellurium 127.60	53 **I** Iodine 126.90	54 **Xe** Xenon 131.30
79 **Au** Gold 196.97	80 **Hg** Mercury 200.59	81 **Tl** Thallium 204.37	82 **Pb** Lead 207.2	83 **Bi** Bismuth 208.98	84 **Po** Polonium (210)	85 **At** Astatine (210)	86 **Rn** Radon (222)

64 **Gd** Gadolinium 157.25	65 **Tb** Terbium 158.93	66 **Dy** Dysprosium 162.50	67 **Ho** Holmium 164.93	68 **Er** Erbium 167.26	69 **Tm** Thulium 168.93	70 **Yb** Ytterbium 173.04	71 **Lu** Lutetium 174.97
96 **Cm** Curium (247)	97 **Bk** Berkelium (247)	98 **Cf** Californium (251)	99 **Es** Einsteinium (254)	100 **Fm** Fermium (257)	101 **Md** Mendelevium (258)	102 **No** Nobelium (255)	103 **Lr** Lawrencium (256)

FUNDAMENTALS OF
CHEMISTRY

EDWARD KOSTINER
University of Connecticut

JESSE R. REA
P. R. Mallory & Co. Inc.

HARCOURT BRACE JOVANOVICH, INC.
New York   San Diego   Chicago   San Francisco   Atlanta

ISBN: 0–15–529430–X

Library of Congress Catalog Card Number: 78–61298

Printed in the United States of America

Cover: "Helix and Crystal" by Ben Shahn, collection of the Fine Arts Gallery, San Diego.

Preface

FUNDAMENTALS OF CHEMISTRY is designed for a one term, pre-professional, introductory chemistry course. No prior exposure to chemistry is assumed; the text provides the student with the working knowledge of chemistry necessary to enter the general chemistry sequence or a one term course in organic or biochemistry. It offers a sound foundation of chemical principles for prospective chemistry majors, as well as for students in nursing, allied health, home economics, education, agriculture, and liberal arts curricula.

The text is self-contained, coupling the historical development of the concepts of modern chemistry with an essentially "nuts and bolts" approach to calculations and manipulations of chemical quantities. This presentation is intended to give the student an appreciation for the significance and development of the science while providing an explanation of its methods and principles.

The basic concepts of introductory chemistry are presented in a logical sequence: measurements, stoichiometry, atomic structure, the periodic table, bonding, states of matter and phase changes, solutions, equilibria, acids and bases, and oxidation-reduction reactions. Chapters on organic chemistry and biochemistry conclude the text. We have chosen to introduce stoichiometric concepts and problem solving at the beginning of the text so as to immediately acquaint the student with handling chemical quantities. Of special interest is Chapter 3, a detailed series of worked-out examples based on the concepts developed in Chapter 2.

We have attempted to demonstrate the application and relevance of chemistry through examples and inserts carried throughout the text. The inserts in particular illustrate how chemistry is involved in many facets of everyday life. Other features of the text include numerous worked-out examples in those sections dealing with quantitative calculations. Problems are given at the end of every chapter, and the answers to all numerical problems are provided at the end of the text. As a further aid to students, guidelines are set out at the beginning of each chapter to indicate what they should know after having studied that chapter. A glossary and index are also provided.

During the past two years, a manuscript version of this textbook has been extensively class tested at the University of Connecticut. Special thanks are due to those students who were kind enough to draw our attention to errors and ambiguities.

We should like to acknowledge Roger Dunn, who cajoled us into undertaking this project, and Bill Bryden, who saw it through to its completion, as well as Susan Harter, our manuscript editor, and the other members of the staff of Harcourt Brace Jovanovich, Inc. J. R. R. would like to express his appreciation to C. C. Liang and P. Bro at Mallory for their support during the latter stages of this project. Finally, we must give thanks to Lane Witherell, our typist, who was always ready to incorporate that "last change."

Edward Kostiner
Jesse R. Rea

Contents

9 Solids, Liquids, and Changes of State   237

10 Solutions   265

11 Chemical Equilibrium   303

12 Acids and Bases   327

*The unnumbered topics are inserts on subjects of interest related to the material discussed in the chapters.

1 Introduction

Guidelines

After completing this chapter the student should be able to

- list the different major fields of chemistry
- perform algebraic manipulations in exponential (scientific) notation
- list the SI units of measurement for length, volume, mass, temperature, and pressure
- list the SI prefixes and use them in calculations
- express the results of calculations in the correct number of significant figures
- use conversion factors and dimensional (or factor-label) analysis in problem solving
- differentiate between physical and chemical properties
- explain the difference between elements and compounds, between pure substances and mixtures, and between heterogeneous and homogeneous mixtures
- explain the difference between potential and kinetic energy and list several different forms of energy

1.1 Why Chemistry?

Many people ask the question "Why study chemistry?" The answer is best provided by dealing with the question in its broader context: "Why study *any* science?" One reason is that, whether we like it or not, science is the foundation of our way of life in the twentieth century. By that we mean that very few people in our society are dependent only on their own resources for food, clothing, and shelter. We are all dependent on the tools, machinery, and sources of energy that science and scientists have provided. It is almost a cliché to say that the standard of living we enjoy would be impossible without science. One cannot truly understand or even know very much about the world we live in without being conversant with the fundamental ideas of science. To study science is to enlarge one's perspective on the world and to begin to understand the twentieth century.

Many of the questions, dilemmas, and problems facing the world today are partially scientific in nature or were brought about by applications of scientific knowledge. Similarly, many of these problems can best be solved by the proper applications of other scientific knowledge. The problem of the alleged destruction of the atmosphere's ozone shield by aerosol propellants, for example, is best approached with a knowledge of what these things are, how they react with other substances, and how quickly they react. To solve the food shortage problem, it is useful to know something about chemical equations and thus be able to predict, for example, the production of fertilizer from a given amount of natural gas and nitrogen. To develop safe and economical alternatives to our current energy sources, we must be able to predict harmful chemical reactions as well as measure the various forms of energy and understand their interconversions. Finally, to produce materials for specific purposes, something

3

must be known about the internal structure of matter. So there *is* such a thing as "better living through chemistry," because chemistry has been a conspicuous contributor to the progress of civilization and to the quality of our existence.

However, even if it had not contributed a single "practical" discovery toward the betterment of our lives, and even if it were not essential for solving some of our current problems, chemistry would still be worthy of serious study. In the seventeenth and eighteenth centuries what we now call science was called "natural philosophy"; even today, the doctoral degree awarded in the sciences is the Ph.D. (doctor of philosophy), as it is in the humanities. Chemistry as a science is a philosophy in the sense that it is a way of regarding the world, a way of organizing phenomena into a particular picture of reality. Chemistry remains one of the liberal arts, and as such its study can lead to clarity of thought, appreciation of beauty, and the opportunity to exercise intuition and creativity.

At present the physical sciences are more orderly than the social sciences, humanities, and fine arts. Procedures are better defined and established, verification is more easily obtained, and usually consensus is more easily reached. Yet even in the physical sciences there are numerous controversies, such as the current discussion over the effects of aerosol propellants on the atmosphere. In fact, almost every scientific law hides an encounter between conflicting ideas. Chemists, also, can be awed at the sometimes paradoxical complexity of the universe.

What *is* chemistry really? It is the science of substances, devoted to increasing our understanding of the universe in the sense of what it is made of, how it is organized and structured, and how it works. In order to attain this understanding, chemists have developed approximations, models, and theories of great imagination and power. The cornerstones of the science of chemistry are among our most outstanding intellectual achievements.

Fields of Chemistry

Historically, chemistry has been divided into two broad fields, organic and inorganic. **Organic chemistry** is concerned exclusively with the chemistry of the element carbon and its compounds, while **inorganic chemistry** is devoted to the chemistry of all the other elements. Specialized areas of organic and inorganic chemistry usually include other fields of science. *Bioorganic* chemists, for example, deal with biologically active organic molecules, and *bioinorganic* chemists are concerned with biologically active molecules that contain metal atoms.

Other fields of chemistry cut across the division between organic and inorganic chemistry. **Analytical chemistry** is concerned with the qualitative ("What is it?") and the quantitative ("How much is there?") aspects of chemistry; it is the chemical analysis of compounds. **Physical chemistry** covers the quantitative aspects of the physical properties of substances and their relationships to chemical structure and composition. As more specialization and compartmentalization occurs, we speak of *biochemistry*, the chemistry of biologically active substances; *radiochemistry*, the chemistry of radioactive materials; *polymer* chemistry, the chemistry of polymeric (long-chain) molecules; and *solid state* chemistry, which focuses on the chemical behavior of solids. Many of these fields overlap with their counterparts in the areas of biology and physics and, in fact, areas such as *x-ray crystallography* (the investigation of the structure of solids using the technique of x-ray diffraction) claim practitioners in chemistry, biology, physics, and geology.

Even the classical distinction of organic versus inorganic chemistry has become blurred. *Organometallic* chemists are concerned with compounds in which a metal atom (normally the province of the inorganic chemist) is bonded to an organic species.

Finally, *chemical engineering* covers the technological aspects of chemistry; its focus is the application of chemistry to industrial use. For example, it is the chemical engineer who designs machinery to manufacture the new insecticide discovered in the laboratory.

The goals of this introductory course are to expose you to experimental facts, principles, and methods of chemistry; to provide you with a facility for dealing with the quantitative manipulations involved in *doing* chemistry; and to give you a greater understanding of nature and of the society we live in.

1.2 Exponents

Before beginning a study of chemical principles, it is essential to review some mathematics and learn the system of measurement used in science. One mathematical tool used extensively in chemistry is that of **scientific** (or **exponential**) **notation**. It is nothing more than a convenient way of writing very large and very small numbers by making use of positive and negative powers of ten.

For numbers greater than one, the exponent to which the number ten "is raised" indicates the number of tens multiplied together:

$$10^0 = 1.$$
$$10^1 = 10.$$
$$10^2 = 10 \times 10 = 100.$$
$$10^3 = 10 \times 10 \times 10 = 1,000.$$
$$10^4 = 10 \times 10 \times 10 \times 10 = 10,000.$$

Note that the exponent is numerically equal to the number of zeros between one and the decimal point.

Similarly, a negative exponent indicates a reciprocal, which gives a number less than one:

$$10^{-1} = \frac{1}{10^1} = \frac{1}{10} = 0.1$$

$$10^{-2} = \frac{1}{10^2} = \frac{1}{10 \times 10} = 0.01$$

$$10^{-3} = \frac{1}{10^3} = \frac{1}{10 \times 10 \times 10} = 0.001$$

$$10^{-4} = \frac{1}{10^4} = \frac{1}{10 \times 10 \times 10 \times 10} = 0.0001$$

Note that the absolute value of the negative exponent (the value regardless of the plus or minus sign) is always one more than the number of zeros between the decimal point and one.

Consider the following very large number as an example:

$$602,200,000,000,000,000,000,000$$

It can be factored (broken down) into the product of a smaller number and a whole-number power of ten:

$$6.022 \times 100,000,000,000,000,000,000,000$$

or

$$6.022 \times 10^{23}$$

Negative exponents are useful for expressing very small numbers, such as:

$$0.000000000000000000000001674$$

When factored, this number becomes

$$1.674 \times 0.000000000000000000000001$$

or

$$1.674 \times 10^{-24}$$

Addition and subtraction of very large or small numbers are often simplified by the use of exponential notation. For example, numbers that have the same exponent are totaled by simply adding the first factor of each number:

$$
\begin{aligned}
2.5 &\times 10^{18} \\
4.6 &\times 10^{18} \\
\underline{0.2} &\times 10^{18} \\
7.3 &\times 10^{18}
\end{aligned}
$$

If the numbers are expressed in different powers of ten, it is necessary to first convert them so that they have identical exponents. To *reduce* an exponent, the decimal point is moved one place to the *right* for each exponential decrease of one (for example, 2.30×10^3 would become 23.0×10^2). Similarly, the decimal point is moved one place to the *left* for each exponential *increase* of one (2.30×10^3 becomes 0.230×10^4).

EXAMPLE 1.2a

$$
\begin{aligned}
7.30 \times 10^{15} &= 7.30 \times 10^{15} \\
11.2 \times 10^{14} &= 1.12 \times 10^{15} \\
3.80 \times 10^{17} &= \underline{380.00 \times 10^{15}} \\
&388.42 \times 10^{15}
\end{aligned}
$$

EXAMPLE 1.2b

$$
\begin{aligned}
4. \times 10^{-7} &= .4 \times 10^{-6} \\
6.8 \times 10^{-6} &= 6.8 \times 10^{-6} \\
0.30 \times 10^{-4} &= \underline{30.0 \times 10^{-6}} \\
&37.2 \times 10^{-6}
\end{aligned}
$$

The same conversion process is used for *subtraction* of numbers that have different exponents:

$$
\begin{array}{rl}
7.30 \times 10^{-17} = & 7.30 \times 10^{-17} \\
-1.6 \ \times 10^{-18} = & -0.16 \times 10^{-17} \\
\hline
& 7.14 \times 10^{-17}
\end{array}
$$

Multiplication and division are also facilitated by use of scientific notation. To *multiply* two powers of ten, the exponents are *added* algebraically:

$$10^4 \times 10^4 \ = 10^{(4+4)} \ \ = 10^8$$

$$10^2 \times 10^3 \ = 10^{(2+3)} \ \ = 10^5$$

$$10^5 \times 10^{-3} = 10^{[5+(-3)]} = 10^2$$

To *divide,* the exponents are *subtracted:*

$$\frac{10^5}{10^3} \ = 10^{(5-3)} \ \ = 10^2$$

$$\frac{10^3}{10^{-4}} = 10^{[3-(-4)]} = 10^7$$

To multiply or divide numbers that are not simply powers of ten, the first factors are simply multiplied or divided (and, of course, the exponents of the second factors are added or subtracted).

$$
\begin{aligned}
(6.022 \times 10^{23}) \times (1.674 \times 10^{-24}) &= (6.022)(1.674) \times (10^{23})(10^{-24}) \\
&= 10.08 \times 10^{-1} \\
&= 1.008
\end{aligned}
$$

EXAMPLE 1.2c   Perform the multiplication:

$$
\begin{aligned}
(4.80 \times 10^4) \times (2.50 \times 10^{-6}) &= (4.80)(2.50) \times (10^4)(10^{-6}) \\
&= 12.0 \times 10^{-2} \\
&= 1.2 \ \times 10^{-1}
\end{aligned}
$$

EXAMPLE 1.2d   Perform the division:

$$\frac{(3.38 \times 10^{-7})}{(5.20 \times 10^4)} = \frac{3.38}{5.20} = \frac{10^{-7}}{10^4}$$

$$= 0.650 \times 10^{-11}$$

$$= 6.50 \ \times 10^{-12}$$

1.3 Measurements

It is absolutely necessary to be able to perform accurate measurements in order to develop the principles necessary to systematize a science. Because chemistry, like all science, is quantitative, experiments must be based on quantitative measurements of various parameters, such as length, mass, volume, and temperature.

In recent years, in an attempt to develop an international standard of scientific measurement, a new system of measurement has been adopted: the International System of Units, or **SI** (*Systeme Internationale*). In the SI, which is based on the **metric system** traditionally used by scientists, there are seven base units (listed with their abbreviations):

1. length   meter   (m)
2. mass   kilogram (kg)
3. time   second   (sec)
4. temperature   kelvin   (K)
5. amount of substance mole   (mol)
6. electric current   ampere   (A)
7. luminous intensity candela   (cd)

Some of these base units will be discussed in this section, along with other useful units of measurement. The units not covered in this section will be dealt with in subsequent chapters.

In addition to the base units, the SI has adopted some standard **prefixes** and their abbreviations to indicate powers of ten:

10^1	deka	(da)	10^{-1} deci	(d)
10^2	hecto	(h)	10^{-2} centi	(c)
10^3	kilo	(k)	10^{-3} milli	(m)
10^6	mega	(M)	10^{-6} micro	(μ)
10^9	giga	(G)	10^{-9} nano	(n)

Length

In the laboratory, length is measured with a meter stick, which reproduces the standard unit of length used in the SI (and metric system). This unit, the **meter** (m), is defined as being equal to 1,650,763.73 times the wavelength of a particular line in the emission spectrum of a form of krypton known as ^{86}Kr. (Wavelengths are discussed in Chapter 4.) A meter stick is divided into 100 parts, each equal to 1 **centimeter** (cm), so that 1 cm $= 10^{-2}$ m. Each centimeter is divided into 10 **millimeters** (mm); thus 1 mm $= 10^{-1}$ cm $= 10^{-3}$ m.

For an idea of the relationship between the SI and English system of linear measurement, note the following equivalencies:

1 meter (m) = 39.4 inches (in), or 3.28 feet (ft)
1 inch (in) = 2.54 centimeters (cm)
1 kilometer (km) = 10^3 meters (m) = 0.621 mile (mi)

A common unit of length which is not formally part of the SI but which will certainly remain in use is the **ångstrom** (Å). It represents a convenient measure of the distances encountered at the atomic level and is equal to 10^{-8} cm. A measurement expressed in ångstroms can easily be converted into **nanometers** (nm), the unit in the SI; one nanometer is equal to 10^{-9} m. As an example of the conversion, consider an atomic bond length of 1.85 Å:

$$1.85 \text{ Å} = 1.85 \times 10^{-8} \text{ cm}$$
$$= 1.85 \times 10^{-10} \text{ m}$$
$$= 0.185 \times 10^{-9} \text{ m}$$
$$= 0.185 \text{ nm}$$

Volume

Volume is not a basic unit but is related to length. A cube 1 cm on each edge has a volume of 1 **cubic centimeter** (1 cm $\times$ 1 cm $\times$ 1 cm = 1 cm^3, or 1 cc). Volume is normally measured with a graduated cylinder or, more accurately, with a pipet or buret (see Figure 1–1).

A commonly used liquid and dry measure is the **liter**, equal to 1,000 milliliters (1 mL = 1 cm^3). In its English system equivalent, a liter is 1.06 liquid quarts (qt).

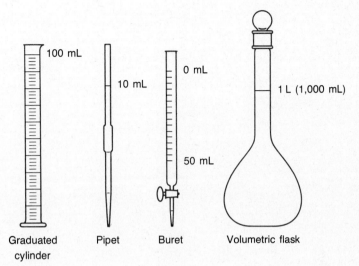

Figure 1–1
Volumetric ware used in the laboratory

Graduated cylinder   Pipet   Buret   Volumetric flask

Mass

Mass is a fundamental property of matter; unlike **weight**, the mass of an object does not vary with the location of the object. The two properties, mass (m) and weight (w), are related by the **gravity** (g) acting on the mass:

$$w = mg$$

Gravity is a quantity that has *direction* as well as magnitude; w is then the force in the direction of g. Mass, on the other hand, is a quantity having only magnitude. Because w depends on g, at $g = 0$, $w = 0$. This, of course, is the situation in outer space, where g is essentially 0 and w is then also 0 (weightlessness). Because the mass of an object is not dependent on gravity, an object in outer space still has mass m.

If two objects are at the same point on the earth, they are affected by the same g.

$$w_1 = m_1 g_1$$
$$w_2 = m_2 g_2$$

Since $g_1 = g_2$, if the first equation is divided by the second, the gs cancel out.

In this case, then, the *ratio* of the masses of the two objects is the same as the ratio of their weights.

$$\frac{w_1}{w_2} = \frac{m_1}{m_2}$$

For this reason one can determine mass by comparing weights on a chemical balance. In chemistry, the term weight (e.g., atomic weight and molecular weight) is frequently used to mean mass.

Although the SI base unit of mass is the **kilogram**, chemical substances are usually handled in **gram** (g) quantities:

$$1 \text{ kilogram (kg)} = 10^3 \text{ g}$$
$$1 \text{ milligram (mg)} = 10^{-3} \text{ g}$$
$$1 \text{ microgram } (\mu\text{g}) = 10^{-6} \text{ g}$$

A kilogram is equal to 2.20 pounds (lb).

Temperature

Heat is nothing more than a form of energy. We say that when a body becomes hot it gains **heat** (or **thermal**) energy. As it gains heat energy, it goes to a state of higher **temperature**, which is simply a *measure* of how hot an object or system is. To compare the temperature of objects, a relative temperature scale, such as the **Celsius** or the **Fahrenheit** scale, is used.

Celsius scale: 0 °C is defined by the freezing point of water.
                    100 °C is defined by the boiling point of water.

Fahrenheit scale: 32 °F is defined by the freezing point of water.
                    212 °F is defined by the boiling point of water.

Figure 1–2 illustrates these two temperature scales, along with a third, the **Kelvin** temperature scale. One degree Celsius (sometimes called centigrade) is defined as $\frac{1}{100}$ of the interval 0–100 °C, and one degree Fahrenheit is defined as $\frac{1}{180}$ of the interval 32–212 °F. A difference of 100 °C, then, is equal to a difference of 180 °F, or, dividing by 20, a difference of 5 °C equals a difference of 9 °F. Thus each °C equals $\frac{9}{5}$ °F.

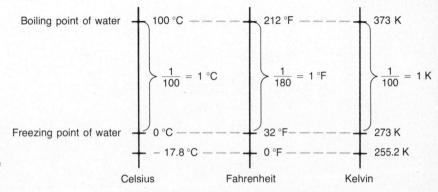

Figure 1–2
A comparison of
the Celsius,
Fahrenheit, and
Kelvin temperature
scales

If a temperature is expressed in °F and we want to convert it to °C, we must account for the 32 °F difference between 0 °F and 0 °C by subtracting it from the Fahrenheit temperature. We then divide this by $\frac{9}{5}$ (or simply multiply by $\frac{5}{9}$) because there are $\frac{9}{5}$ °F to every °C. The formula for converting °F to °C is therefore:

$$°C = \frac{5}{9}(°F - 32)$$

EXAMPLE 1.3a   Convert 98.6 °F (body temperature) to °C.

$$°C = \frac{5}{9}(98.6 - 32)$$

$$= 37.0 \ °C$$

To obtain the formula for converting °C to °F, we simply rearrange the equation:

$$°F = \frac{9}{5}(°C) + 32$$

EXAMPLE 1.3b   Convert 21 °C (room temperature) to °F.

$$°F = \frac{9}{5}(21) + 32$$

$$= 70 \ °F$$

In the third temperature scale, the Kelvin (or thermodynamic) scale, each degree K is the same interval (size) as each degree in the Celsius scale, but 0 K (absolute zero) $= -273$ °C, or 0 °C $= 273$ K.

$$K = °C + 273$$

We shall return to the concept of absolute zero when we consider gases in Chapter 8.

Temperature is most easily measured with a calibrated mercury **thermometer**. Liquid mercury is used because it expands at a constant rate with increasing temperatures.

Pressure

Pressure is defined as the force exerted on an opposing body and is expressed in units of force per unit of area. The earth's atmosphere, which has a substantial mass, exerts a pressure on the surface of the earth. In the mid-seventeenth century, the Italian physicist and mathematician Evangelista Torricelli realized this fact and invented an instrument to measure atmospheric pressure. Now known as a **barometer** (from the Greek word *baros*, meaning weight), the instrument consists of a glass tube about a meter long, sealed at one end and filled with mercury. The open end of the tube is covered (with the finger), the tube is inverted in a beaker of mercury, and the finger is removed. Some mercury will escape from the tube, but a column of mercury 760.0 mm high (29.92 inches) will be supported by the pressure of the atmosphere under average conditions (see Figure 1–3). In essence, a barometer balances the weight of the column of air above the open beaker with the column of liquid mercury confined in the tube; the height of this column of mercury is therefore a measure of the atmospheric pressure. One **standard atmosphere** of pressure (a measure of atmospheric pressure at sea level on an average day) is defined as the pressure that supports a column of mercury 760.0 mm high. In honor of

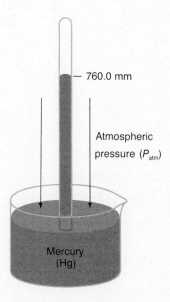

760.0 mm

Atmospheric
pressure (P_{atm})

Mercury
(Hg)

Figure 1–3
The principle of
the barometer

Torricelli, the unit of pressure was named the **torr**:

$$1 \text{ torr} = 1 \text{ mm mercury (Hg)}$$

In the laboratory, pressure is measured with a **manometer**, a U-shaped tube partially filled with mercury. Figure 1–4 illustrates a manometer connected to a gas-filled vessel. The pressure in the vessel is equal to atmospheric pressure plus or minus the difference in the levels of the mercury in the two arms of the U-shaped tube (depending on whether the pressure is greater or less than atmospheric pressure, respectively). The best way to remember how to determine the pressure inside the vessel is to "think it through." If this pressure is greater than atmospheric pressure, then the height of the mercury in arm B of the tube will be greater than that in arm A, and the difference in the heights (in mm) will be *added* to the atmospheric pressure. The converse is true if the pressure within the vessel is less than atmospheric pressure.

Mathematically, this may also be stated as $P_{gas} = P_{atm} + P_{Hg}$, where P_{Hg} is the pressure of the mercury, measured by the difference in height of the mercury columns (height of Hg in arm B − height of Hg in arm A). If the mercury is higher in arm A, then the difference in height is negative, so that in effect P_{Hg} is subtracted from P_{atm}.

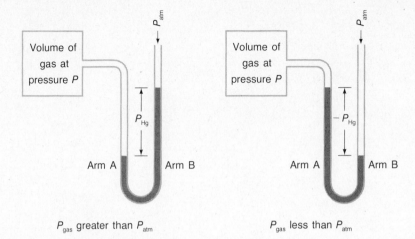

Figure 1–4
The principle of
the manometer

P_{gas} greater than P_{atm} P_{gas} less than P_{atm}

1.4 Significant Figures

When an experiment or a calculation is performed, it is important to know what the error inherent in the measurement is. The number of **significant figures** that are meaningful to a measurement defines the **precision** with which the measurement was made. Precision should not be confused with the **accuracy** of a measurement, which refers to how close a measurement is to the true value. For example, assume that one stopwatch can be read to the nearest 0.5 second and that another can be read to the nearest 0.1 second. A measurement made with the second stopwatch would be more *precise* than the same measurement made with the first stopwatch, but it could be less *accurate* if the second stopwatch were not keeping the correct time.

The precision of a measurement depends to some extent on the equipment used. For example, when measuring 5 mL of water, a large graduated cylinder will give rough precision, a small graduated cylinder will provide better precision, and a buret will give still better precision.

	NUMBER OF SIGNIFICANT FIGURES	VOLUME MEASURED
Large graduated cylinder	1	5 ± 1 mL
Small graduated cylinder	2	5.0 ± 0.1 mL
Buret	3	5.00 ± 0.01 mL

The "plus or minus" notation ($\pm$) indicates the margin of error in the measurement. Note that the more precisely the volume is measured, the greater the number of significant figures. In this book, we shall always assume at least one unit of uncertainty in the last digit, so that if we write 8.02 we mean that the measurement was made to limit the value to the range 8.01 to 8.03 (mathematically, this is written 8.02 $\pm$ 0.01). A few rules will help in recognizing significant figures.

1. Digits other than zero are always significant.
2. Zeros between other digits, whether to the left or the right of the decimal point, are significant. For example, the numbers 202.03 and 40.001 have five significant figures each.
3. Zeros to the right of the decimal point are significant when positioned to the right of the last nonzero digit (as in 23.5700 and 1.40, for example). Zeros to the left of the decimal but to the right of the last nonzero digit in the number may be significant. A number such as 2,300 may be precise to the nearest 100, 10, or 1. If 2,300 is precise to the nearest 1, precision is indicated by writing in the decimal point or by expressing the number in scientific notation. To indicate precision to the nearest 10 or 100, scientific notation should be used.
4. Zeros used to locate the decimal point (those to the left of the first nonzero digit in a number) are not significant. The only significant figures in the number 0.004201, therefore, are the last four digits.

Care must be taken to report the proper number of significant figures in the results of arithmetic operations. When figures are added or subtracted, the number of significant figures in the result is determined by the precision of the least precise measurement.

EXAMPLE 1.4a   Calculate the mass of a solution prepared by adding 40.21 g of sodium chloride to 350. g of water.

    sodium chloride 40.21 g (implies $\pm$ 0.01 g)
             water 350.   g (implies $\pm$ 1. g; therefore this measurement is less precise)
_____
the total mass is 390.   g (implies $\pm$ 1. g)

To say that the solution has a mass of 390.21 g would be misleading, because the water was not weighed to the nearest hundredth of a gram. Since the water was weighed only to the nearest gram, the sum cannot be expressed any more precisely than to the nearest gram.

A different procedure for reporting significant figures is used in multiplication and division problems. In these cases, the number of significant figures in the result is the same as the number in the measurement having the fewest significant figures.

EXAMPLE 1.4b If 1 cm³ of mercury weighs 14.7 g, how many grams does 0.23 cm³ of mercury weigh?

$$\frac{14.7 \text{ g}}{1 \text{ cm}^3} \times 0.23 \text{ cm}^3 = 3.4 \text{ g}$$

The factor 0.23 has the fewer significant figures (two). The results, therefore, must have two significant figures, regardless of the number of digits in the result of the multiplication.

This example illustrates another problem, that of **rounding off**. Although $14.7 \times 0.23 = 3.381$, we "round off" to two significant figures (3.4) to reflect the required degree of precision. To round off a number, excess digits are omitted from the end of the number and the last remaining digits are adjusted as follows. If the first omitted digit is less than 5, all the retained digits remain the same: for example, 5.8345 expressed to three significant figures is 5.83. If this omitted digit is equal to or greater than 5, the last retained digit is raised by one: 3.7937 to two significant figures is 3.8. If the digit to be raised is 9, it becomes 0 and the digit preceding it is raised by one. For example, 8.7967 to three significant figures is 8.80, and 6.99962 to four significant figures would be 7.000.

EXAMPLE 1.4c If 2.50 qt of milk weigh 5.562 lb, what is the weight of 1 qt?

$$\frac{5.562 \text{ lb}}{2.50 \text{ qt}} = 2.2248 \text{ lb/qt}$$

Three significant figures are called for; therefore we round off to 2.22 lb/qt.

EXAMPLE 1.4d   A racing car travels a 4.50 mi track in 1.483 min. What is the average speed of the car in miles per hour?

First, we convert minutes to hours:

$$1.483 \text{ min} \times \frac{1 \text{ h}}{60 \text{ min}} = 0.02472 \text{ h}$$

The car's speed is then:

$$\frac{4.50 \text{ mi}}{0.02472 \text{ h}} = 182 \text{ mi/h} \text{ (only three significant figures are called for)}$$

The number of significant figures is limited only in calculations that involve *inexact* relationships, such as $(1 \text{ in})^2 = (2.54 \text{ cm})^2 = 6.45 \text{ cm}^2$. In exact relationships, no such limitation is required. For example, because 1 ft contains exactly 12 in and 1 m contains exactly 100 cm, the number of significant figures in the relationships $(1 \text{ ft})^2 = (12 \text{ in})^2 = 144 \text{ in}^2$ and $(1 \text{ m})^2 = (100 \text{ cm})^2 = 10^4 \text{ cm}^2$ is not limited.

1.5 Conversion Factors

If two quantities are equivalent, their ratio is equal to 1 even though they may use different units. For example, since 1 in = 2.54 cm, then the ratio 1 in/2.54 cm = 1 or 2.54 cm/1 in = 1. Therefore, we may multiply any quantity by such a ratio to get an equivalent quantity, since mathematically it is equal to multiplying by 1. For example, let us find the number of centimeters equivalent to 25 in. The conversion relationship we need is 1 in = 2.54 cm.

$$25 \text{ in} \times \frac{2.54 \text{ cm}}{1 \text{ in}} = 64 \text{ cm}$$

We chose 2.54 cm/1 in as the **conversion factor** so that inches would "cancel" from the numerator and denominator. If instead we had chosen the conversion factor 1 in/2.54 cm, we would have obtained

$$25 \text{ in} \times \frac{1 \text{ in}}{2.54 \text{ cm}} = 9.8 \frac{\text{in}^2}{\text{cm}}$$

This is, of course, incorrect, since the units of the answer are meaningless. We always choose the ratio (conversion factor) that will eliminate the unwanted unit.

EXAMPLE 1.5a   How many centimeters are there in 2.5 yd?
We must change yards to inches, then inches to centimeters. Therefore, we need the two following conversion relationships: 1 yd = 36 in; 1 cm = 2.54 in. We choose the correct ratios and multiply:

$$2.5 \text{ yd} \times \frac{36 \text{ in}}{1 \text{ yd}} \times \frac{2.54 \text{ cm}}{1 \text{ in}} = 230 \text{ cm}$$

Because only two significant figures are called for, the answer is 230 cm rather than 229 or 228.6 cm. To clearly indicate the precision of the measurement, 230 may be expressed in scientific notation: 2.3×10^2 cm.

Area and Volume Conversions

Sometimes it is necessary to use the same ratio more than once. Suppose we want to find the number of square meters in a rectangular area 7.5 ft by 11.0 ft. The area is given by 7.5 ft × 11.0 ft. To convert first to units of inches, we must multiply twice by 12 in/1 ft to "cancel" both units of feet. We must then multiply twice by the other ratios to convert inches to centimeters and centimeters to meters:

Area = width × length

Area = 7.5 ft × 11.0 ft

$$= \left(7.5 \text{ ft} \times \frac{12 \text{ in}}{1 \text{ ft}}\right) \times \left(11.0 \text{ ft} \times \frac{12 \text{ in}}{1 \text{ ft}}\right)$$

Area = 90. in × 132 in

$$= \left(90. \text{ in} \times \frac{2.54 \text{ cm}}{1 \text{ in}}\right) \times \left(132 \text{ in} \times \frac{2.54 \text{ cm}}{1 \text{ in}}\right)$$

Area = 230 cm × 335 cm

$$= \left(230 \text{ cm} \times \frac{1 \text{ m}}{100 \text{ cm}}\right) \times \left(335 \text{ cm} \times \frac{1 \text{ m}}{100 \text{ cm}}\right)$$

Area = 2.3 m × 3.35 m

Area = 7.7 m²

This would have been briefer if we had derived conversion relationships for the square of the units as follows:

$(1 \text{ ft})^2 = (12 \text{ in})^2 = 144 \text{ in}^2$

$(1 \text{ in})^2 = (2.54 \text{ cm})^2 = 6.45 \text{ cm}^2$

$(1 \text{ m})^2 = (100 \text{ cm})^2 = 10^4 \text{ cm}^2$

We would then multiply the area found by multiplying 7.5 ft × 11.0 ft (83 ft²) by the appropriate ratios:

$$83 \text{ ft}^2 \times \frac{144 \text{ in}^2}{1 \text{ ft}^2} \times \frac{6.45 \text{ cm}^2}{1 \text{ in}^2} \times \frac{1 \text{ m}^2}{10^4 \text{ cm}^2} = 7.7 \text{ m}^2$$

EXAMPLE 1.5b   How many liters are there in one cubic foot?
We must convert cubic feet first to cubic inches, then to cubic centimeters, then to milliliters, and finally to liters. The following conversion relationships are therefore needed:

$(1 \text{ ft})^3 = (12 \text{ in})^3 = 1.73 \times 10^3 \text{ in}^3$

$(1 \text{ in})^3 = (2.54 \text{ cm})^3 = 16.4 \text{ cm}^3$

$1 \text{ cm}^3 = 1 \text{ mL}$

$1 \text{ L} = 10^3 \text{ mL}$

We can now multiply one cubic foot by the appropriate ratios:

$$1 \text{ ft}^3 \times \frac{1.73 \times 10^3 \text{ in}^3}{1 \text{ ft}^3} \times \frac{16.4 \text{ cm}^3}{1 \text{ in}^3} \times \frac{1 \text{ mL}}{1 \text{ cm}^3} \times \frac{1 \text{ L}}{10^3 \text{ mL}} = 28.4 \text{ L}$$

Three significant figures are called for, since the conversion factors are given to three significant figures.

Density

So far we have used conversion relationships only for similar quantities, such as length to length, area to area, and volume to volume. Sometimes it is possible to convert between dissimilar quantities (mass to volume, for example) *if* a suitable conversion factor is given or can be determined. A useful conversion factor relating mass to volume is **density** (d), defined as the mass per unit of volume (m/V).

$$d = \frac{m}{V}$$

The density of a material is a characteristic property of that material. Aluminum, for example, has a density of 2.70 g/cm³. This means that 1 cubic centimeter of aluminum is equivalent to 2.70 g of aluminum (1 cm³ ≡ 2.70 g). Thus 2.70 g/cm³ and 1 cm³/2.70 g are appropriate conversion factors for aluminum. Conversion factors for other elements can be determined from their densities. Gold, for example, with a density of 19.3 g/cm³, has conversion factors of 19.3 g/cm³ and 1 cm³/19.3 g.

EXAMPLE 1.5c   A block of aluminum is measured and found to have a volume of 11.5 cm³. What is its mass? (Density = 2.70 g/cm³.)

$$m = V \times d$$

$$m = 11.5 \text{ cm}^3 \times \frac{2.70 \text{ g}}{\text{cm}^3} = 31.1 \text{ g}$$

EXAMPLE 1.5d   To perform an experiment, 100. g of a certain solution are needed. If the density of the solution is 1.10 g/cm³, what volume of the solution is needed?

$$V = \frac{m}{d}$$

$$V = \frac{100.\ \text{g}}{1.10\ \text{g/cm}^3} = 100.\ \text{g} \times \frac{1\ \text{cm}^3}{1.10\ \text{g}} = 90.9\ \text{cm}^3$$

EXAMPLE 1.5e   A rectangular piece of iron has dimensions of 0.50 cm by 0.60 cm by 0.80 cm and weighs 1.89 g. What is its density?

$$d = \frac{m}{V}$$

$$d = \frac{1.89\ \text{g}}{0.50\ \text{cm} \times 0.60\ \text{cm} \times 0.80\ \text{cm}} = \frac{1.89\ \text{g}}{0.24\ \text{cm}^3} = 7.9\ \text{g/cm}^3$$

The densities of some common materials are listed in Table 1–1. Sometimes when people refer to heaviness ("heavy as lead"), they really mean density. What makes lead seem heavier than most other materials is its greater mass in a given volume (its density).

Table 1–1

Densities of Some Common Materials (in g/cm³ at room temperature)

Ethyl alcohol	0.79	Chalk (calcium carbonate)	2.71
Benzene	0.88	Iron	7.86
Water	1.00	Copper	8.92
Carbon tetrachloride	1.57	Lead	11.3
Table salt (sodium chloride)	2.17	Mercury	13.6
Aluminum	2.70	Gold	19.3

Table 1–2

Units of Measurement and Selected Conversion Factors

MASS	VOLUME
1 g = 1,000 mg	1 mL = 1 cm³ (or 1 cc)
1 mg = 10^{-3} g	1 L = 1,000 mL
1 kg = 1,000 g	1 qt = 0.946 L
1 oz = 28.3 g	1 L = 1.06 qt
1 lb = 454 g	1 gal = 3.79 L
1 kg = 2.20 lb	

LENGTH

1 mm = 10^{-3} m
1 cm = 10 mm
1 cm = 10^{-2} m
1 m = 100 cm
1 km = 1,000 m
1 Å = 10^{-8} cm
1 in = 2.54 cm
1 ft = 0.305 m
1 mi = 1.61 km
1 cm = 0.394 in
1 km = 0.621 mi

PRESSURE

1 torr = 1 mm Hg
1 atm = 760. torr
1 atm = 29.9 in Hg

TEMPERATURE

$$°C = \frac{5}{9}(°F - 32)$$

$$°F = \frac{9}{5}(°C) + 32$$

$$K = °C + 273$$

You will notice that in each example in this section the *units* of each number and conversion factor were included when the problem was set up. This use of **dimensional** (or **factor-label**) **analysis** is extremely helpful in keeping track of units and in ensuring that the problem is set up correctly. The units are treated algebraically and will therefore cancel out to give the correct units for the answer. If the dimensions (the units) of the answer are incorrect, then the problem has been solved improperly. Dimensional analysis in problem solving is used throughout the text and it is advised that you make it routine in setting up and solving problems. Table 1–2 lists some common units of measurement and conversion factors.

1.6   Chemistry, Matter, and Energy

This section is designed to present some basic definitions and ideas, some of which will be discussed in greater detail in subsequent chapters. You should learn to recognize them now because they will be used from time to time before they are reintroduced for detailed discussion. Also, the glossary at the end of the text can be used for reference, or the index can be used to locate the page where a term or concept was first introduced.

Chemistry is the study of the chemical and physical properties of matter (anything that has mass and occupies space). A **physical property** is a characteristic of a substance which can be studied without changing the identity of the substance. The boiling point, melting point, density, and conductivity of a substance are physical properties. A **chemical property** is a characteristic which can be studied only at the risk of changing the identity of the substance. To test the reaction of a metal with an acid is to determine a chemical property, since the metal may react to form a different substance. When hydrogen is burned in oxygen to form water, the chemical properties of hydrogen and oxygen are being exhibited.

Classification of Matter

Matter may be classified as pure substances or as mixtures. **Elements** are pure substances and cannot be *chemically* separated into simpler substances. In principle, any object can be resolved into its component elements. Elements have chemical and physical properties (such as melting point, boiling point, density, crystal structure, and reactivity) which uniquely characterize them. A total of 105 elements have been identified. They are listed along with their symbols (abbreviations) in Table 1–3, and those that are most commonly found in the earth's crust are shown in Table 1–4.

Compounds, which are chemical combinations of elements, are also pure substances. The elements that comprise a given compound are present in fixed proportions. Compounds are uniquely characterized by their properties, which are different from those of the component elements. For example, sodium (a solid) and chlorine (a gas) react to form the compound sodium chloride (table salt), which is a solid. Elements and compounds will be discussed extensively in later chapters.

Table 1–3

The Elements and Their Symbols

ELEMENT	SYMBOL	ELEMENT	SYMBOL	ELEMENT	SYMBOL
Actinium	Ac	Hafnium	Hf	Potassium	K*
Aluminum	Al	Hahnium	Ha	Praseodymium	Pr
Americium	Am	Helium	He	Promethium	Pm
Antimony	Sb*	Holmium	Ho	Protactinium	Pa
Argon	Ar	Hydrogen	H	Radium	Ra
Arsenic	As	Indium	In	Radon	Rn
Astatine	At	Iodine	I	Rhenium	Re
Barium	Ba	Iridium	Ir	Rhodium	Rh
Berkelium	Bk	Iron	Fe*	Rubidium	Rb
Beryllium	Be	Krypton	Kr	Ruthenium	Ru
Bismuth	Bi	Kurchatovium	Ku	Samarium	Sm
Boron	B	Lanthanum	La	Scandium	Sc
Bromine	Br	Lawrencium	Lr	Selenium	Se
Cadmium	Cd	Lead	Pb*	Silicon	Si
Calcium	Ca	Lithium	Li	Silver	Ag*
Californium	Cf	Lutetium	Lu	Sodium	Na*
Carbon	C	Magnesium	Mg	Strontium	Sr
Cerium	Ce	Manganese	Mn	Sulfur	S
Cesium	Cs	Mendelevium	Md	Tantalum	Ta
Chlorine	Cl	Mercury	Hg*	Technetium	Tc
Chromium	Cr	Molybdenum	Mo	Tellurium	Te
Cobalt	Co	Neodymium	Nd	Terbium	Tb
Copper	Cu*	Neon	Ne	Thallium	Tl
Curium	Cm	Neptunium	Np	Thorium	Th
Dysprosium	Dy	Nickel	Ni	Thulium	Tm
Einsteinium	Es	Niobium	Nb	Tin	Sn*
Erbium	Er	Nitrogen	N	Titanium	Ti
Europium	Eu	Nobelium	No	Tungsten	W*
Fermium	Fm	Osmium	Os	Uranium	U
Fluorine	F	Oxygen	O	Vanadium	V
Francium	Fr	Palladium	Pd	Xenon	Xe
Gadolinium	Gd	Phosphorus	P	Ytterbium	Yb
Gallium	Ga	Platinum	Pt	Yttrium	Y
Germanium	Ge	Plutonium	Pu	Zinc	Zn
Gold	Au*	Polonium	Po	Zirconium	Zr

*These elements have symbols derived from their Latin names:

Sb	Stibium	Pb	Plumbum	Na	Natrium
Cu	Cuprum	Hg	Hydrargyrum	Sn	Stannum
Au	Aurum	K	Kalium	W	Wolfram
Fe	Ferrum	Ag	Argentum		

Table 1–4

The Eight Most Common Elements in the Earth's Crust*

	PERCENT BY WEIGHT
Oxygen	46.60
Silicon	27.72
Aluminum	6.47
Iron	5.00
Magnesium	2.09
Calcium	3.63
Sodium	2.83
Potassium	2.59

*From Brian Mason, *Principles of Geochemistry* (New York: John Wiley & Sons, Inc., 1966).

Most matter, however, occurs in the form of **mixtures**. Elements or compounds (or both) may be brought together in any proportions to form mixtures, which have properties that are not significantly different from those of the components. Mixtures are commonly divided into two kinds:

Heterogeneous mixtures are made up of two or more physically discernible parts. For example, a mixture of powdered instant coffee and granulated sugar is heterogeneous, because the particles of each of the components can be detected.

Homogeneous mixtures are those in which the separate components cannot be detected. Dissolving the heterogeneous mixture of instant coffee and sugar in hot water gives a homogeneous mixture, because the component parts cannot be individually detected.

Obviously, the classification of homogeneous versus heterogeneous mixtures depends on how sensitive the means of detecting heterogeneity is. As a result, there is no distinct dividing line between homogeneous and heterogeneous mixtures.

Homogeneous mixtures, which are made up of one or more substances dissolved in another, are usually called **solutions**. In a two-component (binary) system, the major component is known as the **solvent** and the minor component is called the **solute**. Systems with water as the solvent and a solid as the solute are considered the most common examples of solutions (so-called **aqueous solutions**), but solid-solid, gas-liquid, liquid-liquid, and gas-solid solutions are also known. When both components of a system can be mixed in any proportion they are said to be **miscible**. Ethyl alcohol and water are good examples of two miscible liquids. If the solution contains less than 50% ethyl alcohol, water is the solvent and alcohol the solute; if it contains more than 50% alcohol, alcohol is the solvent and water the solute. Finally, any mixture, heterogeneous or homogeneous (solution), should be separable into its component parts by physical means. Figure 1–5 summarizes this classification of matter.

States of Matter

A particular element or compound can exist in any of three states of matter: solid, liquid, or gas. For example, the compound represented by the chemical formula H_2O exists as ice, water, and steam:

$$\text{Ice} \xrightarrow{\text{melting}} \underset{\text{freezing}}{\longleftarrow} \text{Water} \xrightarrow{\text{boiling}} \underset{\text{condensing}}{\longleftarrow} \text{Steam}$$
$$\text{(solid)} \qquad\qquad \text{(liquid)} \qquad\qquad \text{(gas)}$$

A **phase transition** occurs when a substance is transformed from one state (phase) to another. It is a *physical* change as opposed to a *chemical* change, because it does not involve a chemical reaction. The temperature at which a solid is transformed to a liquid is known as the **melting point** of the substance, and the temperature at which the liquid is transformed to a gas is

Figure 1–5
Classification of matter

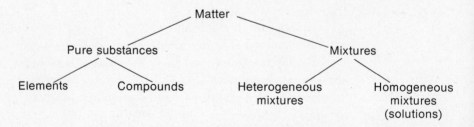

called the **boiling point**. In the reverse direction, the **condensation point** of a substance is the temperature at which the gaseous state becomes the liquid state of the substance, and the **freezing point** marks the temperature of the transition from a liquid to a solid. Transition from the solid state directly to the gaseous state is also possible:

$$\text{solid} \underset{\text{condensation}}{\overset{\text{sublimation}}{\rightleftharpoons}} \text{gas}$$

The temperature at which this transition occurs is known as the **sublimation point**. Phase transitions will be discussed more fully in Chapter 9.

As will be demonstrated later in the text, the three states of matter can be explained more or less successfully by the **kinetic molecular theory**, which states that matter is made up of tiny particles that are always in motion. This motion, called thermal motion, is dependent on the temperature of the material and would, in the absence of attractive interactions, tend to cause the particles to fly about at random. This tendency toward motion is opposed by forces of attraction between the particles.

In solids, where the attraction between particles is strong, the random thermal motion is not violent enough to overcome the attractive forces, which bind the particles into a mass having rigidity and definite volume, two characteristic properties of solids. In liquids, which have weaker forces of attraction, the particles are free to move relative to one another. This restricted freedom of movement results in the characteristic properties of liquids: definite volume but indefinite shape (a liquid assumes the shape of the bottom and sides of its container). Gases have the weakest attractive interactions of the three states of matter. Because there is little restraint on the kinetic motion, gases have the properties of indefinite shape and indefinite volume (a gas will expand to fill its container and thus assume its shape and volume). In Chapters 8 and 9 we will consider the properties and behavior of each of the three states of matter.

Energy

When a physical or chemical change occurs, heat (thermal energy) can be either absorbed or liberated by the system. When heat is *released* by the system to the surroundings, the process is said to be **exothermic**; when heat is *absorbed* by the system from the surroundings, it is said to be

Nuclear Power Reactors as Thermal Polluters

In this era of energy crises nuclear energy has been proclaimed as the energy of the future, the abundant source of energy that will allow us to maintain our relatively high standard of living. Briefly stated, nuclear energy is released by unlocking the energy of the atom, either by *fusion,* in which two light atoms unite to form a heavier atom, or by *fission,* in which a heavier atom is "split" into lighter fragments. In using nuclear energy we seek to convert it to a more usable form, usually electrical energy.

At present only the fission reactor is practical. The nuclear energy released in fission as heat is transmitted to a heat exchanger by a cooling system which is connected to the reactor. This heat exchanger then provides thermal energy which can be used directly or converted to electrical energy by turbine generators. Unfortunately, nearly two-thirds of the thermal energy is lost during the energy conversion process, and this large amount of waste heat must be carried off. Aside from the environmental dangers associated with the possible escape of radioactivity, the *thermal pollution* from the waste heat can be damaging to the nearby area if it raises the average temperature of the environment. An environmental temperature change can

endothermic. The unit of thermal energy is the calorie (abbreviated *cal*); it is defined as the amount of heat required to raise the temperature of 1 gram of water by 1 °C. In an endothermic or exothermic process what occurs is actually the interconversion of chemical energy and thermal energy. The fact that energy can be converted from one form to another but is never created or destroyed is summarized by the Law of Conservation of Energy:

Energy is always conserved and can never be created or destroyed in a chemical reaction.

Similarly, there is a Law of Conservation of Mass:

Matter is always conserved and is neither created nor destroyed in a chemical reaction.

This law implies that in a chemical reaction the mass of the products always equals the mass of the reactants. We say *in a chemical reaction*

upset the natural distribution of plant and animal life by causing certain organisms to die and other organisms (which may actually prefer the new temperature) to multiply.

Nuclear plants are necessarily located near large bodies of water to provide enough cooling water to operate the reactors. When the water is discharged from the plant, it heats up the surrounding water, which leads to an imbalance in the immediate biological environment. In addition, there are problems of radioactive waste disposal, fuel reprocessing, and possible radiation release. Because the products formed in a fission reaction are highly radioactive, the environmental effects resulting from the disposal and possible escape of these products could be serious. The environmental dangers are complicated by the long lifetime of many of these materials, which may extend to tens of thousands of years. Before a method for safe long-term storage of these dangerous materials can be found, the use of nuclear reactors is limited. This example of the factors that complicate the seemingly "clean" generation of electrical energy by nuclear fission illustrates the need for thorough research of all aspects of any proposed solution to a major problem.

because in 1905 Albert Einstein developed a formula for relating energy (E) and mass (m) using the speed of light (c):

$$E = mc^2$$

Thus in nuclear reactions mass and energy can be interconverted.

Broadly speaking, energy may be categorized as either kinetic energy or potential energy. **Kinetic energy** is energy associated with motion and is given by the formula

$$\text{kinetic energy} = \frac{1}{2}mv^2$$

where m = mass (in grams) and v = velocity (in centimeters per second). The units on the right-hand side of the equation will be g cm²/sec², which are the units of the **erg** (1 erg = 1 g cm²/sec²).

Potential energy is stored energy which results from relative position or structure. Because of its elevation, water stored behind a dam has a greater potential energy than water in the ocean; a coiled spring, because of its structure, has greater potential energy than a straight wire.

Work, which is expressed in the same units as energy (ergs), may result from the transfer of energy. Therefore, energy may be considered as the capacity for doing work. To do work, energy must be expended. Although energy is conserved, it can be transferred from one object to another in many forms. Several kinds of kinetic and potential energy are defined as follows:

Thermal energy	energy associated with heat
Radiant energy	energy in the form of radiation
Electrical energy	energy associated with electricity
Mechanical energy	energy associated with mechanical work
Chemical energy	energy stored in chemicals (e.g., in food and in petroleum)
Nuclear energy	energy that binds nuclei together

A good example of the conversions of various forms of energy is provided by tracing a possible course of water on the earth and in the atmosphere. Water in the ocean absorbs the sun's radiant energy, warms up, and evaporates into the atmosphere. Radiant energy from the sun is converted first into thermal energy, heating the water, and then into potential energy as liquid water becomes gaseous (the gaseous water particles in the atmosphere are farther from one another and from the center of the earth than the liquid water particles in the ocean). Eventually the water condenses, releasing thermal energy, and falls as rain. Some of the rain may fall onto a mountain and then flow into a river (potential energy converted into kinetic energy). The moving water could drive a turbine (kinetic into mechanical energy, or work), which could then drive a generator (mechanical into electrical energy). At each step energy is conserved, but because each process is not completely efficient, some energy will be lost to the surroundings as heat.

TERMS
AND
CONCEPTS

- Organic, inorganic, physical, and analytical chemistry
- Scientific (exponential) notation
- SI units and prefixes
- Metric system

- Meter, centimeter, millimeter, ångstrom, and nanometer
- Cubic centimeter, liter, and milliliter
- Mass versus weight
      gravity

- Kilogram and gram
- Heat and temperature
- Celsius (centigrade), Fahrenheit, and Kelvin scales
    thermometer
- *Pressure*
    standard atmosphere of pressure
    torr
    barometer and manometer
- Significant figures
    precision versus accuracy
- "Rounding off"
- Conversion factors
- *Density*
- Dimensional (factor-label) analysis
- Physical and chemical properties
- *Elements and compounds*
- *Heterogeneous and homogeneous mixtures*

- *Solutions*
    solutes and solvents
    aqueous solutions
- *Miscibility*
- *States of matter*
    solids, liquids, and gases
- *Phase transitions*
    melting and boiling points
    freezing and condensation
        points
    sublimation point
- *Kinetic molecular theory*
- *Exothermic and endothermic processes*
    calorie
- Law of Conservation of Energy
- Law of Conservation of Mass
- *Kinetic and potential energy*
    erg

Note: The terms printed in *italics* will be reintroduced and discussed in greater detail in subsequent chapters.

QUESTIONS

1. a. List two or three items from the recent news that you would better understand if you knew more about scientific concepts.
   b. Look around your bedroom or dormitory room and list five materials present that do not exist in nature.
   c. Based on your present knowledge, identify these materials as pure substances or as mixtures.
2. List and define four major fields of chemistry.
3. Express the following numbers in exponential notation:
   a. 0.000365
   b. 631
   c. 7,856
   d. 69.7
   e. 65.007
   f. 0.376
   g. 10.0
   h. 0.000070
   i. 210
   j. 210.
4. Express the following quantities in nonexponential form:
   a. the speed of light, 3.00×10^{10} cm/sec
   b. the mass of an electron, 9.11×10^{-28} g
   c. the circumference of the earth, 2.5×10^4 mi

5. Find the temperature
   a. in °C for a winter night (10 °F)
   b. in °C for body temperature (98.6 °F)
   c. in °F for a winter day in Alaska (−32 °C)
   d. in °F for the record low in Massena, N.Y. (−48 °C)
   e. in K for a warm summer day (21 °C)
   f. in K for a winter day (35 °F)
6. A draftsman wants to measure a line on a drawing. He finds two rulers, a metal one with marks at millimeter intervals and a wooden one marked off at every 0.5 mm. However, each end of the wooden ruler has been broken unevenly. The draftsman measures the line from the end of each ruler and finds a length of 10 mm with the metal ruler and 11.5 mm with the wooden one. Which measurement is more precise? Do you think that the more precise measurement is the more accurate one? How can the draftsman make the measurement to be confident of his accuracy and precision, using the wooden ruler?

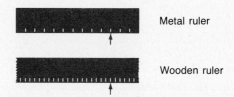

Metal ruler

Wooden ruler

7. Express the results of the following operations using the proper number of significant figures:
   a. $6.731 + 1.208 + 5.914 =$
   b. $6.73 + 1.208 + 5.9 =$
   c. $(2.01 \times 10^{-2}) + (6.78 \times 10^{-1}) + 0.57 =$
   d. $(2.01 \times 10^{-2}) \times (6.78 \times 10^{-1}) \times 0.57 =$
   e. $17.5 \div 8.3 =$
   f. $86.7 \times 0.006 =$
   g. $6.359 \div 0.75 =$
8. Express in exponential notation using three significant figures the number of (a) years, (b) days, and (c) minutes from October 12, 1492, to October 12, 1978. Does the inclusion of the extra time for leap years make a significant difference in the number of days and in the number of minutes?
9. Convert the following quantities:
   a. 25.0 mL = _____L = _____cm³
   b. 0.0375 g = _____mg
   c. 1.2 in = _____cm = _____m

    d. 57 mil = _____cm (1 mil = 0.001 in)

    e. 100. mi = _____km

    f. 1.50 yd² = _____in² = _____cm²

    g. 6.0 in³ = _____ft³ = _____cm³

10. a. The velocity of sound is 1,100 ft/sec. How many meters per second is this equal to?

    b. The speed of light is 3.00 × 10¹⁰ cm/sec. How many miles per second and miles per hour is this?

    c. An upright piano is listed to be 90.0 cm wide. Will it fit through a doorway that is 3.00 ft wide?

11. A 0.500 g sample of a powdered material being tested for use in a solid state battery is placed in a circular steel die of 0.761 cm radius.

    a. The material is pressed into the die at 14,000 lb pressure. How many pounds per square inch pressure is this? (The area of a circle is given by 3.14 r^2, where r is the radius.)

    b. The thickness of the material pressed in the die is 0.098 cm. What is its density in grams per cubic centimeter? (The volume of a cylinder is given by the area of the base times the height, h, or 3.14 r^2h.)

12. A primitive society is found to be living in an abandoned building in a remote area of a large university. The members of this society use a system of measurement based on the *mar*, the width of the marble cornerstone of the building. Investigators find that 1 mar = 18.7 in.

    a. How many centimeters are there in a mar? How many meters?

    b. The largest room in the building measures 30. mar by 33 mar. What is the area in square mars? In square meters? In square feet?

    c. The caldron in which food is fixed is 47 cm in diameter and 95 cm high. What is its volume in cubic mar?

13. If a book measures 6.0 in by 8.0 in by 1.5 in and weighs 3.0 lb, what is its density in grams per cubic centimeter?

14. The density of water is 1.00 g/cm³. Express this quantity in pounds per cubic foot.

15. 25.0 mL of a liquid weigh 39.25 g. What is its density?

16. There are 35.8 mL of liquid in a graduated cylinder. A metallic object weighing 58.9 g is immersed in the liquid, which then reaches to the 67.2 mL mark. What is the density of the object?

17. 27 g of a certain liquid is needed for a reaction. If its density is 0.84 g/mL, what volume is needed?

18. Indicate whether the following statements describe physical properties or chemical properties:

    a. Bromine is a red liquid.

    b. A quartz crystal (SiO_2) will produce an electric pulse when pressure is applied to it.

    c. Fluorine will combine with nearly all of the other elements.

    d. Copper will acquire a green patina when exposed to air and water over a period of time.

    e. Silver chloride is a white solid.

    f. The diamond form of carbon is the hardest of all substances.

19. What are the three states of matter?

20. What is a phase transition?

21. Classify the following as having either potential or kinetic energy:

    a. a car parked on a hill

    b. the car rolling down the hill if the brake fails

    c. the attraction of opposite charges on the two sides of an electrical wall socket

    d. the flow of electric current through an appliance when the two sides are joined by plugging in the cord

    e. a molecule of gasoline

    f. gasoline being burned to drive an engine

2

Stoichiometry

Guidelines

After completing this chapter the student should be able to:

- outline the contributions of early workers to the science of chemistry
- discuss the Laws of Constant and Multiple Proportions
- describe the principles of Dalton's atomic theory
- use the concepts of atomic and molecular weights in calculations
- use the concepts of the mole and stoichiometry in calculations
- determine a compound's empirical formula given its percent composition and calculate its percent composition given the formula
- balance chemical equations and use their molar ratios to perform calculations involving stoichiometry
- determine whether a reaction is exothermic or endothermic given ΔH
- identify the limiting reagent in a chemical reaction and calculate the amount of product
- calculate theoretical and percent yield given an equation and the amounts of starting materials

2.1 Historical Aspects

The early Greeks were the first to ask the question, "Can matter be divided infinitely or is it composed of small, finite particles?" Democritus (ca. 470 B.C.) maintained that all matter is composed of minute particles and that the properties of tangible matter are a result of and determined by the properties of these tiny, ultimate particles. For example, he considered water to be fluid because the minute water particles are smooth and will roll over one another, and iron to be strong because its particles have raw surfaces and stick to one another. In this manner, he believed, it is the properties of the ultimate particles that determine bulk properties.

The name he gave to these ultimate particles was *atomos* (the Greek word for indivisible); our word *atom* is derived from this. Democritus further considered that it was impossible to create or destroy atoms. This was the first statement of the **Law of Conservation of Matter**: that matter cannot be created or destroyed in a chemical process. However, despite the insight and accuracy of this analysis, Aristotle's later postulate (ca. 350 B.C.) that the material world is built up from four elements—earth, air, fire, and water—prevailed at least into the Middle Ages.

During the Middle Ages chemistry became enmeshed with astrology, giving rise to the alchemists. Although alchemy was, in part, concerned with such impossibilities as turning lead into gold, it left modern chemists with a most important legacy. The experimental techniques developed by the alchemists provided apparatus, observations, and even theories that over the years led to the foundations of what we now know as chemistry.

During the seventeenth century, it became recognized that all matter is composed of certain fundamental materials. It was Robert Boyle who, in this period, laid the foundations for modern chemistry. Up until his day, chemistry was wholly involved with the concept of **synthesis**, or the preparation of chemical compounds. Rather than trying to determine what elements are required to make certain compounds, Boyle was the first to ask, "Just what are the basic building blocks of all matter?" In doing so, he introduced the concept of **analysis**, or the separation of compounds into their component elements. In recognition of his novel approach, Boyle is remembered as the first chemist.

Antoine Lavoisier in 1770 was the first chemist to measure the weights of compounds entering into chemical reactions, and by careful experimental measurements he was able to determine the decomposition products of chemical compounds. He was the first to find that under carefully controlled experimental conditions the sum of the weights of the decomposition products of a particular compound was always equal to the weight of the original compound. This was an experimental demonstration of the Law of Conservation of Matter. If a compound was reacted with *other* substances the product of the reaction was *always* heavier than the original material and *never* weighed less. Those substances that did not undergo further decomposition were defined by Lavoisier as *chemical elements*.

Let us look at an example from his work. Exactly 1.00 g of mercury (Hg) will dissolve in an excess of nitric acid (HNO_3). When the excess acid is boiled away, a new white, water-soluble compound, which weighs 1.62 g, is formed. The original reaction takes place with the evolution of a

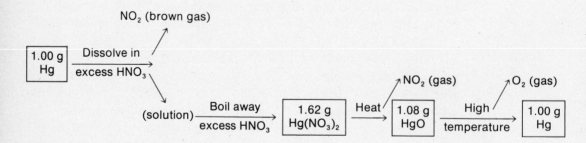

Figure 2–1
Lavoisier's experiment, which proved the existence of fundamental substances known as elements

brown, noxious gas; that is, there is more than one product. What happened to the mercury? Lavoisier's answer was to try to find it again. It turns out that it can be recovered only from the white solid. Further heating of this solid decomposes it into 1.08 g of a red powder and more of the same brown gas. Heating the red powder at a high temperature decomposes it into Hg and a gas which turns out to be oxygen. The weight of the Hg recovered is exactly 1.00 g.

All attempts at preparing something from mercury that weighed *less* than the mercury failed; therefore mercury is an element. In modern terms (see Figure 2–1) the Hg reacted with HNO_3 to form the white solid mercuric nitrate $Hg(NO_3)_2$ (and the brown gas nitrogen dioxide NO_2), which on heating decomposed to the red mercuric oxide HgO (and gave off more NO_2). The HgO in turn decomposed at red heat to yield Hg (and oxygen gas).

2.2 The Laws of Constant and Multiple Proportions

After Lavoisier many investigations into the weight relationships among chemical compounds were carried out, and during the latter part of the eighteenth century an important experimental fact emerged: The composition by weight of any given compound is constant within the available experimental error. For example, mercuric oxide was found to be composed of 93% mercury and 7% oxygen by weight, regardless of how it was made, where it came from, or the size of the sample. This characteristic of constant composition was found time after time for different compounds and led to the formulation of the **Law of Constant Proportions**:

In every compound the constituent elements are present in constant proportions by weight.

This does not mean that a pair of elements cannot form more than one compound with each other. In fact, there are several pairs of elements, such as carbon and oxygen, nitrogen and oxygen, and lead and chlorine, that will combine to give more than one compound. Of course, the Law of Constant Proportions holds for each compound that does form.

Let us use a specific example. When 1.00 g of carbon is burned in air, it reacts with 2.66 g of oxygen to give 3.66 g of a gas which we will call compound A. If 1.00 g of carbon is burned in a limited amount of oxygen, however, 1.33 g of oxygen are used, forming 2.33 g of a *different* gas which we will call compound B.

COMPOUND	WEIGHT OF CARBON	WEIGHT OF OXYGEN	WEIGHT OF GAS
A	1.00 g	2.66 g	3.66 g
B	1.00 g	1.33 g	2.33 g

If enough additional oxygen is supplied, compound B will react further with 1.33 g *more* of oxygen to give 3.66 g of the first gas, compound A (see Figure 2–2). Thus carbon and oxygen will react to form either of two compounds, A or B, each of which obeys the Law of Constant Proportions.

It can be seen at a glance that the proportion of oxygen to carbon is different if the two compounds are compared with each other. In A the proportion is 2.66 g O to 1.00 g C, whereas in B the proportion is 1.33 g O to 1.00 g C. However, if we compare the weight ratios of the oxygen in A and B, we see that they are in the ratio of small whole numbers:

$$\frac{2.66 \text{ g}}{1.33 \text{ g}} = \frac{2}{1}$$

Thus, per gram of carbon, there is twice as much oxygen (by weight) in compound A as in compound B.

Figure 2–2
A demonstration of the validity of the Law of Multiple Proportions

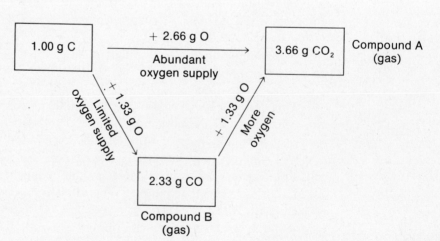

The results of similar investigations of other pairs and triplets of compounds led the English scientist John Dalton to formulate (in 1803) the Law of Multiple Proportions:

When two elements combine to form more than one compound, the masses of one element which combine with a fixed mass of the other element are in a ratio of small whole numbers.

2.3 Dalton's Atomic Theory

From 1803 to 1808 Dalton developed a theory to account for the Laws of Constant and Multiple Proportions. According to his theory, chemical reactions behave as they do because matter is not infinitely divisible but is built up from indivisible particles called **atoms**. All atoms of a particular element, said Dalton, are identical in weight and other properties, and these atoms differ in their properties from atoms of all other elements. Thus an atom is the smallest *characteristic* unit of an *element*. In contrast to the Greeks, Dalton proposed that atoms were hard spheres, or miniature "billiard balls." The property that determined the identity of an atom was its mass.

Dalton went on to say that atoms may combine to form a "compound atom" (now known as a **molecule**), which is the smallest *characteristic* unit of a *compound*. He further theorized that when different atoms combine, they do so in ratios of small whole numbers, i.e., one atom of element X to one of Y, or 2 of X to 3 of Y, etc., with each specific ratio being characteristic of a given compound:

$$X \quad + \quad Y \quad \rightarrow \quad XY$$

1 atom of element X 1 atom of element Y 1 molecule of compound XY

$$2\,X \quad + \quad 3\,Y \quad \rightarrow \quad X_2Y_3$$

2 atoms of element X 3 atoms of element Y 1 molecule of compound X_2Y_3

Thus XY and X_2Y_3 are two different compounds because their molecules contain the atoms of the elements X and Y in different ratios, indicated by the subscripts. (Note that the subscript 1 is always assumed and does not need to be written.)

If atoms have definite constant weights, and if they combine in specific ratios to form molecules, it follows that each molecule of a compound, and thus the bulk compound itself, will have a characteristic composition by weight. This is, then, the atomic explanation of the Law of Constant Proportions.

The Law of Multiple Proportions may also be explained by Dalton's atomic theory. As an illustration, let us return to the example of the two compounds of carbon and oxygen in the previous section. Compound A contained twice as many grams of oxygen per gram of carbon as compound B. Since all atoms of oxygen have the same weight according to the atomic theory, there must be twice as many atoms of oxygen in a molecule of A as in a molecule of B. Furthermore, since atoms always combine in ratios of small whole numbers, the simplest formula for compound A must be CO_2 (carbon dioxide) and for compound B, CO (carbon monoxide).

Dalton's atomic theory was generally accepted by his contemporaries because it provided an explanation for the weight relationships that had been observed between combining elements. However, there were not yet any physical means of proving his postulate, however probable it seemed.

The success of Dalton's theory is reflected in the following quotation from a contemporary chemistry textbook (J. L. Comstock, *Elements of Chemistry*, 1832):

"In respect to the truth or falsity of this (Dalton's) theory, it is obviously without the bounds of demonstration, for we never can ascertain whether the proportions on which it is founded are the smallest in which bodies combine, nor whether, if so, they combine atom to atom, as is supposed. But whether it be true or false, it does not in the least affect the truth of the law of definite proportions, which, as already stated, is founded on experiment alone, and is therefore purely an expression of facts. The atomic theory, however, must always be considered an elegant and probable hypothesis, and while it displays uncommon ingenuity, and great chemical research, has the advantage of agreeing, in general, perfectly with the facts obtained by analysis."

Obviously, the author accepts the postulates of Dalton's theory, but since the existence of atoms had not yet been physically demonstrated, his faith in the atomic theory depends entirely on its ability to explain known chemical facts.

2.4 **Atomic Weights**

We have seen that elements, when combining to form compounds, react in specific proportions by weight. If we subscribe to Dalton's theory that atoms having a characteristic weight are the basic building blocks of matter, then we should be able to place the masses of the different atoms on a relative scale.

It is most convenient to establish a scale of **atomic weights** by defining the mass of one element and then determining the masses of the other elements relative to it. It was necessary to proceed in this manner in the nineteenth century, since the experimental means were not available to determine the absolute mass of an atom. Originally the reference on the scale was the oxygen atom; today it is the atom of ^{12}C, a particular isotope of carbon (see page 97), which is *defined* to have a mass of precisely 12.0000 **atomic mass units (amu)**. Thus one atomic mass unit is $\frac{1}{12}$ of the mass of an atom of ^{12}C. It is now known that *1 amu = 1.66053 × 10^{-24} gram.* Note that the tabulated value of the atomic mass of carbon (Table 2–1) is 12.011 amu. This is the result of the fact that not all carbon atoms have exactly the same mass (page 97).

The atomic weights of other elements were determined by carefully weighing the amounts of elements that react with one another (more sophisticated techniques are now available). Referring to the example of carbon reacting with oxygen, the simplest compound was formed from 1.33 g O and 1.00 g C and had the formula CO. Since the carbon and oxygen atoms are in a one to one ratio in this formula, one atom of oxygen must weigh 1.33 times as much as a carbon atom. Hence the atomic mass of an oxygen atom (which we will call x) is:

$$\frac{1.33 \text{ g}}{1.00 \text{ g}} = \frac{x}{12.01} \text{ amu}$$

$$x = 16.0 \text{ amu}$$

We have just experimentally determined the atomic mass of oxygen. Table 2–1 lists the atomic masses of all the known stable elements, measured by modern equipment and methods. (For convenient reference, the table is also shown inside the back cover of this book.)

Table 2–1

Atomic Weights of the Elements

ELEMENT	SYMBOL	ATOMIC NUMBER*	ATOMIC WEIGHT	ELEMENT	SYMBOL	ATOMIC NUMBER*	ATOMIC WEIGHT
Aluminum	Al	13	26.98154	Neon	Ne	10	20.179
Antimony	Sb	51	121.75	Neptunium	Np	93	237.0482
Argon	Ar	18	39.948	Nickel	Ni	28	58.71
Arsenic	As	33	74.9216	Niobium	Nb	41	92.9064
Barium	Ba	56	137.34	Nitrogen	N	7	14.0067
Beryllium	Be	4	9.01218	Osmium	Os	76	190.2
Bismuth	Bi	83	208.9808	Oxygen	O	8	15.9994
Boron	B	5	10.81	Palladium	Pd	46	106.4
Bromine	Br	35	79.904	Phosphorus	P	15	30.97376
Cadmium	Cd	48	112.40	Platinum	Pt	78	195.09
Calcium	Ca	20	40.08	Potassium	K	19	39.102
Carbon	C	6	12.011	Praseodymium	Pr	59	140.9077
Cerium	Ce	58	140.12	Protactinium	Pa	91	231.0359
Cesium	Cs	55	132.9054	Radium	Ra	88	226.0254
Chlorine	Cl	17	35.453	Rhenium	Re	75	186.2
Chromium	Cr	24	51.996	Rhodium	Rh	45	102.9055
Cobalt	Co	27	58.9332	Rubidium	Rb	37	85.4678
Copper	Cu	29	63.546	Ruthenium	Ru	44	101.07
Dysprosium	Dy	66	162.50	Samarium	Sm	62	150.4
Erbium	Er	68	167.26	Scandium	Sc	21	44.9559
Europium	Eu	63	151.96	Selenium	Se	34	78.96
Fluorine	F	9	18.99840	Silicon	Si	14	28.086
Gadolinium	Gd	64	157.25	Silver	Ag	47	107.868
Gallium	Ga	31	69.72	Sodium	Na	11	22.9898
Germanium	Ge	32	72.59	Strontium	Sr	38	87.62
Gold	Au	79	196.9665	Sulfur	S	16	32.06
Hafnium	Hf	72	178.49	Tantalum	Ta	73	180.9479
Helium	He	2	4.00260	Technetium	Tc	43	98.9062
Holmium	Ho	67	164.9304	Tellurium	Te	52	127.60
Hydrogen	H	1	1.0079	Terbium	Tb	65	158.9254
Indium	In	49	114.82	Thallium	Tl	81	204.37
Iodine	I	53	126.9045	Thorium	Th	90	232.0381
Iridium	Ir	77	192.22	Thulium	Tm	69	168.9342
Iron	Fe	26	55.847	Tin	Sn	50	118.69
Krypton	Kr	36	83.80	Titanium	Ti	22	47.90
Lanthanum	La	57	138.9055	Tungsten	W	74	183.85
Lead	Pb	82	207.2	Uranium	U	92	238.029
Lithium	Li	3	6.941	Vanadium	V	23	50.9414
Lutetium	Lu	71	174.97	Xenon	Xe	54	131.30
Magnesium	Mg	12	24.305	Ytterbium	Yb	70	173.04
Manganese	Mn	25	54.9380	Yttrium	Y	39	88.9059
Mercury	Hg	80	200.59	Zinc	Zn	30	65.38
Molybdenum	Mo	42	95.94	Zirconium	Zr	40	91.22
Neodymium	Nd	60	144.24				

*Atomic number will be discussed in Chapter 4.

Molecular Weights

Chemists also speak of formula mass, or **formula weight**, which is equal to the sum of the masses of all the atoms in the *formula* of a given compound. To determine the formula weight of AlI_3, for example, we must add the mass of one atom of aluminum (26.98 amu) and the masses of three atoms of iodine (126.90 amu for each atom, or 380.70 for three atoms):

$$1 \text{ atom Al} \times 26.98 \text{ amu/atom Al} = 26.98 \text{ amu}$$
$$3 \text{ atoms I} \times 126.90 \text{ amu/atom I} = \underline{380.70 \text{ amu}}$$
$$\text{formula weight of } AlI_3 = 407.68 \text{ amu}$$

Thus there are 407.68 atomic mass units for each formula unit of AlI_3.

The formula weight of a compound is often referred to loosely as a **molecular weight**, although the formula expressed is not always the formula of a discrete molecule. The reason for this will be discussed in Chapter 6.

In calculating a molecular weight, it is essential to include the weights of all the atoms indicated.

EXAMPLE 2.4a Calculate the molecular weight of NaCl (sodium chloride). In a formula unit of NaCl there are:

$$1 \text{ atom Na} \times 22.99 \text{ amu/atom Na} = 22.99 \text{ amu}$$
$$1 \text{ atom Cl} \times 35.45 \text{ amu/atom Cl} = \underline{35.45 \text{ amu}}$$
$$\text{molecular weight of NaCl} = 58.44 \text{ amu}$$

EXAMPLE 2.4b Calculate the molecular weight of $Cu_5(PO_4)_2(OH)_4$ (pseudomalachite, a semiprecious gemstone).

Note that a subscript after a parenthesis indicates that the unit inside the parentheses must be multiplied by that subscript. Thus in a formula unit of pseudomalachite there are two PO_4 groups (each containing four atoms of oxygen) and four OH groups (each containing one atom of oxygen), giving a total of $(2 \times 4) + (4 \times 1) = 12$ oxygen atoms. Similarly, there are two phosphorus atoms and four hydrogen atoms, as well as the five copper atoms, in the molecule.

$$5 \text{ atoms Cu} \times 63.55 \text{ amu/atom Cu} = 317.75 \text{ amu}$$
$$2 \text{ atoms P} \times 30.97 \text{ amu/atom P} = 61.94 \text{ amu}$$
$$12 \text{ atoms O} \times 16.00 \text{ amu/atom O} = 192.00 \text{ amu}$$
$$4 \text{ atoms H} \times 1.008 \text{ amu/atom H} = \underline{4.03 \text{ amu}}$$
$$\text{molecular weight of Cu}_5(\text{PO}_4)_2(\text{OH})_4 = 575.72 \text{ amu}$$

EXAMPLE 2.4c   Calculate the molecular weight of $CuSO_4 \cdot 5H_2O$.
This is an example of a *hydrated* compound. Each formula unit of this compound contains five formula weights of water (as indicated by $\cdot 5H_2O$) so that there is one Cu atom, one SO_4 group, and five H_2O molecules per formula unit. There are therefore $(4 \times 1) + (5 \times 1) = 9$ oxygen atoms and $5 \times 2 = 10$ hydrogen atoms, as well as 1 copper atom and 1 sulfur atom.

$$1 \text{ atom Cu} \times 63.55 \text{ amu/atom Cu} = 63.55 \text{ amu}$$
$$1 \text{ atom S} \times 32.06 \text{ amu/atom S} = 32.06 \text{ amu}$$
$$9 \text{ atoms O} \times 16.00 \text{ amu/atom O} = 144.00 \text{ amu}$$
$$10 \text{ atoms H} \times 1.008 \text{ amu/atom H} = \underline{10.08 \text{ amu}}$$
$$\text{molecular weight of CuSO}_4 \cdot 5H_2O = 249.69 \text{ amu}$$

2.5   The Mole

We have just seen that one atomic mass unit represents an extremely small mass (1.66×10^{-24} g). This small mass is inconvenient for the chemist who normally works with gram quantities of substances. Therefore, the following definition is made:

A *gram-atom* (or *gram-atomic weight*) of an element is that amount of the element that has the same mass in grams as the atomic mass in atomic mass units.

Oxygen, for example, has an atomic weight of 16.00 amu. One gram-atom of O therefore contains 16.00 g O. Carbon has an atomic weight of 12.01 amu; one gram-atom of C contains 12.01 g C.

Since the ratio of the atomic weights of carbon to oxygen is 12 to 16, the ratio of the weights of an equal number of carbon and oxygen atoms will also be 12 to 16. For example, the ratio of weights of two carbon and two oxygen atoms is:

$$\frac{12 \times 2}{16 \times 2} = \frac{12}{16}$$

and the ratio of weights of 10^6 atoms of each is:

$$\frac{12 \times 10^6}{16 \times 10^6} = \frac{12}{16}$$

The converse is also true: If you have a quantity of carbon and a quantity of oxygen, and if the weight ratio of the two quantities is 12 to 16, then you have equal numbers of atoms of carbon and oxygen. Therefore, if you have one gram-atom of carbon (12.01 g C) and one gram-atom of oxygen (16.00 g O), then you have equal numbers of atoms of the two elements. In general, then:

> One gram-atom of any element contains the same number of atoms as one gram-atom of any other element.

A logical question now is, "Just how many atoms *are* there in a gram-atom?" One gram-atom of any element contains **Avogadro's number** of atoms, experimentally determined to be equal to 6.022×10^{23} atoms per gram-atom.

One also speaks of a **gram-formula weight** of a compound, which is simply defined as that amount of a *compound* that has the same mass in grams as the formula mass in amu (cf. definition of a gram-atomic weight). A gram-formula weight will then also contain 6.022×10^{23} formula units (Avogadro's number of formula units). For convenience, we now define the **mole** (abbreviated mol) as being Avogadro's number of formula units for any chemical species (atom, formula unit, molecule, etc.). Thus a mole of carbon, C, is the same quantity as a gram-atom of C, that is, 12.01 g C. A mole of AlI_3 is the same quantity as a gram-formula weight of AlI_3, or 407.68 g AlI_3. From now on we will speak only of moles and not of gram-atoms or gram-formula weights. The chemist uses the mole as a way of counting chemical quantities.

For example, a baker buys eggs by the dozen (units of 12). If he needs 42 eggs then he needs:

$$42 \text{ eggs} \times \frac{1 \text{ dozen eggs}}{12 \text{ eggs}} = 3.5 \text{ dozen eggs}$$

A chemist measures quantities in moles. Therefore, for a particular reaction, 0.50 moles of a chemical might be needed.

Note carefully that although a mole always contains 6.022×10^{23}

formula units, the amount of mass (that is, the molecular weight) in a mole depends on the *chemical* formula:

$$1 \text{ mole AlI}_3 \text{ contains } 407.68 \text{ g AlI}_3$$

$$1 \text{ mole Al}_2\text{I}_6 \text{ contains } 815.36 \text{ g Al}_2\text{I}_6$$

Note also that since the molecular weight has units of grams per mole (g/mol) as well as amu per molecule, the molecular weight may be used as a *conversion factor* to convert from grams to moles, and vice versa.

EXAMPLE 2.5a   How many moles of $MnCl_2$ are in 48.2 g $MnCl_2$?
The molecular weight of $MnCl_2$ is:

$$
\begin{array}{l}
1 \text{ mol Mn} \times 54.94 \text{ g/mol Mn} = 54.94 \text{ g Mn} \\
2 \text{ mol Cl} \times 35.45 \text{ g/mol Cl} = \underline{70.90 \text{ g Cl}} \\
\phantom{2 \text{ mol Cl} \times 35.45 \text{ g/mol Cl} = 70.} 125.84 \text{ g/mol MnCl}_2
\end{array}
$$

When we convert grams to moles, we have:

$$48.2 \text{ g MnCl}_2 \times \frac{1 \text{ mol MnCl}_2}{125.84 \text{ g MnCl}_2} = 0.383 \text{ mol MnCl}_2$$

EXAMPLE 2.5b   How many grams are there in 1.50 moles of B_2O_3?
The molecular weight of B_2O_3 is:

$$
\begin{array}{l}
2 \text{ mol B} \times 10.81 \text{ g/mol B} = 21.62 \text{ g B} \\
3 \text{ mol O} \times 16.00 \text{ g/mol O} = \underline{48.00 \text{ g O}} \\
\phantom{3 \text{ mol O} \times 16.00 \text{ g/mol O} = } 69.62 \text{ g/mol B}_2\text{O}_3
\end{array}
$$

Conversion of moles to grams gives us:

$$1.50 \text{ mol B}_2\text{O}_3 \times \frac{69.62 \text{ g B}_2\text{O}_3}{1 \text{ mol B}_2\text{O}_3} = 104 \text{ g B}_2\text{O}_3$$

EXAMPLE 2.5c   How many atoms are there in 0.0243 gram of gold?

First, we convert grams to moles:

$$0.0243 \text{ g Au} \times \frac{1 \text{ mol Au}}{196.97 \text{ g Au}} = 1.23 \times 10^{-4} \text{ mol Au}$$

Since 1 mol contains Avogadro's number of units (in this case, atoms), we have:

$$(1.23 \times 10^{-4} \text{ mol Au}) \times \left(\frac{6.022 \times 10^{23} \text{ atoms Au}}{1 \text{ mol Au}}\right)$$

$$= 7.41 \times 10^{19} \text{ atoms Au}$$

EXAMPLE 2.5d   How many moles are there in 2.84×10^{24} molecules of H_2O? How many grams?

To answer the first question, we must convert molecules to moles:

$$(2.84 \times 10^{24} \text{ molecules } H_2O) \times \left(\frac{1 \text{ mol}}{6.022 \times 10^{23} \text{ molecules}}\right)$$

$$= 4.72 \text{ mol } H_2O$$

To answer the second question, we must convert moles to grams:

$$\text{molecular weight } H_2O = (2 \times 1.008) + (16.00) = 18.02$$

$$4.72 \text{ mol } H_2O \times \frac{18.02 \text{ g } H_2O}{1 \text{ mol } H_2O} = 85.1 \text{ g } H_2O$$

Diatomic Molecules

Some elements occur as **diatomic molecules**, which are molecules made up of pairs of atoms. Thus oxygen gas is actually composed of O_2 molecules rather than O atoms. Among other elements that occur as diatomic molecules are hydrogen (H_2), fluorine (F_2), chlorine (Cl_2), and nitrogen (N_2). These elements are not found in chemical reactions as atoms because in their elemental states they occur as diatomic molecules. For example, hydrogen and oxygen react to form water:

$$2 \ H_2 + O_2 \longrightarrow 2 \ H_2O$$

For this reason, a mole of oxygen means a mole of O_2 which is equivalent to 32.00 grams of oxygen (2 mol O $\times$ 16.00 g O/mol O).

The Use of the Mole

The concept of the mole is used extensively in the study of stoichiometric relationships in compounds and chemical reactions. **Stoichiometry** (from the Greek *stoicheion,* element, and *metron,* to measure) is the study of weight relationships in chemically equivalent quantities. In general usage, the term refers in particular to ratios of moles of elements in compounds and of compounds in chemical reactions.

Suppose we want to prepare a compound having the *stoichiometry* of three atoms of iodine to one atom of aluminum. Starting with 1.00 g Al, how much I is needed? First, what do we mean? Stoichiometry is the ratio of the component atoms; the stoichiometry of the compound described above is 3 atoms I/1 atom Al. This is nothing more than the formula of the compound, or AlI_3.

The most important concept to remember when approaching problems involving chemical stoichiometry is to first *convert grams to moles* since equal numbers of moles contain equal numbers of atoms. Therefore, there is a one to one correspondence between the subscripts in the chemical formula and the number of moles.

Getting back to the problem stated above, we start with:

$$1.00 \text{ g Al} \times \frac{1 \text{ mol Al}}{26.98 \text{ g Al}} = 0.0371 \text{ mol Al}$$

The chemical formula tells us that we need three times as many moles of I as Al:

$$0.0371 \text{ mol Al} \times \frac{3 \text{ mol I}}{1 \text{ mol Al}} = 0.111 \text{ mol I}$$

To answer the original question, we convert moles of I back to grams:

$$0.111 \text{ mol I} \times \frac{126.90 \text{ g I}}{1 \text{ mol I}} = 14.1 \text{ g I}$$

To sum up: 1.00 g Al needs 14.1 g I to react with it to produce the compound AlI_3.

Other uses of the mole are presented in the following sections, and Chapter 3 is entirely devoted to problems involving the mole. As implied by this extensive coverage, the mole is one of the most important concepts in chemistry.

2.6 Empirical Formula and Percent Composition

The concept of the mole is useful in determining the formulas of chemical compounds because the *simplest formula* (sometimes called the **empirical formula**) is nothing more than the relative number of moles of the elements making up the compound. It may or may not represent the actual composition of a molecule of the compound (the molecular formula).

The empirical formula of a material is usually determined from experimental analytical data.

EXAMPLE 2.6a   Analysis of a compound of calcium and oxygen gives the following weight percentages: 71.47% Ca and 28.53% O. What is the empirical formula of the compound?

For convenience, let us assume a 100.0 g sample since then the percentage by weight can be directly written as the number of grams. If we convert grams to moles by dividing by the atomic weights, we obtain:

$$\frac{71.47 \text{ g Ca}}{40.08 \text{ g/mol Ca}} = 1.783 \text{ mol Ca}$$

$$\frac{28.53 \text{ g O}}{16.00 \text{ g/mol O}} = 1.783 \text{ mol O}$$

We can then write the mole ratios as:

$$Ca_{1.783}O_{1.783}$$

which can be simplified to CaO because we are dealing with ratios.

EXAMPLE 2.6b   Analysis of an organic compound gives the following weight percentages: 32.0% C, 6.7% H, 18.7% N, and 42.6% O. Determine the empirical formula for the compound.

Let us assume a 100.0 g sample and convert grams to moles by dividing by the atomic weights.

$$\frac{32.0 \text{ g C}}{12.01 \text{ g/mol C}} = 2.66 \text{ mol C}$$

$$\frac{6.7 \text{ g H}}{1.008 \text{ g/mol H}} = 6.6 \text{ mol H}$$

$$\frac{18.7 \text{ g N}}{14.01 \text{ g/mol N}} = 1.33 \text{ mol N}$$

$$\frac{42.6 \text{ g O}}{16.00 \text{ g/mol O}} = 2.66 \text{ mol O}$$

The formula (mole ratios) is then:

$$C_{2.66}H_{6.6}N_{1.33}O_{2.66}$$

Since we wish to deal in ratios of small whole numbers, we divide each subscript by the smallest number (1.33):

$$C_{2.00}H_{4.96}N_{1.00}O_{2.00}$$

The slight deviation (4.96 rather than 5.00) is a result of experimental errors in the determination of the elemental percentages. Thus we may write the empirical formula as $C_2H_5NO_2$.

EXAMPLE 2.6c   A compound containing only Zn, Mo, and O analyzes for 38.0% Zn and 37.2% Mo. Calculate its empirical formula.

Assuming a 100.0 g sample, we have 38.0 g Zn and 37.2 g Mo. If we subtract these weights from 100.0 g we find that the compound contains 24.8 g O. Conversion of grams to moles gives:

$$\frac{38.0 \text{ g Zn}}{65.38 \text{ g/mol Zn}} = 0.581 \text{ mol Zn}$$

$$\frac{37.2 \text{ g Mo}}{95.94 \text{ g/mol Mo}} = 0.388 \text{ mol Mo}$$

$$\frac{24.8 \text{ g O}}{16.00 \text{ g/mol O}} = 1.55 \text{ mol O}$$

The mole ratios are

$$Zn_{0.581}Mo_{0.388}O_{1.55}$$

When we divide by the smallest number (0.388), we obtain:

$$Zn_{1.5}MoO_4$$

Since we want the ratios of small whole numbers, we multiply each subscript by 2 (to remove the nonintegral number 1.5) to arrive at the empirical formula:

$$Zn_3Mo_2O_8$$

The opposite process is the calculation of **percent composition** (by weight) of a compound given the empirical formula of the compound. To do this, we must first determine the amount (in grams) of each element in a mole of compound. This is done by multiplying the relative number of moles by the number of grams per mole of element. If we then divide this by the total number of grams in one mole of the compound (i.e., by the formula weight), we find the percentage (by weight) of each element in the compound.

EXAMPLE 2.6d Calculate the percent composition of $Cu_2(PO_4)Cl$.
Each formula unit contains:

$$
\begin{array}{lll}
2 \text{ mol Cu} \times 63.55 \text{ g/mol Cu} = & 127.10 \text{ g Cu} \\
1 \text{ mol P} \;\times 30.97 \text{ g/mol P} \;\; = & 30.97 \text{ g P} \\
4 \text{ mol O} \;\times 16.00 \text{ g/mol O} \;\; = & 64.00 \text{ g O} \\
1 \text{ mol Cl} \times 35.45 \text{ g/mol Cl} = & \underline{35.45 \text{ g Cl}} \\
& 257.52 = \text{molecular weight} \\
& \text{of } Cu_2(PO_4)Cl
\end{array}
$$

$$\text{weight percent Cu} = \frac{127.10 \text{ g Cu}}{257.52 \text{ g}} \times 100\% = 49.36\% \text{ Cu}$$

$$\text{weight percent P} = \frac{30.97 \text{ g P}}{257.52 \text{ g}} \times 100\% = 12.03\% \text{ P}$$

$$\text{weight percent O} = \frac{64.00 \text{ g O}}{257.52 \text{ g}} \times 100\% = 24.85\% \text{ O}$$

$$\text{weight percent Cl} = \frac{35.45 \text{ g Cl}}{257.52 \text{ g}} \times 100\% = 13.77\% \text{ Cl}$$

EXAMPLE 2.6e   A compound of C and H gives, on analysis, the following data:

79.91% C

20.09% H

In a second experiment, the true molecular weight of this compound is determined to be 30.07 g/mol. Determine the empirical formula and the molecular formula for this compound.

First, to determine the empirical formula, we will assume a 100.0 g sample and convert grams to moles using the atomic weights:

$$79.91 \text{ g C} \times \frac{1 \text{ mol C}}{12.01 \text{ g C}} = 6.654 \text{ mol C}$$

$$20.09 \text{ g H} \times \frac{1 \text{ mol H}}{1.008 \text{ g H}} = 19.93 \text{ mol H}$$

We can then write the mole ratios as:

$$C_{6.654}H_{19.93}$$

Then, dividing by the smaller of these numbers, we obtain the empirical formula:

$$CH_{2.995} \quad \text{or} \quad CH_3$$

To determine the true molecular formula, we must realize that the molecular weight is an integral multiple of the "weight" of an empirical formula. For CH_3, the formula weight is $12.01 + 3(1.008) = 15.03$. To

The Empirical Formula of a Protein

Suppose you wanted to determine the empirical formula of a protein, a large biological molecule (see Chapter 15), by ordinary elemental analysis. The results (by weight) for a protein isolated from cod-meal are:

7.25% hydrogen
41.22% carbon
36.10% oxygen
15.06% nitrogen
0.39% sulfur

The relative number of moles of each element is calculated as outlined in the previous section:

H $\quad \dfrac{7.25 \text{ g H}}{1.008 \text{ g/mol H}} = 7.19 \quad$ mol H

C $\quad \dfrac{41.22 \text{ g C}}{12.01 \text{ g/mol C}} = 3.43 \quad$ mol C

O $\quad \dfrac{36.10 \text{ g O}}{16.00 \text{ g/mol O}} = 2.26 \quad$ mol O

N $\quad \dfrac{15.06 \text{ g N}}{14.01 \text{ g/mol N}} = 1.07 \quad$ mol N

S $\quad \dfrac{0.39 \text{ g S}}{32.06 \text{ g/mol S}} = 0.012$ mol S

After dividing each number by the smallest, 0.012, the empirical formula is found to be $H_{599}C_{286}O_{188}N_{89}S$.

Since the formula cannot be expressed in mole ratios of small whole numbers, this protein is a very complex molecule containing a large number of atoms. It should be pointed out that for complex molecules even a very small error in the chemical analyses will produce significant changes in the apparent empirical formula. For example, if the oxygen is analyzed at 36.07% and the sulfur at 0.42%, a change of only 0.03% for each, the new empirical formula becomes $H_{553}C_{264}O_{173}N_{82}S$. Thus the determination of a chemical formula by elemental analysis is not very reliable for a large complex molecule such as a protein. Instead, current practice is to break a protein up into its much smaller chemical subunits (single or small groups of amino acids), each of which is identified individually. In this manner the more accurately determined empirical formula for this protein is $H_{555}C_{265}O_{174}N_{83}S$.

determine the multiple, we divide the molecular weight by the formula weight:

$$\frac{30.07}{15.03} = 2$$

Therefore, the molecular formula is two times the empirical formula, or:

C_2H_6

2.7 Chemical Equations

Chemical equations are nothing more than a chemical shorthand notation:

$$\text{reactants} \longrightarrow \text{products}$$

The chemical equation must satisfy three conditions:

1. It must be consistent with the "chemical facts"; that is, all of the reactants and products that are observed must be included in the equation.
2. It must retain conservation of mass.
3. It must retain conservation of charge.

If conditions two and three are satisfied, the equation is said to be **balanced**. In a balanced equation the arrow, which indicates the direction of the reaction, is equivalent to an equal sign.

At this stage we shall be concerned only with equations that can be easily balanced by inspection. (In Chapter 13 you will be shown how to balance more complex oxidation-reduction equations.) As an example, it is observed that methane (CH_4) burns in oxygen gas (O_2) to form carbon dioxide (CO_2) and water (H_2O). The unbalanced equation for this reaction would be written:

$$CH_4(g) + O_2(g) \longrightarrow CO_2(g) + H_2O(l) \qquad \text{(unbalanced)}$$

Note the use of (g) and (l) which indicate gaseous and liquid states; (s) would be used to indicate a solid and (aq) to indicate an aqueous solution. To balance this equation, note that on the left each CH_4 molecule contains four H atoms, so that a coefficient of 2 must be placed in front of the water molecule on the right to give a total of four H atoms. There are now a total of four O atoms on the right-hand (product) side of the equation (two from the CO_2 molecule and one from each of the two H_2O molecules). Therefore a coefficient of 2 must be placed before the O_2 molecule on the left to provide the necessary four O atoms on the reactant side. The equation is now balanced:

$$CH_4(g) + 2\ O_2(g) \longrightarrow CO_2(g) + 2\ H_2O(l)$$

A balanced chemical equation represents the *stoichiometry* of the reaction, or the relative amounts of reactants that react chemically to form the products. The **coefficients** in a balanced equation indicate the number of molecules or moles of reactants and products. The above equation says that one molecule of CH_4 reacts with two molecules of O_2 to produce one molecule of CO_2 and two molecules of H_2O, *or* one mole of CH_4 reacts with two moles of O_2 to form one mole of CO_2 and two moles of H_2O. But more importantly, an equation gives the **molar ratios** between any pair of chemical species (reactants and/or products) in the specific reaction. Therefore, if we know the balanced equation and the number of moles of one of the species involved in the reaction, we can determine the number of moles of any of the other species involved.

EXAMPLE 2.7a How many moles of O_2 gas will react with 3.25 moles of CH_4 according to the preceding equation?
In the equation, two moles of O_2 react with every one mole of CH_4. So if there are 3.25 moles of CH_4, there must be twice as many moles of O_2, or 6.50 moles. To put this in mathematical form, we simply multiply the number of moles of CH_4 by the molar ratio of O_2 to CH_4.

$$3.25 \text{ mol } CH_4 \times \frac{2 \text{ mol } O_2}{1 \text{ mol } CH_4} = 6.50 \text{ mol } O_2$$

EXAMPLE 2.7b How many moles of H_2O are produced if 0.246 mole of CH_4 is burned in O_2 according to the preceding equation?
Here we must assume that there is enough oxygen present to completely react with 0.246 mole of CH_4. In all future problems we may similarly assume that if the amount of reactant is not given it is present in excess.
Because a balanced equation indicates the relationship between any pair of reactants and/or products, we can calculate the amount of H_2O directly; that is, it is not necessary to first calculate the amount of the other reactant, O_2. Again, to determine the number of moles of H_2O mathematically, we simply multiply the number of moles of CH_4 by the molar ratio of H_2O to CH_4.

$$0.246 \text{ mol } CH_4 \times \frac{2 \text{ mol } H_2O}{1 \text{ mol } CH_4} = 0.492 \text{ mol } H_2O$$

Let us consider some other examples of calculations involving weight relationships in chemical equations. We should note here that in all of our problems involving stoichiometry we are assuming that the reaction will proceed to completion, i.e., that all of at least one reactant will be used up.

EXAMPLE 2.7c How many moles of NH_3 can be formed if 84.0 g N_2 are reacted with excess H_2?
Our first step is to balance the equation:

$$N_2 + H_2 \longrightarrow NH_3 \quad \text{(unbalanced)}$$

The coefficient 2 is added to NH_3 to balance N, and the coefficient 3 is added to H_2 to balance H:

$$N_2(g) + 3\ H_2(g) \longrightarrow 2\ NH_3(g) \quad \text{(balanced)}$$

The second step is to convert grams to moles for N_2:

$$84.0 \text{ g } N_2 \times \frac{1 \text{ mol } N_2}{28.0 \text{ g } N_2} = 3.00 \text{ mol } N_2$$

Finally, we consider the stoichiometry of the reaction:

$$3.00 \text{ mol } N_2 \times \frac{2 \text{ mol } NH_3}{1 \text{ mol } N_2} = 6.00 \text{ mol } NH_3$$

EXAMPLE 2.7d Low-grade coal contains sulfur in the form of the mineral pyrite (FeS_2). When it is burned, SO_2 (a pollutant) is produced according to the reaction:

$$4\ FeS_2(s) + 11\ O_2(g) \longrightarrow 2\ Fe_2O_3(s) + 8\ SO_2(g)$$

How many grams of SO_2 are formed by burning 1.00 kg of coal that contains 2.5% FeS_2?
First, we find the number of grams of FeS_2 in 1.00 kg of coal by multiplying this amount of coal (in grams) by the proportion of pyrite in it:

$$1.00 \text{ kg coal} \times \frac{1{,}000 \text{ g}}{1 \text{ kg}} \times \frac{0.025 \text{ g } FeS_2}{1 \text{ g coal}} = 25 \text{ g } FeS_2$$

We now convert grams to moles:

$$\text{molecular weight FeS}_2 = 55.85 \text{ g/mol Fe} + 2(32.06 \text{ g/mol S})$$
$$= 119.97 \text{ g/mol FeS}_2$$

$$25 \text{ g FeS}_2 \times \frac{1 \text{ mol FeS}_2}{119.97 \text{ g FeS}_2} = 0.21 \text{ mol FeS}_2$$

To determine the amount of SO_2 produced (in moles), we multiply the number of moles of FeS_2 by the molar ratio of SO_2 to FeS_2:

$$0.21 \text{ mol FeS}_2 \times \frac{8 \text{ mol SO}_2}{4 \text{ mol FeS}_2} = 0.42 \text{ mol SO}_2$$

When we convert moles to grams, we obtain:

$$\text{molecular weight SO}_2 = 32.06 \text{ g/mol S} + 2(16.00 \text{ g/mol O})$$
$$= 64.06 \text{ g/mol SO}_2$$

$$0.42 \text{ mol SO}_2 \times \frac{64.06 \text{ g SO}_2}{1 \text{ mol SO}_2} = 27 \text{ g SO}_2$$

2.8 **Energy Changes Associated with Chemical Reactions**

When chemical reactions take place, energy (most often in the form of heat) can be liberated to or absorbed from the surroundings. Recall from Chapter 1 (page 30) that the unit used to measure heat is the *calorie*. We have already defined an *exothermic* process as one which takes place with the *liberation* of heat and an *endothermic* process as one in which heat is *absorbed*. The change in heat content, or the change in **enthalpy** (**H**), is expressed mathematically as:

$$\Delta H = H_{\text{products}} - H_{\text{reactants}}$$

(The Greek letter delta, Δ, indicates "difference in.") By convention, an exothermic reaction is one in which H_{products} is less than $H_{\text{reactants}}$ and ΔH is therefore negative. In other words, the heat content of the products is less than that of the starting materials, indicating that heat has been given off during the reaction. The reverse is true for an endothermic reaction, of course. As an example of the exothermic process, consider a reaction between A and B in which the change in enthalpy is -100 kcal:

$$A + B \longrightarrow products; \Delta H = -100 \text{ kcal}$$

This means that heat is a product in this reaction.

$$\Delta H = H_{products} - H_{reactants}$$
$$H_{reactants} = H_{products} - \Delta H$$
$$= H_{products} + 100 \text{ kcal}$$

We may now rewrite the reaction as:

$$A + B \longrightarrow products + 100 \text{ kcal}$$

In an endothermic reaction, in which heat is absorbed and ΔH is positive, heat is a reactant:

$$C + D + heat \longrightarrow products$$

As an example, consider an endothermic reaction where $\Delta H = +75$ kcal:

$$\Delta H = H_{products} - H_{reactants}$$

After substitution and rearrangement, we have:

$$H_{reactants} + 75 \text{ kcal} = H_{products}$$

Compounds of carbon and hydrogen, called *hydrocarbons*, burn in air (oxygen), with the carbon being converted to CO_2 and the hydrogen to H_2O. If one mole of methane is burned in two moles of oxygen, 213 kcal of heat is liberated. In equation form, this becomes:

$$CH_4(g) + 2 \text{ } O_2(g) \longrightarrow CO_2(g) + 2 \text{ } H_2O(l) + 213 \text{ kcal}$$

For this reaction, then, $\Delta H = -213$ kcal. The enthalpy given off, or "lost," in the reaction is "gained" as heat by the surroundings.

So far we have discussed the amount of heat liberated or absorbed only for reactions involving a fixed amount of materials. The enthalpy associated with a reaction, however, can be used to calculate the heat produced by any amount of materials.

EXAMPLE 2.8a How many grams of CH_4 must react with O_2 to produce 100. kcal of heat according to the above reaction?
Because 213 kcal are given off for every mole of CH_4 burned, we may use this ratio as a conversion factor:

$$100. \text{ kcal} \times \frac{1 \text{ mol } CH_4}{213 \text{ kcal}} = 0.469 \text{ mol } CH_4$$

Conversion of moles to grams gives:

$$\text{molecular weight } CH_4 = 12.01 + 4(1.008) = 16.04 \text{ g/mol } CH_4$$

$$0.469 \text{ mol } CH_4 \times 16.04 \text{ g/mol } CH_4 = 7.52 \text{ g } CH_4$$

EXAMPLE 2.8b Ethane (C_2H_6) burns according to the reaction:

$$2 \text{ } C_2H_6 + 7 \text{ } O_2 \longrightarrow 4 \text{ } CO_2 + 6 \text{ } H_2O \qquad \Delta H = -746 \text{ kcal}$$

How much heat is liberated by burning 84.0 g ethane?
First we convert grams to moles:

$$\text{molecular weight } C_2H_6 = 2(12.01) + 6(1.008) = 30.07 \text{ g/mol } C_2H_6$$

$$\frac{84.0 \text{ g } C_2H_6}{30.07 \text{ g/mol } C_2H_6} = 2.79 \text{ mol } C_2H_6$$

According to the equation, 746 kcal are liberated for every 2 moles of C_2H_6 burned:

$$2.79 \text{ mol } C_2H_6 \times \frac{746 \text{ kcal}}{2 \text{ mol } C_2H_6} = 1.04 \times 10^3 \text{ kcal}$$

EXAMPLE 2.8c   1.44 kcal are required to melt 1.00 mol of ice at 0 °C.

$$H_2O(s) \longrightarrow H_2O(l) \qquad \Delta H = +1.44 \text{ kcal}$$

How much energy is required to melt a 40.0 g ice cube?
Conversion of grams to moles gives:

$$\text{molecular weight } H_2O = 2(1.008) + 16.00 = 18.02 \text{ g/mol } H_2O$$

$$40.0 \text{ g } H_2O \times \frac{1 \text{ mol } H_2O}{18.02 \text{ g } H_2O} = 2.22 \text{ mol } H_2O$$

We can now calculate the new ΔH:

$$2.22 \text{ mol } H_2O \times \frac{1.44 \text{ kcal}}{1 \text{ mol } H_2O} = 3.20 \text{ kcal}$$

2.9 Limiting Reagent

Consider the following problem: How many grams of H_2O will be formed
when a mixture of 1.93 g C_2H_4 and 5.92 g O_2 is ignited?

$$C_2H_4(g) + 3 O_2(g) \longrightarrow 2 CO_2(g) + 2 H_2O(l)$$

Unless the C_2H_4 and O_2 are present in precisely the proper *molar ratio*
(1 to 3, in this case), one of the reactants will be used up before the other
when the reaction occurs. The reactant that disappears first is called the
limiting reagent because it determines the amount of product formed. (A
reagent is simply a substance that participates in a chemical reaction.)
To solve this particular problem, we begin by converting grams to
moles:

$$\frac{1.93 \text{ g } C_2H_4}{28.05 \text{ g/mol } C_2H_4} = 0.0688 \text{ mol } C_2H_4$$

$$\frac{5.92 \text{ g } O_2}{32.00 \text{ g/mol } O_2} = 0.185 \text{ mol } O_2$$

But the stoichiometry of the equation indicates that we need 3 mol O_2 to every 1 mol C_2H_4; is there enough O_2 to burn 0.0688 mol C_2H_4?

$$0.0688 \text{ mol } C_2H_4 \times \frac{3 \text{ mol } O_2}{1 \text{ mol } C_2H_4} = 0.206 \text{ mol } O_2$$

No, we need 0.206 mol and there is only 0.185 mol O_2 present; therefore O_2 is the limiting reagent. (If there were excess O_2, or more than 0.206 mol O_2 in this case, C_2H_4 would be the limiting reagent.)
Our next step is to determine the amount of water that is formed by completely reacting the O_2:

$$0.185 \text{ mol } O_2 \times \frac{2 \text{ mol } H_2O}{3 \text{ mol } O_2} = 0.123 \text{ mol } H_2O$$

Conversion of moles to grams gives us:

$$0.123 \text{ mol } H_2O \times 18.02 \text{ g/mol } H_2O = 2.22 \text{ g } H_2O$$

EXAMPLE 2.9a   How many grams of $FeSb_2$ can be made from 2.000 g Fe and 3.000 g Sb? The formula for this compound indicates that the molar ratio of Fe to Sb is 1 mol Fe/2 mol Sb. One may also write a hypothetical equation to represent the formation of $FeSb_2$:

$$1 \text{ Fe} + 2 \text{ Sb} \longrightarrow FeSb_2$$

When we convert grams to moles, we obtain:

$$\frac{2.000 \text{ g Fe}}{55.85 \text{ g/mol Fe}} = 0.03581 \text{ mol Fe}$$

$$\frac{3.000 \text{ g Sb}}{121.75 \text{ g/mol Sb}} = 0.02464 \text{ mol Sb}$$

We then must identify the limiting reagent:

$$0.02464 \text{ mol Sb} \times \frac{1 \text{ mol Fe}}{2 \text{ mol Sb}} = 0.01232 \text{ mol Fe (we have enough)}$$

or

$$0.03581 \text{ mol Fe} \times \frac{2 \text{ mol Sb}}{1 \text{ mol Fe}} = 0.07162 \text{ mol Sb (we do } not \text{ have enough)}$$

Taken either way, Sb is the limiting reagent.
We can now determine the amount of $FeSb_2$ formed:

$$0.02464 \text{ mol Sb} \times \frac{1 \text{ mol FeSb}_2}{2 \text{ mol Sb}} = 0.01232 \text{ mol FeSb}_2$$

Conversion of moles to grams gives us:

$$0.01232 \text{ mol FeSb}_2 \times 299.35 \text{ g/mol FeSb}_2 = 3.688 \text{ g FeSb}_2$$

2.10 Theoretical and Percent Yield

The maximum amount of product that can be produced in a given reaction (under ideal conditions) is known as the **theoretical yield**. The **actual yield** is the yield obtained experimentally (under laboratory conditions) and is less than or equal to the theoretical yield. The **percent yield** is then defined as:

$$\text{percent yield} = \frac{\text{actual yield}}{\text{theoretical yield}} \times 100$$

Consider the production of aspirin:

$$\underset{\text{salicylic acid}}{2\ C_7H_6O_3} + \underset{\text{acetic anhydride}}{C_4H_6O_3} \longrightarrow \underset{\text{aspirin}}{2\ C_9H_8O_4} + H_2O$$

If we start with 1.50 kg salicylic acid and 2.00 kg acetic anhydride, what is the theoretical yield of aspirin?
Conversion of grams to moles gives:

$$\frac{1.50 \times 10^3 \text{ g acid}}{138.12 \text{ g/mol acid}} = 10.9 \text{ mol C}_7H_6O_3$$

$$\frac{2.00 \times 10^3 \text{ g anhydride}}{102.09 \text{ g/mol anhydride}} = 19.6 \text{ mol C}_4H_6O_3$$

We then determine the limiting reagent:

Since the equation indicates that we need 2 mol acid/1 mol anhydride, it is obvious that the limiting reagent is $C_7H_6O_3$ (that is, $C_4H_6O_3$ is in excess).

We can now calculate theoretical yield:

$$10.9 \text{ mol } C_9H_8O_4 \times 180.15 \text{ g/mol } C_9H_8O_4 = 1960 \text{ g } C_9H_8O_4$$
$$= 1.96 \text{ kg } C_9H_8O_4$$

Assume that in an experiment using these amounts of reactants, 1.75 kg of aspirin are isolated. Calculate the percent yield.

$$\text{percent yield} = \frac{1.75 \text{ kg}}{1.96 \text{ kg}} \times 100\%$$

$$= 89.3\%$$

This means that the yield of the laboratory reaction is only 89.3% of the yield under hypothetical, ideal conditions.

TERMS AND CONCEPTS

- Law of Conservation of Mass
- Chemical synthesis versus analysis
- Laws of Constant and Multiple Proportions
- Dalton's atomic theory
  atoms and molecules
- Atomic mass unit (amu)
- Atomic weight, formula weight, and molecular weight
- Gram-atomic weight (gram-atom) and gram-formula weight
- Avogadro's number
- Mole

- Diatomic molecules
- Stoichiometry
- Empirical formula
- Percent composition
- Chemical equation
- Balanced equation
  coefficient
- Molar ratio
- Enthalpy (H)
  change in enthalpy (ΔH)
- Reagent and limiting reagent
- Theoretical, actual, and percent yields

QUESTIONS

1. Briefly trace the history of modern chemistry. Include the contributions of Democritus, the alchemists, Boyle, Lavoisier, and Dalton.

2. Briefly define or explain the following:
   a. the Law of Conservation of Matter
   b. synthesis versus analysis
   c. the Law of Constant Proportions
   d. the Law of Multiple Proportions
   e. Dalton's atomic theory

3. Calculate the molecular weights of the following compounds (in g/mol):
   a. CO_2 (carbon dioxide)
   b. CH_4 (methane)
   c. $C_6H_3Cl_3$ (trichlorobenzene)
   d. FeS_2 (pyrite)

4. a. What is the weight (in grams) of one mole of Pb (lead)?
   b. How many atoms are there in a mole of Pb?
   c. What is the weight (in grams) of one atom of Pb?

5. a. What is the weight (in grams) of one billion gold atoms?
   b. How many gold atoms would weigh as much as a grain of sand (0.1 mg)?
   Express the answers to a and b in exponential and nonexponential notation.

6. Calculate the number of moles present for each of the following:
   a. 12.5 g $Al_2(SO_4)_3$
   b. 23.0 g NaOH
   c. 125 mL octane (C_8H_{18}); density = 0.703 g/mL
   d. 0.375 g $ZnCl_2 \cdot 6H_2O$
   e. 0.735 g $Ni(C_4H_7N_2O_2)_2$

7. The chemical formula of pyrite (fool's gold) is FeS_2.
   a. How many moles are there in 5.00 g of pyrite?
   b. How many molecules of FeS_2 is this?
   c. How many atoms of Fe? of S?

8. Calculate the number of grams present in
   a. 0.0500 mol LiI
   b. 0.960 mol H_2SO_4
   c. 2.37 mol $Ca_3(PO_4)_2$
   d. 6.45 mol $Co_3(PO_4)_2 \cdot H_2O$
   e. 1.50 L ethyl alcohol (C_2H_5OH); density = 0.789 g/mL
   f. How many atoms of each element are there in the quantities in a and c?

9. How many moles are there in 4×10^{22} molecules of a compound? How many grams are there in 4×10^{22} molecules of H_2SO_4?

10. Ascorbic acid (vitamin C) has the molecular formula $C_6H_8O_6$. How many moles of ascorbic acid are there in a 500 mg tablet of vitamin C? How many molecules are there?

11. On chemical analysis, the aromatic flavor called oil of wintergreen is found to contain:

63.18% C
5.26% H
31.56% O

Calculate its empirical formula.
12. The insecticide parathion has the following composition:

41.24% C	4.81% N
4.81% H	10.65% P
27.49% O	11.00% S

Calculate its empirical formula.
13. Red Dye Number 2, once used extensively as a food coloring agent, has been banned because it may produce cancer over a long period of time. Its composition is:

11.46% Na	15.95% S
39.87% C	23.92% O
1.83% H	6.98% N

Calculate its empirical formula.
14. Calculate the percent composition by weight of
  a. the hallucinogens
     (1) mescaline, $C_{11}H_{17}NO_3$
     (2) psilocin, $C_{12}H_{15}N_2O$
     (3) lysergic acid diethylamide (LSD), $C_{20}H_{25}N_3O$
     (4) methoxyamphetamine (STP), $C_{12}H_{17}NO_2$
  b. the tranquilizers
     (1) chlordiazepoxide (Librium), $C_{16}H_{14}N_3OCl$
     (2) meprobamate (Miltown), $C_9H_{18}N_2O_4$
     (3) diazepam (Valium), $C_{16}H_{13}N_2OCl$
15. It is found that arsenic forms two different compounds with fluorine. For example, 1.50 g As will combine with 1.14 g F to form compound X. In another experiment 0.950 g As is found to combine with 1.20 g F to form compound Y.
  a. Show (without using atomic weights) that the Law of Multiple Proportions is satisfied in these observations. (Hint: First find by ratios and proportions the amount of F that will combine with 1.00 g As for each compound.)
  b. What are the percent compositions of As and F in the compounds X and Y? (Assume that you do not know the formulas of the compounds.)
  c. From the percent compositions find the empirical formulas of the compounds X and Y.

16. The explosive TNT (trinitrotoluene) has the molecular formula $C_7H_5N_3O_6$. Calculate the percent composition for each element in this compound.

17. The weed killer 2,4,5-T has the chemical formula $C_6H_2Cl_3OCH_2COOH$. Calculate the weight percentage of chlorine in this compound.

18. Which of the following minerals has the highest percentage of boron?
    a. $Na_2B_4O_7 \cdot 10H_2O$ (borax)
    b. $Na_2B_4O_7 \cdot 4H_2O$ (kernite)
    c. $Ca_2B_6O_{11} \cdot 5H_2O$ (colemanite)

19. Balance the following equations:
    a. $Mg + N_2 \longrightarrow Mg_3N_2$
    b. $P_2O_5 + H_2O \longrightarrow H_3PO_4$
    c. $Ca_3P_2 + H_2O \longrightarrow Ca(OH)_2 + 2\ PH_3$
    d. $V_2O_5 + Al \longrightarrow V + Al_2O_3$
    e. $Al + H_2SO_4 \longrightarrow Al_2(SO_4)_3 + H_2$
    f. $MgNH_4PO_4 \longrightarrow Mg_2P_2O_7 + NH_3 + H_2O$
    g. $ZnS + O_2 \longrightarrow ZnO + SO_2$

20. How many grams of $Al_2(SO_4)_3$ can be made from 24.5 g of $AlCl_3$ by the reaction:

$$2\ AlCl_3 + 3\ H_2SO_4 \longrightarrow Al_2(SO_4)_3 + 6\ HCl$$

21. Of the following elements, which burns with the most energy per gram?

$$\Delta H$$

$$2\ Ca + O_2 \longrightarrow 2\ CaO \qquad -303.8\ \text{kcal}$$

$$4\ Al + 3\ O_2 \longrightarrow 2\ Al_2O_3 \qquad -800.6\ \text{kcal}$$

$$Si + O_2 \longrightarrow SiO_2 \qquad -210.3\ \text{kcal}$$

$$4\ P + 5\ O_2 \longrightarrow P_4O_{10} \qquad -720\ \text{kcal}$$

22. Butane, C_4H_{10}, burns in air according to the reaction:

$$2\ C_4H_{10}(g) + 13\ O_2(g) \longrightarrow 8\ CO_2(g) + 10\ H_2O(l); \Delta H = -1{,}376\ \text{kcal}$$

    a. How much heat per mole of butane is liberated on burning?
    b. What weight of butane is needed to produce 1.0×10^5 kcal of heat?
    c. What weight of oxygen is needed to react with the butane in part b?

23. You are asked to prepare 40.0 g of $Co_3(PO_4)_2$ by the reaction:

$$2(NH_4)_3PO_4 + 3\ CoCO_3 \longrightarrow Co_3(PO_4)_2 + 3\ CO_2 + 6\ NH_3 + 3\ H_2O$$

    a. How many grams of $CoCO_3$ will you need?
    b. How many grams of NH_3 will be produced as a byproduct?

24. a. How many grams of Na_2CO_3 do you need to completely react with $(NH_4)_2WO_4$ to prepare 175 g of $Na_2W_2O_7$?

$$Na_2CO_3 + 2\ (NH_4)_2WO_4 \longrightarrow Na_2W_2O_7 + CO_2 + 4\ NH_3 + 2\ H_2O$$

   b. How many grams of H_2O are formed as a byproduct?

25. One gallon of gasoline contains about 25 moles of the hydrocarbon octane, C_8H_{18}. How many moles of O_2 are needed to burn this amount of octane, and how many moles of CO_2 are formed according to the equation:

$$2\ C_8H_{18}(l) + 25\ O_2(g) \longrightarrow 16\ CO_2(g) + 18\ H_2O(l)$$

26. How many grams of $CaSO_4$ can be produced by mixing solutions containing 20. g $CaCl_2$ and 20. g Na_2SO_4, respectively, according to the reaction:

$$CaCl_2(aq) + Na_2SO_4(aq) \longrightarrow CaSO_4(s) + 2\ NaCl(aq)$$

27. If only 40.0 g $BaCO_3$ and 150.0 g Fe_2O_3 are available, how many grams of $BaFe_{12}O_{19}$ can be made according to the reaction:

$$BaCO_3 + 6\ Fe_2O_3 \longrightarrow BaFe_{12}O_{19} + CO_2$$

3

Stoichiometry
Problems

This chapter will be devoted to a series of completed examples of problems that involve weight relationships among elements and compounds as represented by the empirical formulas of the compounds and by chemical equations.

In solving problems of stoichiometry, two points are especially important to remember:

1. The empirical formula of a chemical compound indicates the *relative number of moles* of each element in the compound.
2. The coefficients before each compound in a balanced equation indicate the *relative number of moles* of each compound involved in the reaction.

Also, in any balanced equation, such as:

$$2 \text{ A} + 3 \text{ B} \longrightarrow \text{A}_2\text{B}_3$$

the arrow may be considered to be *equivalent* to an equal sign. This makes it possible to set up the molar ratios required to convert mole quantities of one species into mole quantities of another.

A general outline to follow in solving problems that involve balanced equations is:

1. Convert grams of species A into moles of species A, using the molecular weight of A as a conversion factor.
2. Convert moles of species A into moles of species B, using the molar ratios given by the chemical formula or the balanced equation.
3. Convert moles of species B back into grams of species B (if called for), using the molecular weight of B as a conversion factor.

EXAMPLE 3.1   The mineral hydroxyapatite, which has the ideal formula $Ca_5(PO_4)_3OH$, is an important source of phosphate for fertilizer and is also the major inorganic component of biological hard tissues (teeth and bones).

_____

PROBLEM

(1) Calculate the molecular weight of $Ca_5(PO_4)_3OH$.

(2) Calculate the weight percentage of Ca and P in hydroxyapatite.

SOLUTION

(1) The molecular weight of a compound is numerically equal to the sum of the atomic weights of the elements in the formula of the compound, and to the number of grams in one mole of the compound. A mole of $Ca_5(PO_4)_3OH$ contains:

$$5 \times 1 = 5 \text{ mol Ca}$$
$$3 \times 1 = 3 \text{ mol P}$$
$$(3 \times 4) + 1 = 13 \text{ mol O}$$
$$1 \times 1 = 1 \text{ mol H}$$

We then determine the weights of these amounts and add them to find the molecular weight.

$$
\begin{array}{llll}
5 \text{ mol Ca} & \times\ 40.08 & \text{g/mol Ca} = 200.40 & \text{g Ca} \\
3 \text{ mol P} & \times\ 30.97 & \text{g/mol P} = 92.91 & \text{g P} \\
13 \text{ mol O} & \times\ 16.00 & \text{g/mol O} = 208.00 & \text{g O} \\
1 \text{ mol H} & \times\ 1.008 & \text{g/mol H} = \underline{1.008} & \text{g H} \\
& & 502.32 & \text{g/mol } Ca_5(PO_4)_3OH
\end{array}
$$

(2) To find the weight percentage of one element in a compound, the mass of that element is divided by the formula weight, and this result is multiplied by 100%.

$$\text{weight percent Ca} = \frac{200.40 \text{ g Ca}}{502.32 \text{ g hydroxyapatite}} \times 100\% = 39.89\% \text{ Ca}$$

$$\text{weight percent P} = \frac{92.91 \text{ g P}}{502.32 \text{ g hydroxyapatite}} \times 100\% = 18.50\% \text{ P}$$

EXAMPLE 3.2   A compound of barium, iron, and oxygen, which has a crystal structure similar to the mineral magnetoplumbite, is widely used in the manufacture of hard ("permanent") magnets.

PROBLEM

Given the following analytical data, calculate the empirical formula of this compound:

12.36 weight percent Ba
60.29 weight percent Fe
27.35 weight percent O

SOLUTION

We may assume that a sample of the compound contains exactly 100 g; the analytical data will then represent the number of grams of each element in the sample. Because the empirical formula represents the simplest *mole ratio* of the component elements, we will convert grams to moles, using the atomic weights as the conversion factors.

$$12.36 \text{ g Ba} \times \frac{1 \text{ mol Ba}}{137.34 \text{ g Ba}} = 0.09000 \text{ mol Ba}$$

$$60.29 \text{ g Fe} \times \frac{1 \text{ mol Fe}}{55.85 \text{ g Fe}} = 1.079 \text{ mol Fe}$$

$$27.35 \text{ g O} \times \frac{1 \text{ mol O}}{16.00 \text{ g O}} = 1.709 \text{ mol O}$$

When expressed in the form of an empirical formula, this ratio of moles becomes:

$$Ba_{0.09000}Fe_{1.079}O_{1.709}$$

To simplify, we divide each of the subscripts by the smallest subscript (0.09000):

$$BaFe_{12}O_{19}$$

EXAMPLE 3.3

Sulfuric acid, H_2SO_4, is manufactured in large quantities in many countries throughout the world. It is considered a "heavy chemical," not because of its weight but because of the amounts in which it is produced and used (more than 30 million tons per year in the U.S. alone). Commercially, sulfuric acid is produced by first burning sulfur, which occurs in nature in the elemental state as the S_8 molecule, and then reacting the product with water in a multistep reaction. The overall reaction is:

$$S_8 + O_2 + H_2O \longrightarrow H_2SO_4 \quad \text{(unbalanced)}$$

This equation is balanced by adding a coefficient of 8 to the H_2SO_4 to balance the sulfur, then a coefficient of 8 to the H_2O to balance the hydrogen, and finally a coefficient of 12 to the O_2 to balance the oxygen:

$$S_8(s) + 12\ O_2(g) + 8\ H_2O(l) \longrightarrow 8\ H_2SO_4(l) \quad \text{(balanced)}$$

PROBLEM

How many kilograms of H_2SO_4 can be produced by reacting 4.00 kg of S by the above reaction?

SOLUTION

(1) When we convert g S to mol S_8, we obtain:

$$\text{molecular weight } S_8 \text{(in g/mol)} = 8 \times 32.06 = 256.48 \text{ g/mol}$$

$$4.00 \times 10^3 \text{ g S} \times \frac{1 \text{ mol } S_8}{256.48 \text{ g S}} = 15.6 \text{ mol } S_8$$

(2) We can convert mol S_8 to mol H_2SO_4 by using the balanced equation:

$$15.6 \text{ mol } S_8 \times \frac{8 \text{ mol } H_2SO_4}{1 \text{ mol } S_8} = 125 \text{ mol } H_2SO_4$$

(3) Conversion of mol H_2SO_4 to g H_2SO_4 gives:

$$\text{molecular weight } H_2SO_4 = 2(1.008) + 1(32.06) + 4(16.00)$$
$$= 98.08 \text{ g/mol } H_2SO_4$$

$$125 \text{ mol } H_2SO_4 \times 98.08 \text{ g/mol } H_2SO_4 = 12{,}260 \text{ g } H_2SO_4$$
$$= 12.3 \text{ kg } H_2SO_4$$

Thus 4.00 kg S can yield 12.3 kg H_2SO_4 in the above reaction.

EXAMPLE 3.4   Acetylene, C_2H_2, was one of the most important gases used for lighting prior to the perfection of the electric light bulb. It was also a source of many chemicals now produced from petroleum and was the object of much research now applied in the petrochemical industry. Acetylene is still used in large quantities to produce very hot flames when burned with oxygen. Although most acetylene is now produced from petroleum, large amounts are still made by the original technique of treating quicklime (calcium oxide, CaO) with coke (carbon) to form calcium carbide, CaC_2, and then treating the calcium carbide with water in a second reaction to produce acetylene.

$$2\ CaO(s) + 4\ C(s) \longrightarrow 2\ CaC_2(s) + O_2(g)$$

$$CaC_2(s) + H_2O(l) \longrightarrow CaO(s) + C_2H_2(g)$$

PROBLEM

How many grams of acetylene can be made from 1.00 kg of quicklime?

SOLUTION

This problem is different from others encountered thus far in that it involves two chemical reactions. However, the approach to solving it is exactly the same as before.

(1) We convert g CaO to mol CaO:

$$\text{molecular weight CaO} = 40.08 + 16.00 = 56.08 \text{ g/mol}$$

$$1.00 \times 10^3 \text{ g CaO} \times \frac{1 \text{ mol CaO}}{56.08 \text{ g CaO}} = 17.8 \text{ mol CaO}$$

(2) We cannot convert mol CaO directly to mol C_2H_2 since the two do not appear in the same equation. Instead we must first convert mol CaO to mol CaC_2, the intermediate, using the stoichiometry of the first equation:

$$17.8 \text{ mol CaO} \times \frac{2 \text{ mol } CaC_2}{2 \text{ mol CaO}} = 17.8 \text{ mol } CaC_2$$

We must now convert mol CaC_2 to mol C_2H_2 using the stoichiometry of the second equation:

$$17.8 \text{ mol } CaC_2 \times \frac{1 \text{ mol } C_2H_2}{1 \text{ mol } CaC_2} = 17.8 \text{ mol } C_2H_2$$

(3) Finally, we can convert mol C_2H_2 to g C_2H_2, using the molecular weight of the compound:

$$\text{molecular weight } C_2H_2 = 2(12.01) + 2(1.008) = 26.04 \text{ g/mol}$$

$$17.8 \text{ mol } C_2H_2 \times \frac{26.04 \text{ g } C_2H_2}{1 \text{ mol } C_2H_2} = 464 \text{ g } C_2H_2$$

EXAMPLE 3.5   The following equation represents the primary method of extracting iron (Fe) from its ore, iron oxide (Fe_2O_3), in a blast furnace.

$$Fe_2O_3(s) + 3 \text{ CO}(g) \longrightarrow 2 \text{ Fe}(l) + 3 \text{ CO}_2(g)$$

PROBLEM

How many grams of iron per gram of iron oxide are produced, assuming that there are no impurities in the ore?

SOLUTION

First we must be clear about what the problem is. Stated another way, it is, "Starting with 1.00 g of pure Fe_2O_3, how many grams of Fe can theoretically be produced?"
(1) We first convert g Fe_2O_3 to mol Fe_2O_3:

$$\text{molecular weight } Fe_2O_3 = 2(55.85) + 3(16.00) = 159.70 \text{ g/mol}$$

$$1.00 \text{ g } Fe_2O_3 \times \frac{1 \text{ mol } Fe_2O_3}{159.70 \text{ g } Fe_2O_3} = 6.26 \times 10^{-3} \text{ mol } Fe_2O_3$$

(2) We then convert mol Fe_2O_3 to mol Fe using the stoichiometry of the balanced equation:

$$6.26 \times 10^{-3} \text{ mol } Fe_2O_3 \times \frac{2 \text{ mol Fe}}{1 \text{ mol } Fe_2O_3} = 1.25 \times 10^{-2} \text{ mol Fe}$$

(3) Finally, we convert mol Fe to g Fe:

$$1.25 \times 10^{-2} \text{ mol Fe} \times \frac{55.85 \text{ g Fe}}{1 \text{ mol Fe}} = 0.698 \text{ g Fe}$$

EXAMPLE 3.6 Certain organisms (e.g., yeast) are able to degrade sugar $(C_6H_{12}O_6)$ to CO_2 and ethyl alcohol (C_2H_5OH) and to use the energy released in this reaction for their own life processes.

PROBLEM

(1) According to the following reaction, how much energy is released when 1.00 g of sugar is degraded?
(2) How much energy is released per gram of alcohol produced?

$$C_6H_{12}O_6(s) \longrightarrow 2 \text{ } CO_2(g) + 2 \text{ } C_2H_5OH(l) + 20.0 \text{ kcal}$$

SOLUTION

(1) First we convert grams to moles:

$$\text{molecular weight } C_6H_{12}O_6 = 6(12.01) + 12(1.008) + 6(16.00)$$
$$= 180.16 \text{ g/mol}$$

$$1.00 \text{ g } C_6H_{12}O_6 \times \frac{1 \text{ mol } C_6H_{12}O_6}{180.16 \text{ g } C_6H_{12}O_6} = 5.55 \times 10^{-3} \text{ mol } C_6H_{12}O_6$$

Because 20.0 kcal of heat is given off per mole of $C_6H_{12}O_6$ reacted, the energy of the reaction may be used as a conversion factor to change mol $C_6H_{12}O_6$ to kcal:

$$5.55 \times 10^{-3} \text{ mol } C_6H_{12}O_6 \times \frac{20.0 \text{ kcal}}{1 \text{ mol } C_6H_{12}O_6} = 0.111 \text{ kcal}$$

(2) Again, we first convert grams to moles:

$$\text{molecular weight } C_2H_5OH = 2(12.01) + 6(1.008) + 1(16.00)$$
$$= 46.07 \text{ g/mol}$$

$$1.00 \text{ g } C_2H_5OH \times \frac{1 \text{ mol } C_2H_5OH}{46.07 \text{ g } C_2H_5OH} = 2.17 \times 10^{-2} \text{ mol } C_2H_5OH$$

In converting mol C_2H_5OH to energy, note that the balanced equation indicates that 2 mol C_2H_5OH are produced for every 20.0 kcal released.

$$2.17 \times 10^{-2} \text{ mol } C_2H_5OH \times \frac{20.0 \text{ kcal}}{2 \text{ mol } C_2H_5OH} = 0.217 \text{ kcal}$$

EXAMPLE 3.7   One commercial method for preparing hydrochloric acid, which is used in pickling steel (a cleaning process) and in activating oil wells, among other uses, is represented by the following equation:

$$2 \text{ NaCl}(s) + H_2SO_4(l) \longrightarrow Na_2SO_4(s) + 2 \text{ HCl}(g)$$

PROBLEM

(1) Starting with 0.652 mol NaCl, how many moles of HCl and of the by-product Na_2SO_4 are produced? How many grams of each are produced?
(2) Starting with 114 g NaCl and 120. g H_2SO_4, how many grams of HCl are produced? How much starting material is left over?

SOLUTION

(1) Because the quantity of the reagent is given in moles, we can convert

the NaCl directly to moles of HCl and Na_2SO_4, using the molar ratios given by the balanced equation:

$$0.652 \text{ mol NaCl} \times \frac{2 \text{ mol HCl}}{2 \text{ mol NaCl}} = 0.652 \text{ mol HCl}$$

$$0.652 \text{ mol NaCl} \times \frac{1 \text{ mol Na}_2\text{SO}_4}{2 \text{ mol NaCl}} = 0.326 \text{ mol Na}_2\text{SO}_4$$

This answers the first part of (1). To answer the second part, we convert moles to grams using the molecular weights of the compounds as conversion factors.

$$\text{molecular weight HCl} = 1.008 + 35.45$$
$$= 36.46 \text{ g/mol}$$

$$\text{molecular weight Na}_2\text{SO}_4 = 2(22.99) + 1(32.06) + 4(16.00)$$
$$= 142.04 \text{ g/mol}$$

$$0.652 \text{ mol HCl} \times \frac{36.46 \text{ g HCl}}{1 \text{ mol HCl}} = 23.8 \text{ g HCl}$$

$$0.326 \text{ mol Na}_2\text{SO}_4 \times \frac{142.04 \text{ g Na}_2\text{SO}_4}{1 \text{ mol Na}_2\text{SO}_4} = 46.3 \text{ g Na}_2\text{SO}_4$$

(2) First we must calculate the number of moles of the two starting materials in order to determine the limiting reagent.

$$\text{molecular weight NaCl} = 22.99 + 35.45 = 58.44 \text{ g/mol}$$

$$\text{molecular weight H}_2\text{SO}_4 = 2(1.008) + 32.06 + 4(16.00)$$
$$= 98.08 \text{ g/mol}$$

$$114 \text{ g NaCl} \times \frac{1 \text{ mol NaCl}}{58.44 \text{ g NaCl}} = 1.95 \text{ mol NaCl}$$

$$120. \text{ g H}_2\text{SO}_4 \times \frac{1 \text{ mol H}_2\text{SO}_4}{98.08 \text{ g H}_2\text{SO}_4} = 1.22 \text{ mol H}_2\text{SO}_4$$

To determine the limiting reagent, we calculate how many moles of

H_2SO_4 are required to react completely with the 1.92 mol NaCl according to the balanced equation:

$$1.95 \text{ mol NaCl} \times \frac{1 \text{ mol } H_2SO_4}{2 \text{ mol NaCl}} = 0.975 \text{ mol } H_2SO_4$$

Because we have 1.22 mol H_2SO_4 and only 0.975 mol is required for the reaction, H_2SO_4 is present in excess. Therefore, NaCl is the limiting reagent and determines the amount of product formed.

To calculate the mass of HCl produced (in grams), we must first know the number of moles of HCl. We can convert mol NaCl to mol HCl using the stoichiometry of the balanced equation:

$$1.95 \text{ mol NaCl} \times \frac{2 \text{ mol HCl}}{2 \text{ mol NaCl}} = 1.95 \text{ mol HCl}$$

We can now convert mol HCl to g HCl using the molecular weight of the compound:

$$1.95 \text{ mol HCl} \times \frac{36.46 \text{ g HCl}}{1 \text{ mol HCl}} = 71.1 \text{ g HCl}$$

To answer the second part of (2), we began with 1.22 mol H_2SO_4 and calculated that 0.975 mol H_2SO_4 would be used up in the reaction. Therefore, $1.22 - 0.975 = 0.25$ mol H_2SO_4 is left over. Conversion to grams gives:

$$0.25 \text{ mol } H_2SO_4 \times \frac{98.08 \text{ g } H_2SO_4}{1 \text{ mol } H_2SO_4} = 25 \text{ g } H_2SO_4$$

EXAMPLE 3.8   Nitrogen, phosphorus, and potassium are plant nutrients that are provided for most crops in large quantities. Often chemicals containing these three nutrients are mixed in varied proportions to make fertilizers of different compositions. The composition of a given mixture is usually indicated by three numbers printed on the fertilizer bag. The first number is the percentage of nitrogen in the mixture; the second gives the amount of phosphorus as if it were present as P_2O_5 (that is, as the percentage of P_2O_5

in the mixture); the third gives the amount of potassium as if it were present as K_2O in the mixture. For example, the numbers 15–10–5 indicate a composition of 15% total nitrogen, an amount of phosphorus equivalent to 10% P_2O_5, and an amount of potassium equivalent to 5% K_2O.

PROBLEM A

Calculate the weights (in grams) of nitrogen, phosphorus, and potassium in a 1.00 kg sample of a 15–10–5 fertilizer.

SOLUTION

Recall that percentage means "parts per hundred"; 15% N means 15 g N per 100. g fertilizer. Therefore, we can use percentage as a conversion factor to convert grams of fertilizer to grams of nitrogen.

$$1.00 \times 10^3 \text{ g fertilizer} \times \frac{15 \text{ g N}}{100. \text{ g fertilizer}} = 150 \text{ g N}$$

Similarly,

$$1.00 \times 10^3 \text{ g fertilizer} \times \frac{10 \text{ g } P_2O_5}{100. \text{ g fertilizer}} = 100 \text{ g } P_2O_5$$

To find the weight of P, we first convert g to mol:

$$\text{molecular weight } P_2O_5 = 2(30.97) + 5(16.00) = 141.94 \text{ g/mol}$$

$$100 \text{ g } P_2O_5 \times \frac{1 \text{ mol } P_2O_5}{141.94 \text{ g } P_2O_5} = 0.705 \text{ mol } P_2O_5$$

Next we convert to moles of P, using the mole ratio of the chemical formula (there are 2 moles of the element P in every mole of the compound P_2O_5):

$$0.705 \text{ mol } P_2O_5 \times \frac{2 \text{ mol P}}{1 \text{ mol } P_2O_5} = 1.41 \text{ mol P}$$

Finally, we convert moles back to grams:

$$1.41 \text{ mol P} \times \frac{30.97 \text{ g P}}{1 \text{ mol P}} = 44 \text{ g P}$$

The four steps in calculating the weight of phosphorus could have been condensed to one by multiplying the amount of fertilizer by the successive conversion factors. We shall use this simplified method to calculate the weight of potassium:

$$1.00 \times 10^3 \text{ g fertilizer} \times \frac{5.0 \text{ g K}_2\text{O}}{100. \text{ g fertilizer}} \times \frac{1 \text{ mol K}_2\text{O}}{94.20 \text{ g K}_2\text{O}}$$

$$\times \frac{2 \text{ mol K}}{1 \text{ mol K}_2\text{O}} \times \frac{39.10 \text{ g K}}{1 \text{ mol K}} = 42 \text{ g K}$$

Although the amount of phosphorus is usually reported as % P_2O_5, P_2O_5 is never used as a component of fertilizer. One compound that is used is ammonium phosphate, $(NH_4)_3PO_4$.

PROBLEM B

Calculate the weight of $(NH_4)_3PO_4$ present in 1.00 kg of the fertilizer in the preceding problem, assuming that all of the phosphorus is in the form of $(NH_4)_3PO_4$.

SOLUTION

In the preceding problem we found 44 g P in 1.00 kg of the 15–10–5 fertilizer. We now need the weight of $(NH_4)_3PO_4$ equivalent to this weight of phosphorus. According to our standard procedure, we convert g P to mol P, mol P to mol $(NH_4)_3PO_4$, and mol $(NH_4)_3PO_4$ to g $(NH_4)_3PO_4$:

$$44 \text{ g P} \times \frac{1 \text{ mol P}}{30.97 \text{ g P}} \times \frac{1 \text{ mol }(NH_4)_3PO_4}{1 \text{ mol P}} \times \frac{149.10 \text{ g }(NH_4)_3PO_4}{1 \text{ mol }(NH_4)_3PO_4}$$

$$= 210 \text{ g }(NH_4)_3PO_4$$

PROBLEM C

Calculate the weight of nitrogen in 210 g of $(NH_4)_3PO_4$ and compare this to the total weight of nitrogen found in the 1.00 kg of 15–10–5 fertilizer of Problem A. Assuming that the rest of the nitrogen is in the form of ammonium nitrate, NH_4NO_3, calculate the weight of NH_4NO_3 present.

SOLUTION

For the first step we calculate the weight of nitrogen:

$$210 \text{ g } (NH_4)_3PO_4 \times \frac{1 \text{ mol } (NH_4)_3PO_4}{149.10 \text{ g } (NH_4)_3PO_4} \times \frac{3 \text{ mol N}}{1 \text{ mol } (NH_4)_3PO_4}$$

$$\times \frac{14.01 \text{ g N}}{1 \text{ mol N}} = 59 \text{ g N}$$

We have a total of 150 g N from the first answer to Problem A:

$$\begin{array}{r} 150 \text{ g N} \\ - \ 59 \text{ g N in } 210 \text{ g } (NH_4)_3PO_4 \\ \hline 91 \text{ g N left, which is in the form of } NH_4NO_3 \end{array}$$

For the second step, we calculate the weight of NH_4NO_3 that contains 91 g N, noting that there are 2 mol N in 1 mol NH_4NO_3:

$$91 \text{ g N} \times \frac{1 \text{ mol N}}{14.01 \text{ g N}} \times \frac{1 \text{ mol } NH_4NO_3}{2 \text{ mol N}} \times \frac{80.05 \text{ g } NH_4NO_3}{1 \text{ mol } NH_4NO_3}$$

$$= 260 \text{ g } NH_4NO_3$$

EXAMPLE 3.9   It is quite common for chemists to analyze the composition of material in the following manner. A known amount of a compound of unknown composition is dissolved to form a solution and a reagent is added. The reaction of the solution with the reagent produces a known solid precipitate which contains one of the elements present in the original compound. This new compound is separated and weighed, and the number of moles of the original element is determined. From this information the empirical formula of the original compound can be determined.

PROBLEM

A 5.000 g portion of a compound of nickel and oxygen is dissolved in acid and analyzed by precipitating the nickel as the sulfide NiS. Measurement of the precipitate indicates that 6.075 g of NiS have been isolated. Calculate the amount of nickel in the original sample. What is the empirical formula of the nickel oxide?

SOLUTION

We first determine the number of moles of the isolated nickel sulfide:

$$\text{molecular weight NiS} = 58.71 + 32.06 = 90.77 \text{ g/mol}$$

$$6.075 \text{ g NiS} \times \frac{1 \text{ mol NiS}}{90.77 \text{ g NiS}} = 0.06693 \text{ mol NiS}$$

Because there is 1 mole of Ni in every mole of NiS, we may use this ratio to convert moles of NiS to moles of Ni:

$$0.06693 \text{ mol NiS} \times \frac{1 \text{ mol Ni}}{1 \text{ mol NiS}} = 0.06693 \text{ mol Ni}$$

The original sample also contained 0.06693 mol Ni, because the amount of nickel in the sulfide is equal to the amount contained in the oxide. Conversion of moles to grams gives us:

$$0.06693 \text{ mol Ni} \times \frac{58.71 \text{ g Ni}}{1 \text{ mol Ni}} = 3.929 \text{ g Ni}$$

The second part of the problem asks for the empirical formula of the nickel oxide. Because the compound contained only Ni and O, we may subtract the amount of nickel (3.929 g) from the total mass of the oxide (5.000 g) to determine the amount of oxygen in the original compound:

$$\begin{array}{r} 5.000 \text{ g NiO} \\ - 3.929 \text{ g Ni} \\ \hline 1.071 \text{ g O} \end{array}$$

Conversion of g to mol gives:

$$1.071 \text{ g O} \times \frac{1 \text{ mol O}}{16.00 \text{ g O}} = 0.06694 \text{ mol O}$$

We combine this with the number of moles of Ni (0.06693 mol) to determine the empirical formula of the oxide:

$$Ni_{0.06693}O_{0.06694}$$

or

$$NiO$$

QUESTIONS

1. The sodium salt of saccharin ("soluble saccharin") gives the following elemental analysis:

40.98% C	23.39% O
1.97% H	15.63% S
6.83% N	11.31% Na

   a. Determine the empirical formula of this compound.

   b. A $\frac{1}{4}$ grain tablet of saccharin has a sweetening power equivalent to one teaspoon of sugar. If 1 grain = 64 mg, calculate the number of moles of saccharin in this tablet.

   c. A person suffering from high blood pressure has to restrict the intake of sodium. How many mg of sodium (Na) are consumed by using this $\frac{1}{4}$ grain tablet? How many moles?

2. In certain organisms urea is converted to ammonia by the following reaction:

$$\underset{\text{urea}}{H_2NCONH_2} + H_2O \longrightarrow \underset{\text{ammonia}}{2\ NH_3} + CO_2$$

   a. How many moles of ammonia are formed from each mole of urea?

   b. How many grams of ammonia are formed from each gram of urea?

3. When white phosphorus is reacted at 40 °C with a three to one mixture of oxygen and nitrogen, a compound is produced which is 56.3% P and 43.7% O. When this compound is burned in excess oxygen, a new compound having the composition 43.6% P and 56.4% O is formed.

   a. What are the empirical formulas of the two compounds?

b. If the molecular weights of the two compounds are 219.9 and 283.9, respectively, what are their molecular formulas?

4. Antimony trichloride, $SbCl_3$, is found to react with water, giving HCl and an unknown compound which is found to be composed of 76.3% Sb, 12.5% O, and 11.1% Cl. What is its empirical formula? Write a balanced chemical equation for the reaction.

5. $$Al_2O_3(s) + C(s) + Cl_2(g) \longrightarrow AlCl_3(s) + CO(g)$$

a. Balance the above equation.
b. How many moles of C and Cl_2 are needed to react completely with 2.50 mol Al_2O_3?
c. How many moles of $AlCl_3$ can be made from 2.50 mol Al_2O_3?
d. How many grams of carbon are needed to react with 0.31 mol Al_2O_3?
e. How many grams of chlorine are needed to react with 21.0 g Al_2O_3? How many grams of $AlCl_3$ are produced?
f. How many grams of $AlCl_3$ are produced from 100. g Al_2O_3 and 40.0 g C?

6. Thionyl chloride $(SOCl_2)$ can be used to remove water from a system according to the reaction:

$$SOCl_2(l) + H_2O(l) \longrightarrow SO_2(g) + 2\ HCl(g)$$

If 6.128 g of HCl is isolated after treating a sample with $SOCl_2$, how many grams of water were originally present?

7. The mineral bauxite ranges in composition from $Al_2O_3 \cdot H_2O$ to $Al_2O_3 \cdot 3H_2O$.
a. What is the range for the aluminum content in weight percent?
b. How much aluminum metal may theoretically be produced from 1.00×10^3 kg of $Al_2O_3 \cdot 3H_2O$? If the actual yield is 300. kg, what is the percent yield?

8. Large quantities of carbon tetrachloride, CCl_4, a common cleaning agent, are made by bubbling Cl_2 into CS_2:

$$CS_2(l) + Cl_2(g) \longrightarrow S_2Cl_2(l) + CCl_4(l)$$

a. Balance the above equation.
b. How many grams of chlorine are needed to produce 1.00 kg CCl_4?
c. How much CCl_4 may be produced from 50.0 g CS_2 and 150. g Cl_2?
d. If 86.4 g CCl_4 are actually obtained from the experiment described in c, what is the percent yield?

9. Tetraethyl lead, $Pb(C_2H_5)_4$, the antiknock agent found in leaded gasoline, may be made by reacting ethyl chloride with sodium-lead alloy:

$$NaPb(s) + C_2H_5Cl(g) \longrightarrow Pb(C_2H_5)_4(l) + Pb(s) + NaCl(s)$$

a. Balance this equation.
b. How much tetraethyl lead may be produced from 150. g C_2H_5Cl?
c. If 200. g NaPb are to be reacted with 50.0 g C_2H_5Cl, which is the limiting reagent, and how much tetraethyl lead may theoretically be produced?
d. If 59.8 g of tetraethyl lead are actually obtained in experiment c, what is the percent yield?
e. Calculate the weight percentage of Pb in tetraethyl lead.
f. Leaded gasoline contains an average 3.5 g of $Pb(C_2H_5)_4$ per gallon. Assuming that all of the Pb goes into the atmosphere through the car's exhaust, calculate the number of grams of Pb introduced into the atmosphere by driving a car 12,000 mi at an average rate of 14 mi/gal.

10. The element phosphorus is produced from the mineral fluorapatite, $Ca_5(PO_4)_3F$. Pretreatment of the mineral to remove fluoride results in the compound calcium phosphate, $Ca_3(PO_4)_2$, which is heated to 1500 °C with silica (sand), and then with carbon, giving the following reactions:

$$Ca_3(PO_4)_2(s) + SiO_2(s) \longrightarrow CaSiO_3(s) + P_4O_{10}(g)$$

$$P_4O_{10}(g) + C(s) \longrightarrow P_4(g) + CO(g)$$

a. Balance the equations above.
b. What weight of phosphorus may theoretically be produced from 1.00 kg of $Ca_3(PO_4)_2$?
c. What weights of SiO_2 and C are necessary for the reaction in b?
d. Assuming that no phosphorus is lost in the pretreatment, how much fluorapatite is necessary to give 1.00 kg of $Ca_3(PO_4)_2$?
e. If five tons of fluorapatite are processed with an expected efficiency of 90%, what weight of phosphorus is expected?

11. A sample containing chloride was dissolved in water, and excess silver nitrate was added, giving a precipitate of silver chloride, AgCl. The AgCl weighed 0.620 g after drying.
a. How much chloride is present in the original sample?
b. If the original sample weighed 0.260 g, what is the percentage of chloride in the sample?

12. The reagent dimethylglyoxime $(C_4H_8N_2O_2)$ is used to determine the amount of nickel in a solution by the formation of a scarlet-red solid according to the reaction:

$$NiCl_2(aq) + 2\ C_4H_8N_2O_2(aq) \longrightarrow Ni(C_4H_7N_2O_2)_2(s) + 2\ HCl(aq)$$

If 2.483 g of $Ni(C_4H_7N_2O_2)_2$ is isolated after the treatment of a solution of $NiCl_2$, how many grams of $NiCl_2$ were initially present?

13. Hydrocarbons of the type C_xH_y, where x and y are integers, burn in oxygen

to form CO_2 and H_2O. If 11.05 g of H_2O are recovered after complete combustion of 7.365 g of a hydrocarbon, what is its empirical formula?

14. When 7.525 g of a compound containing C and H are burned in oxygen, 12.31 g H_2O and an amount of CO_2 are formed.
    a. What is the weight percentage of H in the original compound?
    b. What is the empirical formula of the original compound?
    c. How many grams of CO_2 were formed on burning the sample?

15. a. What is the percentage of Ta in $TaCl_5$? in $TaCl_5 \cdot 2C_5H_5N$?
    °b. A substance known to be $TaCl_5 \cdot xC_5H_5N$ is analyzed and found to be 46.7% Ta. What is the value of x in the formula?

16. a. Find the percentage of Sr in $SrCl_2 \cdot 6H_2O$.
    °b. A sample of $SrCl_2 \cdot 6H_2O$ is heated in a vacuum for a time at 120 °C. Subsequent analysis reveals 42.0% Sr. What is the value of x in $SrCl_2 \cdot xH_2O$? (Assume that only water has been driven off.)
    °c. Further heating yields a solid which is 55.3% Sr. What is the value of x now?

°Difficult or advanced questions

4

Atomic Structure

Guidelines

After completing this chapter the student should be able to:

- describe the current picture of the atom

- explain the concept of isotopes

- define the concepts of wavelength and frequency for waves

- explain the significance of line absorption and emission spectra

- describe the experiments of Thomson, Millikan, and Rutherford and explain their contributions to the modern description of the atom

- discuss the emission of α-, β-, and γ-rays from radioactive isotopes

- discuss the Bohr model of the atom in terms of quantum energy levels

- describe the consequences of the Uncertainty Principle and wave/particle duality

- draw diagrams of s, p, and d orbitals

- construct the electronic configurations of the first 36 elements

4.1 The Current Picture of the Atom

We have seen that since the time of the ancient Greeks, matter has been thought to be composed of tiny discrete particles called atoms. Once these atoms were considered to be indivisible, but the field of high energy physics has shown that atoms consist of even smaller particles: protons, neutrons, and electrons. Indeed, as the structure of the atomic nucleus is probed at deeper levels, other particles have been identified—muons and pions, for example—which cement the nucleus together.

The chemist, however, tends to disregard these smaller, higher energy particles and considers the atom as a positively charged **nucleus** surrounded by a "cloud" of negatively charged **electrons** (see Figure 4–1). Most of the mass of the atom is concentrated in the nucleus, which is composed of two types of particles, the positively charged **proton** and the neutral **neutron**. The charge on the electron is -1.6022×10^{-19} coulomb

Figure 4–1
The modern concept of the atom (as seen by the chemist)

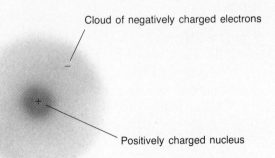

Cloud of negatively charged electrons

Positively charged nucleus

Table 4–1

Properties of Atomic Particles

	MASS		CHARGE	
	g	amu	coulomb	electronic charge unit
Electron	9.1095×10^{-28}	0.00054858	-1.6022×10^{-19}	-1
Proton	1.67265×10^{-24}	1.007276	$+1.6022 \times 10^{-19}$	$+1$
Neutron	1.67495×10^{-24}	1.008665	0	0

(expressed as -1 in electronic charge units); the proton has an equal but opposite (positive) charge. Table 4–1 summarizes some properties of these three elementary particles.

The nucleus occupies a very small fraction of the volume of an atom: the radius of a whole atom is on the order of 1×10^{-8} cm (1 Å), whereas the radius of the nucleus is on the order of 1×10^{-13} cm. Therefore, there is an extremely high concentration of mass (and positive charge) in a small part of the atom, the nucleus.

The number of protons in the nucleus of an atom is the **atomic number** (Z), which tells us the number of positive charges in the nucleus, since each proton has a $+1$ charge. In a neutral atom, Z is also equal to the number of electrons surrounding the atom. As we shall see, Z determines the identity of a particular element.

4.2   Isotopes

With time it was discovered that atoms of different samples of the same element sometimes had different apparent atomic masses. This is due to the fact that for a given atomic number, the number of neutrons in the nucleus can vary from atom to atom. The **atomic mass number** (A) is equal to the number of protons plus the number of neutrons in the nucleus; therefore, A fixes the nuclear mass. If Q is the chemical symbol of the element, the addition of a preceding subscript Z and a preceding superscript A represents the particular isotope:

$$^A_Z Q$$

Isotopes of a given element are atoms that have the same number of protons in the nucleus (the same Z) but different numbers of neutrons (different A). Carbon has two isotopes which occur in significant amounts, $^{12}_{6}C$ and $^{13}_{6}C$; their atomic weights and overall percent abundances on earth are given as:

	ISOTOPIC MASS	ABUNDANCE
$^{12}_{6}C$	12.0000 amu	98.89%
$^{13}_{6}C$	13.0034 amu	1.11%

The observed atomic weight of carbon is given by the *weighted average* of the two naturally occurring isotopes:

$$observed\ atomic\ weight = 0.9889(12.0000\ amu)$$
$$+ 0.0111(13.0034\ amu)$$
$$= 11.8668\ amu + 0.144\ amu$$
$$= 12.011\ amu$$

The occurrence of samples of an element with different atomic masses is a result of different relative abundances of the isotopes in the sample. For example, if the atoms in a sample of carbon are found to have an apparent atomic mass less than 12.011 amu, then the sample must be composed of a greater percentage of ^{12}C than the normal 98.89%. If the atoms in another sample are found to have an apparent atomic mass greater than 12.011 amu, then the sample must be composed of a greater percentage of ^{13}C than normal. The atomic or molecular masses of common laboratory chemicals are taken never to vary from those calculated on the basis of overall averages for those chemicals.

As another example, consider the element oxygen, which has three naturally occurring isotopes:

	ISOTOPIC MASS	ABUNDANCE
$^{16}_{8}O$	15.9949 amu	99.759%
$^{17}_{8}O$	16.9991 amu	0.037%
$^{18}_{8}O$	17.9992 amu	0.204%

The observed atomic weight is 15.9994 amu.

Nuclear Binding Energy

Calculation of the atomic mass of any isotope of an element will show that the actual mass of an isotope is always *less than* the sum of the masses of the individual protons, neutrons, and electrons.

For example, the mass of a single helium atom is given as 4.00260 amu. The He nucleus contains two protons and two neutrons and is surrounded by two electrons. Their masses are (from Table 4–1):

p: 2×1.007276 amu $= 2.014552$ amu
n: 2×1.008665 amu $= 2.017330$ amu
e: 2×0.00054858 amu $= 0.0010972$ amu
total mass: 4.032979 amu

The difference between the sum of the masses of the individual protons, neutrons, and electrons and the mass of a helium atom is:

sum of the masses: 4.032979 amu
atomic mass of He: 4.00260 amu
difference: 0.03038 amu

This difference corresponds to:

$$0.03038 \text{ amu} \times \frac{1.66053 \times 10^{-24} \text{ g}}{1 \text{ amu}}$$

$$= 5.045 \times 10^{-26} \text{ g}$$

This "missing mass" is the **binding energy** of the helium nucleus. That is, a tiny fraction of the mass of the separate atomic components is converted to the energy that holds the parts of the nucleus together. The expression of energy as mass invokes Einstein's famous equation (page 31) that shows the relationship of mass and energy, $E = mc^2$, where $c = 2.998 \times 10^{10}$ cm/sec. Using this relationship, we can calculate the magnitude of the binding energy, which turns out to be 4.534×10^{-5} g cm^2/sec^2, or 4.534×10^{-5} ergs, per helium nucleus. In other words, *each* He nucleus is held together by more than 4.5×10^{-5} ergs, which is equal to 6.8×10^{18} ergs per gram of He. This measurement represents an enormous amount of energy. It is many orders of magnitude larger than the energies that are involved in chemical reactions (the making and breaking of chemical bonds), and it is therefore never reached during chemical reactions. Because the binding energy of an atom must be exceeded in order to break the nucleus apart, for their purposes most chemists view the nucleus as an indestructible entity.

4.3   Electromagnetic Radiation

The focus in the two preceding sections was on the modern picture of the atom. Now we will begin to discuss the historical developments that led to this description. This section will describe the interaction of light with matter and the next section will discuss atomic emission spectra.

In the latter part of the seventeenth century, Sir Isaac Newton performed experiments which proved that sunlight (or "white light") was a mixture of all of the colors and that it could be split up into its component colors by passage through a glass prism (see Figure 4–2). We now know that this occurs because the beams of each of the various colors present in white light are bent to different extents as they pass through the prism. This bending process separates the beams and makes them individually visible as in a rainbow.

Visible light is nothing more than that portion of the **electromagnetic spectrum** to which the human eye is sensitive. All **electromagnetic radiation** making up the electromagnetic spectrum can be considered as being composed of waves which travel at the **speed of light** ($c = 2.998 \times 10^{10}$ cm/sec) and which are characterized by a **wavelength** (λ, lambda) and **frequency** (ν, nu).

The spectrum of electromagnetic radiation spreads over a wide range of wavelengths and frequencies. Figure 4–3 schematically illustrates the electromagnetic spectrum from the low ν (long λ) radio waves through the visible range and into the high ν (low λ) cosmic ray region. Note that the visible region of the electromagnetic spectrum is only a small portion, ranging from a wavelength of about 4,000 Å to 8,000 Å.

The wave nature of electromagnetic radiation is analogous to the waves with which you are familiar in everyday life, such as ocean waves.

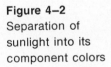

Figure 4–2
Separation of sunlight into its component colors

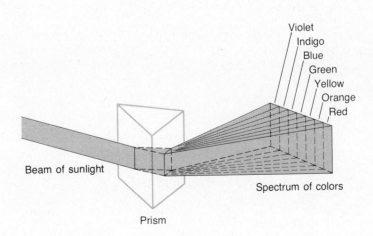

Violet
Indigo
Blue
Green
Yellow
Orange
Red

Beam of sunlight

Spectrum of colors

Prism

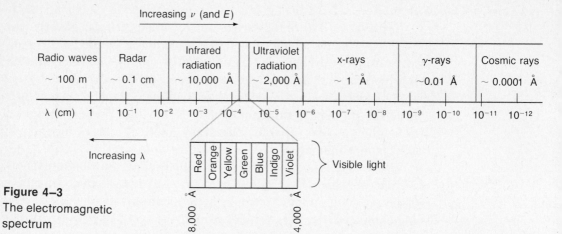

Figure 4–3
The electromagnetic
spectrum

Figure 4–4 illustrates the amplitude (magnitude) of an electromagnetic wave versus the distance along the wave at that instant of time. Just as the length of an ocean wave is given by the distance between crests of the wave, an electromagnetic wavelength λ is measured by the distance between crests. With time an entire wave moves past a given reference point; the number of waves passing this point per second is the frequency ν in $\sec^{-1}$ (waves per second). (The unit $\sec^{-1}$, usually called reciprocal seconds, means 1/sec.) The relationship between wavelength and frequency is given by:

$$\lambda \times \nu = c \qquad (4\text{–}1)$$

$$\text{(cm)} \quad (\sec^{-1}) \quad \text{(cm/sec)}$$

Figure 4–4
Measurement of an
electromagnetic
wave

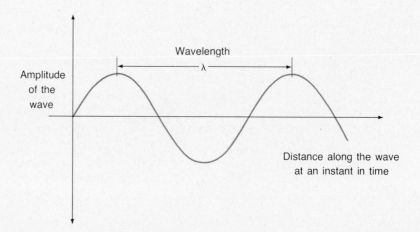

Is Light Composed of Particles or Waves?

When, in 1672, Isaac Newton first advanced a theory of light to explain his observations on sunlight, he decided that light was made up of tiny "corpuscles" traveling at great speeds. Almost immediately, the Dutch physicist Christian Huyghens suggested that light consisted of waves. Each of these two explanations of the behavior of light could account for some but not all of its observed properties, and it was not until the beginning of the twentieth century that this dichotomy was resolved.

In 1900 Max Planck suggested (1) that all types of electromagnetic radiation consist of streams of massless particles (called **photons**) which have discrete amounts of energy and (2) that the energy associated with each photon of a particular radiation is proportional to its frequency:

$$E \propto \nu$$

The proportionality constant, whose value was obtained by experiment, has been named **Planck's constant**: $h = 6.626 \times 10^{-27}$ erg-sec. The energy (in ergs) associated with each frequency of radiation is then given by:

$$E = h\nu \qquad (4\text{--}2)$$

Because the unit of energy, the erg, has dimensions of $g\ cm^2/sec^2$, Planck's constant has the dimensions:

$$h = \frac{E}{\nu} = \frac{g\ cm^2/sec^2}{sec^{-1}}$$

$$h = \frac{g\ cm^2}{sec^2} \times sec$$

$$h = g\ cm^2/sec$$

The equation $E = h\nu$ was the first quantitative statement of the complementary nature of the wave and particle descriptions of radiation. A photon of electromagnetic radiation characterized by a frequency ν has a "packet" of energy associated with it (called a **quantum** of energy, after the Latin *quantus,* meaning "how much") whose magnitude is equal to the frequency times Planck's constant (Equation 4–2).

Information about the nature of electromagnetic radiation and its interaction with matter was accumulating rapidly during the latter part of the nineteenth century. Additional discoveries about radiation in relation to the atom contributed to the gradually developing model of the atom. These discoveries are discussed in the next section.

4.4   Atomic Emission Spectra

A spectroscope is an instrument that breaks white light into its component colors using the same principle as that of the prism. If a small amount of ordinary table salt (sodium chloride) is heated in a flame and the emitted light is then viewed through a spectroscope, a **line emission spectrum** is observed (see Figure 4–5). The observed emission spectrum contains colored lines characteristic of the element sodium. Each of the lines has a wavelength corresponding to its color. With further experiment, one would find this spectrum to be characteristic of sodium in any chemical compound. (The wavelengths emitted by chlorine are not seen in the spectroscope because they lie outside the visible region of the electromagnetic spectrum.) Every chemical element has an emission spectrum which is uniquely characteristic of that element.

In addition, each element exhibits a similar characteristic spectrum when white light is examined after it has passed through a sample of the element. This **absorption spectrum** shows the same characteristic wavelengths of radiation as those in the line emission spectrum, but they appear as dark lines rather than the characteristic colored lines. The reason for this appearance is that each element absorbs certain characteristic wavelengths of radiation, and when white light is passed through the element those wavelengths appear as dark lines in the transmitted light.

Dalton's atomic model considered the atom to be a miniature "billiard ball" that had physical and chemical characteristics of the bulk ele-

Figure 4–5
A typical line
emission spectrum

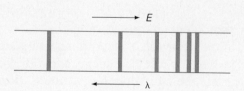

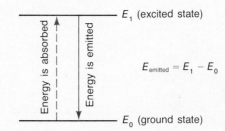

Figure 4–6
Emission of energy
from an excited
atom

E_1 (excited state)

Energy is absorbed

Energy is emitted

$E_{\text{emitted}} = E_1 - E_0$

E_0 (ground state)

ment. Such a simple model cannot explain the occurrence of atomic line spectra.

The origin of both the emission and absorption spectra can be explained by considering an atom of an element in a characteristic ground state of energy designated E_0 on an energy scale. Suppose that you can excite this atom so that by absorbing energy it goes into an excited state of energy E_1, where E_1 is greater than E_0. The energy emitted (Figure 4–6) upon relaxation or return to the energetically lower ground state is:

$$E_{\text{emitted}} = E_1 - E_0 = h\nu \qquad (4\text{--}3)$$

Therefore:

$$\nu = \frac{E_1 - E_0}{h} \qquad (4\text{--}4)$$

where $E_1 - E_0$ is the difference in energy between the two energy levels.

This atomic model explains the existence of line spectra because it views the atom as changing its energy level as it absorbs or emits radiation or other forms of energy. Furthermore, the model links the change in energy level ($E_1 - E_0$) to the frequency of the radiation wave (ν). Additional details must be supplied to the model, however, before it can account for the specific mechanism by which the atom can go from one energy level to another and before it can explain why atoms exist only in certain discrete energy states.

A discovery made toward the end of the nineteenth century eventually led to the development of a model that explained why the hydrogen atom, at least, could exist only in discrete energy states. It was found that the frequencies that appear in the atomic emission spectrum of hydrogen, the element with the simplest atom, obey a simple empirical

The Contributions of the Spectroscope

In the 1860s two German chemists Gustav Kirchhoff and Robert Bunsen (inventor of the common laboratory gas burner) first used the spectroscope as a tool for the identification of elements. They developed techniques whereby the common elements could be identified by the characteristic lines in their emission spectra. During the course of their investigations they found that certain samples of compounds exhibited lines that were not characteristic of any element known at the time. In 1861 they identified the previously unknown elements cesium and rubidium from their emission spectra.

At about this time the spectroscope was also used in conjunction with the telescope to analyze light from the sun and other stars. In 1868 the French astronomer Jules Janssen used a spectroscope in this manner to analyze the chromosphere (the luminescent region near the sun's surface) during a total eclipse of the sun. He found hitherto unknown lines in the visible spectrum; in particular, he observed a yellow line not attributable to any element known on earth. The English astronomer Norman Lockyer, certain that this line represented a new element, named the element helium, after the Greek word *helios,* meaning sun. It was not until 1888 that William Hillebrand, an American, discovered an inert gas which was released when the mineral uranite was dissolved in sulfuric acid. This gas was identified by its emission spectrum, which was identical to the lines observed for helium in the sun's chromosphere.

The subsequent marriage of the spectroscope to the telescope has yielded extremely fruitful results in astronomy and other fields. For example, one investigation led to the identification of the elemental composition of the stars. Another resulted in the discovery of the "red shift," which is a shift in wavelength of characteristic emission lines toward the red region (the longer wavelength region) of the electromagnetic spectrum. The observance of this shift provides evidence that the universe is expanding; that is, that the stars are moving with extremely high velocities away from us and from each other.

In addition, emission spectroscopy has become a valuable analytical tool for the identification of elements in chemical compounds. It has been developed to the extent that parts per billion of an element (1 part in 10^9) can be determined using routine spectrographic analytical techniques.

relationship. The wavelengths of the emitted radiations could be fit into the formula:

$$\frac{1}{\lambda} = R\left(\frac{1}{n_0{}^2} - \frac{1}{n_1{}^2}\right) \tag{4–5}$$

where n_0 is an integer (1, 2, 3, . . .) and n_1 another integer greater than n_0. R is a constant equal to 1.097×10^5 cm^{-1}; it is called the **Rydberg constant** after the man who systematically analyzed these atomic spectra. Any new model of the atom would have to account for this experimentally observed relationship between the wavelengths in the emission spectrum of the hydrogen atom. It was the eventual development of the Bohr atomic model (Section 4.7) that finally explained this observation satisfactorily.

4.5 The Discovery of the Electron

At about the same time that atomic spectra were being investigated, other important discoveries about the nature of matter were being made by chemists and physicists. This section will describe the experiments that led to the discovery of the electron, and the next section will describe the discovery of the nucleus.

In the late nineteenth century physicists were investigating the phenomenon that gases could conduct electricity. In one experiment, two metal electrodes were introduced into a glass tube which was then partially evacuated (see Figure 4–7). The electrodes were connected to a source of direct-current electricity of high voltage ($\approx$20,000 V). Rays were found to be emitted from the negative electrode (the cathode) and to travel toward the positive electrode (the anode). These **cathode rays** were shown to transfer electric charge, but it was not known whether they behaved as waves or as streams of particles.

In 1897 Joseph J. Thomson carried out experiments to determine the nature of these cathode rays. He placed a slit in the discharge tube which

Figure 4–7

A gas discharge tube

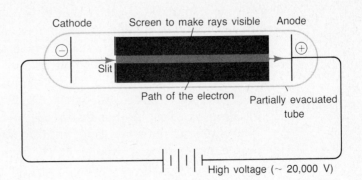

Cathode   Screen to make rays visible   Anode

Slit

Path of the electron   Partially evacuated tube

High voltage ($\sim$ 20,000 V)

allowed a beam of cathode rays to strike a screen coated with a phosphor, a material that emits visible radiation when bombarded with high energy rays. Thomson was able to show, by placing an electric field across the path that the beam of cathode rays traveled, that they were deflected into a curved path toward the positive region of the electric field. In other words, the cathode rays were attracted to the new positive charge, implying that the rays were composed of negatively charged particles. Thomson called these particles electrons (a name actually proposed several years earlier by G. J. Stoney).

An important result of Thomson's experiments was that this phenomenon was observed with any gas in the tube and with any conducting metal used for the electrodes. Therefore, he concluded that these negatively charged particles called electrons were *fundamental particles;* that is, they were to be found in all elements.

In another experiment, Thomson placed a magnetic field at right angles to the electric field that deflected the cathode rays. By adjusting the magnetic field to balance out this deflection, he was able to determine the ratio of the charge to the mass of the electron. He found that:

$$\text{electron charge/electron mass} = e/m$$

$$e/m = -1.76 \times 10^8 \text{ coulomb/gram}$$

Further experiments showed that this **charge/mass ratio** was also independent of the particular tube, gas, and electrodes.

Thomson discovered the existence of the electron, determined that it was negatively charged, and measured its charge/mass ratio. The next step, the determination of the actual charge on the electron, was made in 1909 by Robert A. Millikan in his famous "oil drop" experiment. Figure 4–8 schematically shows the experimental apparatus. Minute oil droplets were sprayed between a pair of parallel plates across which an electric field could be applied. In the absence of an electric field the drops will settle on the bottom plate due to gravity. Millikan put a negative charge on the droplets by using x-ray irradiation or by otherwise inducing a static electric charge on them. Then he applied an electric field across the plates and adjusted it to exactly counteract the force of gravity, causing the drops to "float" rather than settle.

In this very simple experiment, Millikan was able to directly measure the charge on a particular drop of oil. He found that every drop carried a charge of -1.60×10^{-19} coulomb or (if the drop collected more than

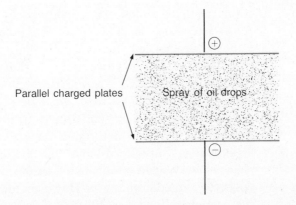

Figure 4–8
Robert Millikan's
oil drop experiment

one electric charge) a whole-number multiple of this number. He concluded that -1.60×10^{-19} coulomb must be a fundamental unit of charge. Furthermore, because it was known that $e/m = -1.76 \times 10^8$ coulomb/gram, the mass on the electron could be determined as:

$$m = -1.60 \times 10^{-19} \text{ coulomb} \times \frac{1 \text{ gram}}{-1.76 \times 10^8 \text{ coulomb}}$$

$$m = 9.09 \times 10^{-28} \text{ gram}$$

The observed mass is actually 9.11×10^{-28} gram; the discrepancy is due to rounding off and to more accurate modern values of the charge and the charge/mass ratio.

4.6 The Experimental Evidence for the Nucleus

At the time that Thomson carried out his experiments on the nature of the electron, he proposed a model for the atom that consisted of electrons embedded in uniform spheres of positive electricity (having radii $\approx 10^{-8}$ cm), which then packed together to build up matter. He envisioned the distribution of the negatively charged electrons within the positively charged spheres as one that would give the most stable electrostatic energy; that is, he viewed them as being distributed evenly and randomly, somewhat like raisins in a pudding.

Other observations soon altered that view. In 1911 Ernest Rutherford made an important discovery while investigating the properties of the newly discovered radioactive particles known as alpha (α) particles.

Alpha particles, which arise from the decay of certain radioactive isotopes, are nothing more than helium atoms from which both electrons have been removed, so that only the helium nuclei remain. Rutherford was investigating the scattering of α-particles by thin metal foils. In one experiment, he directed a beam of α-particles toward a very thin gold foil; after passing through the foil the particles were detected by a phosphor screen. By measuring the angle at which the α-particles were deflected by the foil, Rutherford hoped to determine the size of the atom. Contrary to his expectations, Rutherford found that the paths of most of the α-particles changed very little after passing through the foil, although some were deflected at moderate angles. However, much to his surprise, a very few of the particles (about 1 in 100,000) were deflected back toward the direction from which they came. At the time, considering Thomson's model of the atom, Rutherford was so astonished he stated that it was as if "a cannon ball was fired at a piece of tissue paper and that it bounced back."

Thomson's model of the atom would have suggested a very slight deflection of the α-particles. As the particles hit the gold foil, they would have been deflected by the evenly distributed positive charges in the atoms of the foil, but at very small angles. The very light electrons would have been pushed aside by the heavier α-particles, also limiting the amount of deflection. Rutherford's experiment entirely disproved this model. First, the fact that most of the α-particles passed through the foil without any deflection indicated the then-surprising fact that most of the volume of the atom seemed to be empty space. Second, since a few of the α-particles were deflected back toward the source, there seemed to be a very high concentration of positive charge and mass in a very small volume, because such an arrangement would be necessary to cause this "bouncing back" of the α-particles.

Figure 4–9
Ernest Rutherford's experiment with α-particles

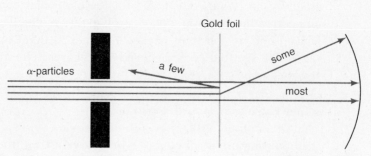

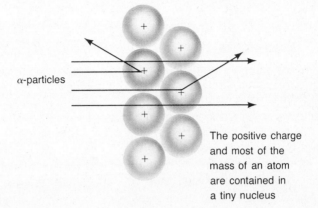

α-particles

The positive charge
and most of the
mass of an atom
are contained in
a tiny nucleus

Figure 4–10
Rutherford's model
of the atom

Figure 4–10 diagrams Rutherford's model of the atom based on this experimental data. A very small nucleus with a high concentration of positive charge and mass lies in the center of a diffuse cloud of negative electronic charge distributed over most of the atomic volume. This model explains why most α-particles act as if they are passing through "empty space" and why only a very few are deflected back toward the source. From the measured scattering angles and from the relative numbers of scattered α-particles, Rutherford was able to make a calculation as to the size of the nucleus. He found that nuclear radii were on the order of 10^{-13} cm. Recalling that atomic radii are on the order of 10^{-8} cm, this means that if the nucleus were 1 inch ($\approx 2\frac{1}{2}$ cm) in radius the whole atom would have a radius of about $1\frac{1}{2}$ miles ($\approx 2\frac{1}{2}$ km).

4.7 The Bohr Model of the Atom

By 1913 Niels Bohr, a Danish physicist, was able to construct a satisfactory model of the whole atom by taking into account the evidence of atomic spectra and the existence of the electron and the nucleus. What Bohr did was to develop a theory to account for the empirical relationship found in the emission spectrum of the element hydrogen (page 103). He constructed a planetary, or "solar system," model for the hydrogen atom, which is made up of only a single electron traveling about a nucleus that contains only one proton.

In developing his model, Bohr assumed that electrons are particles that travel in circular paths, or "orbits," around a positively charged

Radioactivity

During the last decade of the nine-teenth century, the French physicist Henri Becquerel accidentally discovered that $K_2UO_2(SO_4)_2$, potassium uranyl sul-phate, emitted a peculiar type of radiation capable of passing through matter and having the property of being able to darken a photographic plate. Becquerel found that the emission of this type of radiation was characteristic of uranium salts and that the radiation acted some-what similarly to the recently discovered x-rays (Figure 4–3). Marie Curie, one of his students, carried on his investigations and proceeded to identify several other elements (some of them previously un-known) that exhibited this phenomenon of radioactivity. Then at the Cavendish Laboratory in England, Ernest Rutherford identified three unique types of radiation that are emitted from naturally occurring radioactive elements:

alpha radiation   (α-rays)
beta radiation   (β-rays) and
gamma radiation   (γ-rays)

He was able to characterize these radia-tions because they were affected differ-ently by passage through an electric or magnetic field.

Subsequent investigations character-ized the three types of radiation according to their mass, charge, and velocity. Alpha (α) radiation (or α-particles) turned out to be identical to helium atoms that had lost both electrons, leaving only the nucleus (page 107). They move with a velocity of up to 10% of the speed of light. The helium nucleus consists of two protons and two neutrons and has a mass of approximately 4 amu. Since both electrons have been removed, the charge on the alpha particle is $+2$. Like the helium atom, the helium nucleus can be represented by the symbol ^4_2He, where the subscript 2 is the number of protons and the superscript 4 repre-sents the combined number of protons and neutrons (pages 95 and 96).

When the nucleus of a radioactive element emits an alpha particle, it loses two protons and two neutrons and thereby transmutes into another element. The new nucleus resulting from the emission will have an atomic number (Z) of two less and an atomic mass number (A) of four less than the original nucleus. For ex-ample, when a certain isotope of uranium, $^{238}_{92}U$, emits an alpha particle, it becomes an isotope of thorium that has an atomic mass of 234 and an atomic number of 90:

$$^{238}_{92}U \longrightarrow {}^{234}_{90}Th + {}^4_2He$$

Madame Curie also discovered that radium can emit an alpha particle, forming the radioactive gas radon:

$$^{226}_{28}Ra \longrightarrow {}^{222}_{86}Rn + {}^4_2He$$

These equations describe nuclear pro-cesses, because the nucleus of one ele-ment has been transformed into the nucleus of another. In nuclear equations, as in chemical equations, the products and reactants must be balanced. In other words, the sum of the atomic mass num-bers and the sum of the atomic numbers of the nuclei on each side of the equa-tion must be equal.

The second type of radiation, the beta (β) particle, turned out to be identical in mass and charge to the electron; that is, it has a mass of essentially 0 (0.0005 amu) and a charge of -1. It was found to travel at velocities of up to 90% of the speed of light. When the nucleus of a radioactive element emits a beta particle, it becomes the nucleus of a new element that has the

Table 4I–1
Nuclear Radiations

RADIATION	SYMBOL	MASS (amu)	CHARGE (ELECTRON UNITS)	VELOCITY	PENETRATION
alpha	α, ^4_2He	4	+2	up to 0.1 c	paper
beta	β, $_{-1}^{0}e$	≈ 0	−1	up to 0.9 c	0.5 cm Pb
gamma	γ	0	0	c	10 cm Pb

same mass and an atomic number one greater than the original element. A β-particle is represented by the notation $_{-1}^{0}e$, since, in balancing nuclear equations, we treat the electron as if its atomic number were −1. The nucleus of thorium formed by the alpha decay of uranium will emit a beta particle and form the nucleus of protactinium:

$$^{234}_{90}Th \longrightarrow {}^{234}_{91}Pa + {}_{-1}^{0}e$$

The third type of radiation is gamma (γ) radiation. Gamma rays are nothing more than photons of energy traveling at the speed of light with energies higher than those usually observed for x-rays. They have zero mass and charge, and they are usually emitted from nuclei along with α- or β-particles. Table 4I–1 summarizes the characteristics of all three types of nuclear radiations.

Due to their different characteristics, these three types of radiation interact with matter in different ways. For example, alpha particles are easily stopped by several sheets of paper or by human skin. Beta particles will penetrate several millimeters into human skin but are stopped by 0.5 cm of lead, whereas gamma rays can pass through the human body and indeed through several feet of concrete but are stopped by 10 cm of lead.

The amount of radiation emitted from a sample is proportional to the amount of radioactive material in that sample. Since emission is a property of the nucleus, it is not affected by the chemical state of the radioactive species. Thus a change in temperature or pressure of a radioactive substance will not have any effect on its emission of radiation. However, the amount of radiation emitted from a sample decreases with time, due to the fact that the concentration of the radioactive nuclei is decreasing with time. The rate at which the amount of radioactive material decreases is determined by the half-life of the nucleus. The **half-life** is defined as the time required for one-half of the number of the nuclei to disintegrate. For example, ^{238}U has a half-life of 4.5×10^9 years, and ^{234}Th has a half-life of only 24.1 days. This means that if we start with 1,000 ^{234}Th nuclei, at the end of 24.1 days 500 nuclei will be left, and after 48.2 days (two half-lives) only 250 will remain. Very unstable nuclei may have half-lives of less than 10^{-9} seconds, while very stable materials may have half-lives of millions of years.

The discovery of radioactivity and the identification of the three different types of radiation in the early part of the twentieth century have led to many important applications. Among these are the use of radioactive isotopes for medical diagnosis and treatment and for industrial testing, as well as the development of atomic and hydrogen bombs.

nucleus, just as a planet travels about the sun. In terms of Newtonian classical mechanics, this assumption implies that an orbit is stable when the force of attraction between the protons and neutrons is exactly counterbalanced by the centrifugal force associated with a particle moving in a curved path. (The centrifugal force is the force that causes a pebble to fly off a rotating potter's wheel; in an atomic system it would tend to drive the moving electron away from the nucleus.) However, in terms of the laws of classical mechanics, *any* orbit of this type can exist. In other words, a planetary orbit may have any radius and an electron may have any energy.

All of this leads to what was called the "failure of classical mechanics." The theories of classical mechanics state that if any charged particle is moving in a curved path (such as an electron in a particular planetary orbit) it will continuously radiate energy. If an electron were to do this, it would lose energy through radiation and spiral down into the nucleus (since it is still under the influence of electrostatic attraction), causing the atomic system to collapse. It was known in Bohr's time that contrary to the laws of classical mechanics, atoms do not emit radiation continuously, and they are not unstable. In addition, it was known that radiation is emitted only at certain discrete wavelengths (the line spectra described on page 102).

Bohr's stroke of genius was to develop a postulate for the **quantum condition** of an atom which stated that an atom could have only a certain set of electron orbits around its nucleus rather than orbits of any radius. By combining the equations of classical mechanics with this postulate, Bohr was able to derive a new model for the hydrogen atom that explained its stability and the origin of the line emission spectrum. The net result of the addition of this quantum constraint was that the energies an electron could have in an orbit were limited to certain values given by the equation:

$$E = -\frac{1}{n^2}(A) \qquad (4\text{--}6)$$

where n is an integer representing the orbit ($n = 1, 2, 3, \ldots$) and A is a numerical constant characteristic of the element. The radii of these orbits are then given by the equation:

$$r = n^2(B) \qquad (4\text{--}7)$$

where B is a second numerical constant characteristic of the element. The radii of the first four orbits ($n = 1, 2, 3, 4$) for an electron in the hydrogen atom, for example, are given by Equation 4–7, with $r = B, 4B, 9B, 16B$. Their corresponding energies are given by Equation 4–6, with $E = -A$, $-\frac{1}{4}A$, $-\frac{1}{9}A$, $-\frac{1}{16}A$. The assignment of negative energies might seem confusing, but it must be remembered that we are speaking of *relative* energies, where zero energy exists when the electron is removed from the atom and where the most stable orbit, the ground state, has the lowest and therefore most negative energy.

Using these values for the possible energies of the electron in a hydrogen atom, we are now in a position to set up an energy level diagram for hydrogen which plots each allowed electron orbit as a function of energy (see Figure 4–11). Note that the spacing between energy levels decreases as n increases and that $n = \infty$ ($E = 0$) corresponds to the complete removal of the electron from the atom ($r = \infty$). The absorption of light occurs when an electron absorbs energy and is excited into a higher energy level ($E_0 \longrightarrow E_1$ or higher level), and the emission of light occurs when an electron emits energy and drops down from a higher energy level into a lower one.

Bohr went on to use simple numerical manipulation of Equation 4–6 to exactly derive the value of the constant found by Rydberg (page 105) in the empirical formula describing the emission spectrum of the hydrogen atom. This feat, the theoretical derivation of an experimentally deter-

Figure 4–11
An energy level diagram for hydrogen

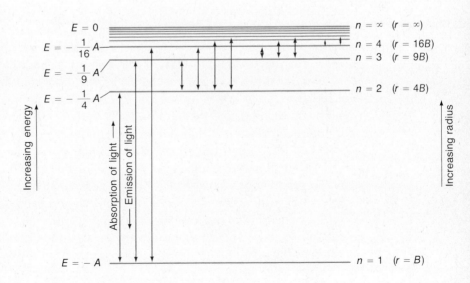

mined physical constant, was one of the outstanding intellectual achievements of the early twentieth century. Bohr's introduction of the quantum condition and his development of a new atomic model based on this condition were also great contributions to the progress of scientific knowledge. However, he introduced the concept of the quantum condition without providing any theoretical justification for it, and his atomic model was limited in that it gave quantitative results only for a one-electron atom such as the hydrogen atom. Thus the ever-developing model of the atom had to be refined still further to account for the electrons in all of the elements.

4.8 The Wave Mechanical Picture of the Atom

The next step in describing the properties of electrons in atoms was taken by Louis de Broglie who, in 1924, proposed that the motion of a very small particle such as an electron has associated with it a wave motion. This was a far-reaching postulate. Recall from Section 4.3 (page 101) that some properties of light indicate that it is corpuscular in nature (Newton), whereas other properties point to a wave-like behavior (Huyghens). De Broglie stated that electrons, which we have been considering as particles, can be treated as waves. They can then be viewed according to the laws of wave mechanics rather than those of Newtonian classical mechanics, which apply to macroscopic particles and which, as we have seen, fail to account for atomic systems. Thus, the reason that classical mechanics failed was that electrons were being treated as particles using a theory originally developed to explain macroscopic objects. When de Broglie applied his concept to Bohr's planetary model of the atom, one result was that Bohr's postulate of the quantum condition was justified.

Note that this approach to electrons provides a complementary view of the same thing. Particles such as electrons can at some times behave and be considered as if they are particles and at other times behave and be better described as if they are waves. This seemingly paradoxical situation is usually called the **wave/particle duality**.

This dual nature of electrons was formalized in 1926 by the German physicist Erwin Schrödinger. Using equations that had been previously developed to describe wave motion, Schrödinger worked out a rather complex equation to describe an electron in an atom in terms of its **wave function**, ψ (psi). The symbol ψ represents a mathematical function that describes the behavior of the wave-like electron in the atom. The beauty of using the equation of wave mechanics to describe the electron is that the square of a wave function (ψ^2) is, in the language of wave mechanics, a **probability function**; it gives the probability of locating an electron in a unit volume of space.

If an electron in an atom is in a certain energy state ($E_1, E_2, E_3, \ldots$), Schrödinger's equation can be solved to give the corresponding wave function ($\psi_1, \psi_2, \psi_3, \ldots$). This wave function will completely describe the electron of the atom in that energy state. In addition, as we shall see in the next section, the form of ψ^2 tells us about the *shape* of the region of space in which there is a maximum probability of finding the electron.

A further development which reinforced the implications of wave mechanics was made in 1927 by the physicist Werner Heisenberg in his statement of the **Uncertainty Principle**. This is a fundamental limitation on the measurement of pairs of related observables, such as time and energy or position and momentum (momentum = mass × velocity, or mv). Heisenberg made the assertion that it is impossible to simultaneously determine both the position and momentum of an electron (or of anything else) with absolute accuracy. If one of these variables is measured with complete certainty, the other cannot be known accurately.

$$\begin{pmatrix} \text{uncertainty} \\ \text{in position} \end{pmatrix} \times \begin{pmatrix} \text{uncertainty} \\ \text{in momentum} \end{pmatrix} \geq h$$

or

$$(\Delta x)(\Delta mv) \geq h$$

where h is Planck's constant, 6.626×10^{-27} g cm^2/sec, and Δ signifies uncertainty.

For a macroscopic object such as a baseball weighing 225 g ($\approx \frac{1}{2}$ lb) moving at 4.0×10^3 cm/sec ($\approx$90 mph), the uncertainty in position and momentum is a trivial fraction of its position and momentum. The momentum (mv) is equal to $(225 \text{ g})(4.0 \times 10^3 \text{ cm/sec})$, or 9.0×10^5 g cm/sec. If we know mv to one part in one million, the uncertainty in momentum (Δmv) would be $(10^{-6})(9.0 \times 10^5 \text{ g cm/sec})$, or 0.90 g cm/sec. Therefore, substituting this answer for Δmv in the relationship $(\Delta x)(\Delta mv) \geq h$, we can solve for Δx, the uncertainty in position:

$$\Delta x \geq \frac{6.626 \times 10^{-27} \text{ g cm}^2/\text{sec}}{0.90 \text{ g cm/sec}}$$

$$\Delta x \geq 7.4 \times 10^{-27} \text{ cm}$$

The Impossible X-Ray Microscope

When discussing atomic systems we are dealing with such small dimensions that we cannot build a microscope to directly observe these systems. The resolving power of any microscope (the smallest dimensions that can be resolved) is dependent on the wavelength of the radiation used to make the observation. Microscopes that use visible light with wavelengths of about 7,000 Å, for example, are limited to seeing things on the order of 7,000 Å (7.0×10^{-5} cm). If we want to observe distances on the atomic scale, on the order of 1 Å, we must construct a microscope that can use radiation with a wavelength of this order of magnitude. Wavelengths of 1 Å correspond to radiation in the x-ray region of the electromagnetic spectrum (Figure 4–3). The energy of radiation of a 1.0 Å wavelength can be calculated from the equation $E = h\nu = h(c/\lambda)$ (page 101):

$$E = (6.626 \times 10^{-27} \text{ erg-sec})$$
$$\left(\frac{3.0 \times 10^{10} \text{ cm/sec}}{1.0 \times 10^{-8} \text{ cm}} \right)$$

$$E = 2.0 \times 10^{-8} \text{ erg}$$

However, the energy associated with an electron moving with a typical velocity of 1.00×10^8 cm/sec, calculated from the equation $E = \frac{1}{2} mv^2$ (page 31), is:

$$E = \frac{1}{2}(9.11 \times 10^{-28} \text{ g})$$
$$\times (1.00 \times 10^8 \text{ cm/sec})^2$$

$$E = 4.56 \times 10^{-12} \text{ erg}$$

This is more than four orders of magnitude smaller than the energy of the radiation used in the microscope to try to observe the electron. Therefore, the incident radiation (the x-rays) will greatly disturb the atomic system, because this radiation has greater energy than the electron in the atom under observation.

This inability to observe the electron directly reinforces the concept that it is impossible to precisely locate an electron within an atom. When we try to use radiation of suitable resolving power to study an electron through a microscope, we completely disrupt the atomic system. When we discuss solids (in Chapter 9) we shall see that x-rays can be used to investigate the structure of matter, but only indirectly through the process of diffraction.

This is a minuscule dimension that becomes negligible on the macroscopic scale of a baseball.

The uncertainty in the position of an electron, on the other hand, is not at all negligible on the microscopic scale of an atom. Consider, for example, an electron moving at 1.00×10^8 cm/sec, with its momentum known to one part per million:

$$\Delta mv = \left(\frac{1}{10^6}\right)(9.11 \times 10^{-28} \text{ g})(1.00 \times 10^8 \text{ cm/sec})$$

$$= 9.11 \times 10^{-26} \text{ g cm/sec}$$

Then, solving for Δx in the relationship $(\Delta x)(\Delta mv) \geq h$, we have:

$$\Delta x \geq \frac{6.626 \times 10^{-27} \text{ g cm}^2/\text{sec}}{9.11 \times 10^{-26} \text{ g cm/sec}}$$

$$\Delta x \geq 7.27 \times 10^{-2} \text{ cm}$$

which is much larger than the wavelengths corresponding to an electron and many orders of magnitude larger than atomic distances. Thus, because of the Uncertainty Principle it is impossible to locate an electron precisely at a given point within the atom. There is therefore no point in talking about fixed electron orbits as in the planetary model of the atom. It is more accurate to describe electrons in the language of *probability*— that is, to give the probability of finding the electron in a particular volume of space, rather than to give its exact position.

4.9 The Electronic Configuration of the Elements

Energy Levels, Sublevels, and Orbitals

Every wave function ψ that is a valid solution of the Schrödinger equation describes the behavior of an electron within the atom. In this section we shall see how these wave functions describe **orbitals**, the regions in space in which there is a maximum probability of finding the electron. Specifically, we will concern ourselves with how each electronic orbital looks (what its shape is) and how the orbitals order themselves energetically within the atom.

It is the mathematical form of the wave function that identifies an orbital's energy and shape. Each wave function contains four constants known as **quantum numbers** which are used to describe the behavior of an electron in an atom. The principal quantum number n (which turns out to be the same as Bohr's quantum number for the hydrogen atom) defines the **energy level**. Recall that as n increases ($n = 1, 2, 3, 4, \ldots$), the energy ($E = -A, -\frac{1}{4}A, -\frac{1}{9}A, -\frac{1}{16}A, \ldots$) and the electron's distance from the nucleus ($r = B, 4B, 9B, 16B, \ldots$) also increase.

The electronic energy levels within the atom are made up of energy **sublevels,** called the s, p, d, and f sublevels. Within a given energy level, the energy of the sublevels increases in the order listed, so that s has the least amount of energy and f has the most. The number of sublevels that an energy level contains is equal to the numerical value of n. For example, the $n = 3$ energy level contains three sublevels, the $s, p,$ and d sublevels.

Each sublevel is in turn made up of the orbitals that the electrons occupy. Only a certain number of electron orbitals can exist in each type of sublevel: an s sublevel contains only one orbital, a p sublevel contains three orbitals, a d sublevel contains five orbitals, and an f sublevel contains seven orbitals.

We identify particular orbitals in the following manner. The orbital in the $n = 2$ energy level and the s sublevel is called the $2s$ orbital; an orbital in the $n = 3$ level and the d sublevel is labeled a $3d$ orbital. The identification of orbitals is summarized in Table 4–2.

Each orbital in an atom can be occupied by two electrons, so that:

one s orbital can contain two s electrons

Table 4–2

Electronic Energy Levels, Sublevels, and Orbitals

LEVEL	SUBLEVEL	ORBITALS	
$n = 1$	s	one	$1s$
$n = 2$	s	one	$2s$
	p	three	$2p$
$n = 3$	s	one	$3s$
	p	three	$3p$
	d	five	$3d$
$n = 4$	s	one	$4s$
	p	three	$4p$
	d	five	$4d$
	f	seven	$4f$

three p orbitals can contain six p electrons
five d orbitals can contain ten d electrons
seven f orbitals can contain fourteen f electrons

In general, a level of principal quantum number n can contain up to a total of $2\,n^2$ electrons. For example, in the $n = 3$ energy level, there are $2(3)^2 = 18$ possible electrons, which corresponds to the sum of the possible number of electrons in the s, p, and d orbitals ($2 + 6 + 10 = 18$).

An electron in an orbital may be pictured as a spinning electric charge that generates a tiny magnetic field. The two possible electrons in an orbital of an atom differ only in the direction of this **spin**. For one atom, the spin may be considered as a clockwise, or "upward," motion (↑); for the other, the spin is considered to be counterclockwise, or "down" (↓).

Shapes of the Orbitals

What do the electronic orbitals of an atom look like? Keep in mind that we are really asking, "What is the region in space that an electron is most likely to be found in?" or "What does the square of the wave function, ψ^2, look like?"

All s orbitals are spherically symmetrical; that is, the region of maximum probability of finding an s electron is a sphere in space whose size (and energy) increases with n, the principal quantum number. Three p orbitals exist within the p subshell. They are "dumbbell"-shaped regions oriented along the mutually perpendicular x, y, and z directions (see Figure 4–12). We shall call them the p_x, p_y, and p_z orbitals, respectively. Each of the electrons in a p orbital occupies *both* lobes of the dumbbell-shaped orbital. Remembering that the electron can be considered as a wave, Figure 4–13 illustrates how an electron can exist simultaneously in both lobes of a p orbital.

The five d orbitals are more complex in shape (Figure 4–12). The d_{xy}, d_{yz}, and d_{xz} orbitals are two dumbbell-shaped lobes in the xy, yz, and xz planes, respectively. They are thinner than the p orbitals and are oriented at 45° to the axes. The $d_{x^2-y^2}$ orbital lies in the xy plane along the xy axes, and the d_{z^2} orbital has a dumbbell-shaped region along the z direction and a toroidal-shaped (doughnut-shaped) region in the xy plane. Again, each electron may be found in any part of a particular orbital.

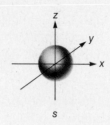

(spherically symmetric)

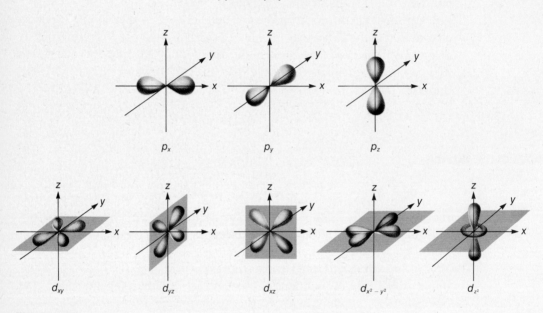

Figure 4–12
The shapes of the electronic orbitals

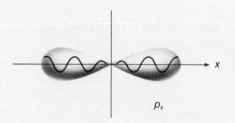

Figure 4–13
An electron in the lobes of a p_x orbital

Filling the Orbitals

Electrons fill the available orbitals in a particular manner: they fill the lowest energy orbital first. The order of increasing energy of the orbitals has been determined by a careful examination of a wealth of atomic spectroscopic data. Starting with the lowest energy orbital, the order is:

$$1s, \; 2s, \; 2p, \; 3s, \; 3p, \; 4s, \; 3d, \; 4p, \; 5s, \; 4d, \; 5p, \; 6s, \; 4f, \; 5d, \; 6p, \; 7s, \; 5f, \; 6d, \; 7p$$

Figure 4–14 is a schematic energy level diagram of these electronic orbitals. The order of filling of electronic energy levels can be remembered by the simple mnemonic illustration in Figure 4–15: starting at the upper right of each line, the order of increasing energies is diagonally down to the left and then back to the upper right of the next diagonal.

Let us start with the simplest element, hydrogen, which has an atomic number of 1 ($Z = 1$). The one electron in the neutral hydrogen atom will be located in the lowest energy orbital, the $1s$ orbital. We

Figure 4–14
A schematic
energy level
diagram

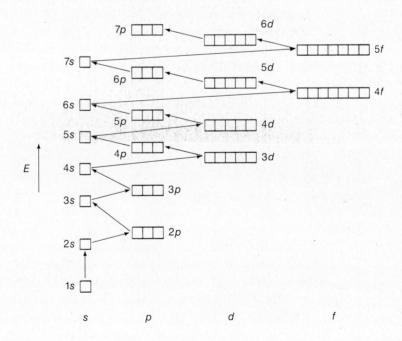

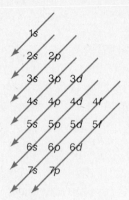

Figure 4–15
A mnemonic
illustration for the
order of filling of
energy levels

therefore say that the **electronic configuration** of hydrogen is:

$$1s^1$$

where $1s$ is the orbital and the superscript 1 represents the number of electrons in that orbital.

In constructing the electronic configurations of the successive elements we follow the so-called **aufbau principle** (from the German aufbau, meaning "to build up"). In going to the next element (one higher in Z) we add a proton to the nucleus and an electron to the configuration that exists for the previous element. A neutral helium atom $(Z = 2)$ has a second electron (with opposite spin) which can enter the $1s$ orbital:

$$_2\text{He: } 1s^2$$

Another way of indicating this is to use the notation we previously introduced for spin:

$$\frac{\uparrow\downarrow}{1s}$$

Notice that the $1s^2$ configuration represents a filled orbital, a filled sublevel, and a filled energy level $(n = 1)$. This stable configuration tells us that helium gas must have a high degree of stability.

The next element is lithium $(Z = 3)$. We have already filled the $1s$ orbital, so the third electron has to go into the next orbital, the $2s$ orbital:

$$_3\text{Li: } 1s^2 2s^1$$

Beryllium $(Z = 4)$ will fill the $2s$ orbital:

$$\text{}_4\text{Be:} \quad 1s^2 2s^2 \quad \text{or} \quad \frac{\uparrow\downarrow}{2s}$$

$$\frac{\uparrow\downarrow}{1s}$$

The next electron, which will form boron $(Z = 5)$, must go into one of the three available $2p$ orbitals which make up the $2p$ sublevel:

$$\text{}_5\text{B: } 1s^2 2s^2 2p^1 \quad \text{or} \quad \frac{\uparrow\downarrow}{2s} \quad \frac{\uparrow}{} \ \underline{\ \ } \ \underline{\ \ }$$

$$\qquad\qquad\qquad\qquad\qquad\qquad \underset{2p}{}$$

$$\frac{\uparrow\downarrow}{1s}$$

Now we have a problem: carbon $(Z = 6)$, with an electronic configuration of $1s^2 2s^2 2p^2$, can have two electrons in a single $2p$ orbital or an electron in each of two of the **degenerate** (same energy) $2p$ orbitals:

$$\frac{\uparrow\downarrow}{}\ \frac{\uparrow\downarrow}{}\ \underline{\ \ }\ \underline{\ \ } \quad \text{or} \quad \frac{\uparrow\downarrow}{}\ \frac{\uparrow}{}\ \frac{\uparrow}{}\ \underline{\ \ }$$

$$\frac{\uparrow\downarrow}{} \qquad \text{(a)} \qquad\qquad \frac{\uparrow\downarrow}{} \qquad\qquad \text{(b)}$$

This ambiguity is resolved by **Hund's Rule:** If two or more electrons are going into the same sublevel, the more stable configuration will be that in which the electrons are not in the same orbital. Therefore, for $_6$C, (b) is the configuration with lowest energy. In general, Hund's Rule means that you will always find the *maximum number of unpaired spins* when faced with a choice of configurations.

Continuing on, we have:

$2p$ sublevel

$_7$N:	$1s^2 2s^2 2p^3$	$\frac{\uparrow}{}$ $\frac{\uparrow}{}$ $\frac{\uparrow}{}$	(electron goes into third p orbital)
$_8$O:	$1s^2 2s^2 2p^4$	$\frac{\uparrow\downarrow}{}$ $\frac{\uparrow}{}$ $\frac{\uparrow}{}$	(pairing of electrons begins)
$_9$F:	$1s^2 2s^2 2p^5$	$\frac{\uparrow\downarrow}{}$ $\frac{\uparrow\downarrow}{}$ $\frac{\uparrow}{}$	
$_{10}$Ne:	$1s^2 2s^2 2p^6$	$\frac{\uparrow\downarrow}{}$ $\frac{\uparrow\downarrow}{}$ $\frac{\uparrow\downarrow}{}$	

At neon, we have filled the $n = 2$ level; we will abbreviate this stable noble gas configuration as:

$$1s^2 2s^2 2p^6 \equiv [\text{Ne}]$$

The next element is sodium ($Z = 11$). Since the neon configuration is a filled energy level, the next electron goes into the $3s$ orbital:

$$_{11}\text{Na:} \quad 1s^2 2s^2 2p^6 3s^1 \quad \text{or} \quad [\text{Ne}]3s^1$$

Magnesium ($Z = 12$) completes the $3s$ orbital:

$$_{12}\text{Mg:} \quad 1s^2 2s^2 2p^6 3s^2$$

The next six elements ($Z = 13\text{--}18$) fill the $3p$ sublevel in a similar manner:

$$_{13}\text{Al:} \quad 1s^2 2s^2 2p^6 3s^2 3p^1$$
$$_{14}\text{Si:} \quad 1s^2 2s^2 2p^6 3s^2 3p^2$$
$$_{15}\text{P:} \quad 1s^2 2s^2 2p^6 3s^2 3p^3$$
$$_{16}\text{S:} \quad 1s^2 2s^2 2p^6 3s^2 3p^4$$
$$_{17}\text{Cl:} \quad 1s^2 2s^2 2p^6 3s^2 3p^5$$
$$_{18}\text{Ar:} \quad 1s^2 2s^2 2p^6 3s^2 3p^6 \equiv [\text{Ar}]$$

Argon has the same outer level electronic configuration as neon ($ns^2 np^6$); we will abbreviate the 18-electron argon configuration as [Ar].

The next sublevel to be filled contains the $4s$ orbital:

$$_{19}\text{K:} \quad [\text{Ar}]4s^1$$
$$_{20}\text{Ca:} \quad [\text{Ar}]4s^2$$

According to our order of filling diagram, the next sublevel contains the $3d$ orbitals. Since there are five degenerate d orbitals in the sublevel, we must fill them following Hund's Rule:

		4s sublevel	3d sublevel				
$_{21}$Sc:	$[Ar]4s^2 3d^1$	↑↓	↑	—	—	—	—
$_{22}$Ti:	$[Ar]4s^2 3d^2$	↑↓	↑	↑	—	—	—
$_{23}$V:	$[Ar]4s^2 3d^3$	↑↓	↑	↑	↑	—	—
$_{24}$Cr:	$[Ar]4s^1 3d^5$	↑	↑	↑	↑	↑	↑
$_{25}$Mn:	$[Ar]4s^2 3d^5$	↑↓	↑	↑	↑	↑	↑
$_{26}$Fe:	$[Ar]4s^2 3d^6$	↑↓	↑↓	↑	↑	↑	↑
$_{27}$Co:	$[Ar]4s^2 3d^7$	↑↓	↑↓	↑↓	↑	↑	↑
$_{28}$Ni:	$[Ar]4s^2 3d^8$	↑↓	↑↓	↑↓	↑↓	↑	↑
$_{29}$Cu:	$[Ar]4s^1 3d^{10}$	↑	↑↓	↑↓	↑↓	↑↓	↑↓
$_{30}$Zn:	$[Ar]4s^2 3d^{10}$	↑↓	↑↓	↑↓	↑↓	↑↓	↑↓

Notice that Cr and Cu seem to behave anomalously. This is due to the extra stability associated with the half-filled or completely filled d sublevel. Cr therefore has the configuration $[Ar]4s^1 3d^5$ rather than $[Ar]4s^2 3d^4$ since the former gives a single electron in each of the five $3d$ orbitals, making the s and the d sublevels exactly half-filled.

The elements gallium through krypton (Z = 31–36) fill the $4p$ sublevel:

$$_{31}\text{Ga:} \quad [Ar]4s^2 3d^{10} 4p^1$$

$$_{32}\text{Ge:} \quad [Ar]4s^2 3d^{10} 4p^2$$

$$_{33}\text{As:} \quad [Ar]4s^2 3d^{10} 4p^3$$

$$_{34}\text{Se:} \quad [Ar]4s^2 3d^{10} 4p^4$$

$$_{35}\text{Br:} \quad [Ar]4s^2 3d^{10} 4p^5$$

$$_{36}\text{Kr:} \quad [Ar]4s^2 3d^{10} 4p^6 \equiv [Kr]$$

The 36-electron krypton configuration is abbreviated [Kr].

By following the order of filling of orbitals, the electronic configuration of all the elements can be constructed.

TERMS
AND
CONCEPTS

- Nucleus
  - neutrons and protons
- Electrons
- Atomic number and atomic mass number
- Isotope
- Nuclear binding energy
- Electromagnetic spectrum
- Electromagnetic radiation
  - wavelength, λ
  - frequency, ν
  - speed of light, c
- Photons and quanta of energy
  - Planck's constant, h
- Line emission and absorption spectra
- Rydberg constant
- Thomson's experiment
  - cathode rays
- Charge/mass ratio of the electron
- Millikan's oil drop experiment
- Rutherford's experiment with α-particles

- Radioactivity
  - alpha radiation, α-rays
  - beta radiation, β-rays
  - gamma radiation, γ-rays
- Half-life
- Bohr model of the atom
  - quantum condition
  - energy level diagram
- Wave mechanical picture of the atom
  - wave/particle duality
  - wave function, ψ
  - probability function
  - Heisenberg's Uncertainty Principle
- Electronic configuration
  - quantum numbers
  - energy levels, sublevels, and orbitals
- Electron spin
- Aufbau principle
- Hund's Rule
  - degenerate orbitals

QUESTIONS

1. Explain the difference between atomic mass number and atomic number. Which one determines the identity of an element? Which one is used to identify isotopes?

2. Give the number of protons and neutrons in the nucleus of each of the following:

   a. $^{18}_{8}O$ d. $^{40}_{19}K$ g. $^{1}_{1}H$
   b. $^{16}_{8}O$ e. $^{238}_{92}U$ h. $^{2}_{1}H$ (deuterium)
   c. $^{40}_{18}Ar$ f. $^{235}_{92}U$ i. $^{3}_{1}H$ (tritium)

   For each of the above, give the number of electrons in the neutral atom.

3. a. From the general magnitudes of nuclear and atomic radii given in Section 4.1 calculate the ratio of the radius of a nucleus to the radius of a whole atom.

   b. If a nucleus were as large as a period on a page (radius approximately 0.25 mm), how far away would the electron be (measured in units of feet)?

4. Boron has two naturally occurring isotopes, ^{10}B and ^{11}B. Their atomic weights and percent abundances are

$$\begin{aligned} ^{10}\text{B:} &\quad 10.0129 \text{ amu; } 19.78\% \\ ^{11}\text{B:} &\quad 11.0093 \text{ amu; } 80.22\% \end{aligned}$$

Calculate the atomic mass of naturally occurring boron *from this data*. Does your answer agree with the tabulated value?

5. On a summer day each square centimeter on the surface of the earth receives approximately 10^6 ergs of solar energy per second. Assuming that all of this radiation has a wavelength of 6,000 Å (it actually spans a good part of the spectrum), calculate the number of photons bombarding 1 cm^2 each second.

6. Which has more energy, a photon of red light or a photon of blue light?

7. The average distance from the sun to the earth is 93×10^6 miles. Calculate the time required for light from the sun to reach the earth.

8. The emission spectrum of sodium has a bright yellow line at a wavelength of 0.589 μm.

   a. What is the frequency of the line?

   b. What is the energy in ergs for a photon of this frequency?

9. What information is available from atomic spectra?

10. How is an atomic line emission spectrum generated?

11. What are "cathode rays"? (A common modern version of Thomson's cathode ray tube is the television picture tube. You may want to investigate how it works.)

12. Briefly describe Rutherford's experiment and the conclusions that he drew from it.

13. Why was Bohr's description of the atom considered a breakthrough in developing the modern picture of the atom?

14. a. Do the energies of the electrons in the Bohr atom increase or decrease as the radius of the orbit increases?

    b. It is easier to remove an electron from an atom the higher its energy is. Does this mean that it is easier to remove an electron from an outer orbit or an inner orbit?

15. Discuss the differences between the Bohr model and the wave mechanical model of an atom with respect to the:

    a. nature of the electron

    b. position of the electron

    c. structure of the atom

16. Why couldn't Newton's Laws governing the motion of larger objects be applied with success to describe the motion of an electron? Is an electron an "object"?

17. List the number of sublevels, orbitals, and electrons which can occupy the $n = 1, 2, 3,$ and 4 levels.

18. Indicate whether the following sublevels exist, and, if so, how many orbitals can be contained in each:

$$2s \quad 4d \quad 3d \quad 1p \quad 3f \quad 5s$$
$$3p \quad 1s \quad 2p \quad 2d \quad 1d \quad 4f$$

19. Give the number of unpaired electrons for each element from $Z = 19$ to $Z = 36$.

20. Write electronic configurations for the following sets of elements and ions and comment on the similarities in the outer shell of electrons in each set.
    a. Li, Na, K
    b. F, Cl, Br
    c. Ne, Ar, Kr
    d. O^{2-}, F^-, Ne, Na^+, Mg^{2+}, Al^{3+}

5

The Periodic Table

Guidelines

After completing this chapter the student should be able to:

- discuss the contributions of Newlands, Mendeleev, and Moseley to the development of the modern periodic table

- state the periodic law

- list the families in the periodic table

- explain the relationship between the shape of the periodic table and the electronic configuration of the elements

- explain the concepts of ionization potential and electron affinity

- identify and explain the periodic trends of ionization potentials and electron affinities

- discuss the concept of atomic size in terms of atomic and ionic radii

- identify an isoelectronic series of ions

5.1 Historical Background

In Chapter 2 we discussed the atomic theory advanced by John Dalton in the first decade of the nineteenth century. Almost immediately there were attempts to correlate the chemical and physical properties of the known elements with their atomic weights. For example, in 1817 Johann Dobereiner described a relationship among the atomic weights of certain "triads" of elements having similar properties. One such triad consisted of lithium, sodium, and potassium—all very active metals which have similar physical and chemical properties. Dobereiner noticed that the atomic weight of sodium (23 amu) was the average of the atomic weights of lithium and potassium (7 and 39 amu, respectively). He found other triads that exhibited the same relationship. However, his scheme was limited, since he could find no unifying concept to relate the several triads.

In fact, there were no notable advances made in correlating elemental properties with atomic weight for almost fifty years. This was due in part to inaccuracies in the measurement of the atomic weights known at the time and to the fact that there were undiscovered elements. But, as more and more elements were isolated and identified, more chemists tried to correlate their chemical properties in an attempt to seek a pattern. The first partly successful systemization of the elements was proposed in 1866 by the English chemist John Newlands. He noted that if the known elements were listed in order of increasing atomic weight, elements with similar properties tended to appear at regular intervals. Each of the elements in the list was similar to the seventh element preceding and/or following it, so that an interval from the first to the eighth element, for example, formed a series of eight, or an octave. Hence, Newlands said

Table 5–1

Newlands' Law of Octaves

H	Li	Be	B	C	N	O
1.0	6.9	9.0	10.8	12.0	14.0	16.0
F	Na	Mg	Al	Si	P	S
19.0	23.0	24.3	27.0	28.0	31.0	32.0
Cl	K	Ca	Cr	Ti	Mn	Fe
35.5	39.1	40.0	52.0	47.9	55.0	55.8

that the elements were related by a "law of octaves." A part of Newlands' list of elements, with the similar elements occurring in columns, is shown in Table 5–1. (The atomic weights in the table are those known in Newlands' time.) Note that Dobereiner's triad of lithium, sodium, and potassium appears in the second column.

Unfortunately, Newlands' "law of octaves" was not entirely consistent (the metals cobalt and nickel would be in the same row as the gases fluorine and chlorine, for example), and he was subjected to some ridicule, especially since he proposed a relationship between this arrangement and musical octaves. Furthermore, his scheme worked well only for the first two rows, and he was unable to predict or accommodate the discovery of new elements. Nevertheless, his notion that elements with similar properties occur at certain intervals (or *periods*) in a listing according to atomic weight was at the heart of the later and more successful efforts of Mendeleev and Meyer.

Mendeleev's and Meyer's Tables

In 1869 the Russian chemist Dimitri Mendeleev and the German chemist Lothar Meyer independently proposed a more consistent, complete, and sophisticated grouping of all of the then-known elements based on their atomic weights. Like Newlands, they recognized that the properties of elements occurred periodically according to atomic weights. To illustrate this, let us look at one property of elements, the melting point, which varies with atomic weight. It can be seen at a glance from Figure 5–1 that the melting point does vary in cycles when plotted against atomic weight. Furthermore, elements having similar chemical properties lie in

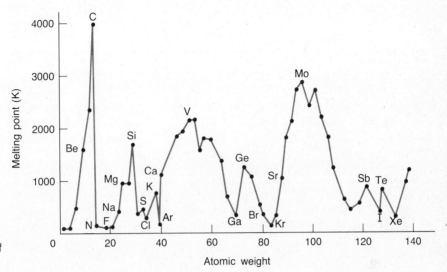

Figure 5–1
A plot of the melting points in relation to the atomic weights of the elements

similar positions within a particular cycle. For example, Be, Mg, Ca, and Sr, which have chemical similarities, all lie on ascending portions of the curve in Figure 5–1. F, Cl, and Br, another group of similar elements, fall near the low points of the curve. The periodic nature of elemental properties could also be illustrated using such properties as conductivity, hardness, or atomic volume.

Mendeleev and Meyer summarized their observations in their statement of the periodic law: The properties of the elements are periodic functions of their atomic weights. In addition, they arranged the groupings of elements that had similar properties in a periodic table. One of Mendeleev's early periodic tables is shown in Figure 5–2. The elements are listed according to atomic weight from left to right in continuing rows, with the elements having similar properties placed under one another. So far, this seems little different from what Newlands did, but Mendeleev paid more careful attention to his groupings and left blank spaces where he thought undiscovered elements should lie. He even predicted the atomic weights of these elements, as well as their chemical and physical properties. Dramatic proof of his system came in the following years when three of the elements he predicted in 1871 were discovered: gallium in 1875, scandium in 1879, and germanium in 1886.

The most serious problem with Mendeleev's periodic table was that as the measurement of atomic weights became more precise, it was found that there were three places where pairs of elements had to be reversed

Figure 5–2
Mendeleev's periodic table (with the atomic weights as known in his time given in parentheses)

Row	Group I	Group II	Group III	Group IV	Group V	Group VI	Group VII	Group VIII	
1	H (1)								
2	Li (7)	Be (9)	B (11)	C (12)	N (14)	O (16)	F (19)		
3	Na (23)	Mg (24)	Al (27)	Si (28)	P (31)	S (32)	Cl (35.5)		
4	K (39)	Ca (40)	__ (44)	Ti (48)	V (51)	Cr (52)	Mn (55)	Fe (56)	Co (59)
								Ni (59)	Cu (63)
5	[Cu (63)]	Zn (65)	__ (68)	__ (72)	As (75)	Se (78)	Br (80)		
6	Rb (85)	Sr (87)	?Yt (88)	Zr (90)	Nb (94)	Mo (96)	__ (100)	Ru (104)	Rh (104)
								Pd (106)	Ag (108)
7	[Ag (108)]	Cd (112)	In (113)	Sn (118)	Sb (122)	Te (125)	I (127)		
8	Cs (133)	Ba (137)	?Di (138)	?Ce (140)	__	__	__	__ __	__ __
9	__	__							
10	__		?Er (178)	?La (180)	Ta (182)	W (184)		Os (195)	Ir (197)
								Pt (198)	Au (199)
11	[Au (199)]	Hg (200)	Tl (204)	Pb (207)	Bi (208)		__		
12	__	__	__	Th (231)	__	U (240)		__ __	__ __

from the normal sequence of increasing atomic weight so that they would fall into their proper chemical groupings. For example, tellurium (at. wt. 127.6) had to be placed before iodine (at. wt. 126.9) so that it would fall into its proper group with oxygen, sulfur, and selenium, and so that iodine would be properly grouped with fluorine, chlorine, and bromine. These disturbing irregularities hinted that there might be a property other than atomic weight (but closely related to it) that actually determines the elemental properties.

Moseley's Experiment

This notion was confirmed by Henry Moseley in 1913. Moseley carried out a series of experiments in which he bombarded various elements with a beam of electrons, an action that produced x-rays having a frequency characteristic of the element. In analyzing his results, Moseley discovered that if the elements were ordered according to the increasing frequency of their x-rays, they fell into a sequence identical to that of their atomic weights, except that the three anomalous pairs were now in their proper positions (e.g., tellurium came before iodine). He was then able to formulate a mathematical relationship between the number of an element's position on the list, Z, and the frequency of the characteristic x-ray of that element; furthermore, his experiments provided strong evidence for the hypothesis that Z, the atomic number (page 96), was actually the number of positive charges on the nucleus. This was subsequently shown to be true.

Thus the properties of the elements are determined not by their atomic weights but by the number of positive charges in their nuclei, that is, by their atomic numbers. Hence the **periodic law** as understood by Mendeleev had to be restated in its presently accepted form:

The properties of the elements are periodic functions of their atomic numbers.

It is understandable that Mendeleev and his contemporaries emphasized the importance of atomic weight, since the atomic weight usually does increase as the atomic number increases. It is now known, as we shall see in Chapter 6, that chemical properties arise from the interactions of electrons in the outer shells of the different atoms involved. These electronic interactions are, in turn, determined by the number of positive charges on the nuclei, that is, by the atomic numbers of the elements. Thus, in the final analysis, it is the atomic number that determines the chemical properties and thus the identity of an element.

5.2 The Modern Periodic Table

The form of the periodic table most used today is the so-called "long form," shown in Figure 5–3. The elements are, of course, arranged in order of their atomic numbers and, as we shall see in the next section, there are good theoretical reasons for the table having the shape it does.

In general, the elements to the left of the zig-zag line (the **Zintl border**) that runs from aluminum ($Z = 13$) to polonium ($Z = 84$) are metals, while those to the right of the line are nonmetals. **Metals** have the physical properties of luster, ductility, malleability, and electrical and thermal conductivity. (A substance that is ductile can be stretched into a wire; a substance that is malleable can be hammered into a sheet.) **Nonmetals,** on the other hand, are either gaseous or, in the solid state, dull-looking, brittle, and only weakly conductive, if at all. Some of the elements in the immediate neighborhood of the zig-zag line have both metallic and nonmetallic properties and are called **metalloids.**

IA	IIA	IIIB	IVB	VB	VIB	VIIB	VIIIB			IB	IIB	IIIA	IVA	VA	VIA	VIIA	VIIIA
			H 1														He 2
Li 3	Be 4											B 5	C 6	N 7	O 8	F 9	Ne 10
Na 11	Mg 12											Al 13	Si 14	P 15	S 16	Cl 17	Ar 18
K 19	Ca 20	Sc 21	Ti 22	V 23	Cr 24	Mn 25	Fe 26	Co 27	Ni 28	Cu 29	Zn 30	Ga 31	Ge 32	As 33	Se 34	Br 35	Kr 36
Rb 37	Sr 38	Y 39	Zr 40	Nb 41	Mo 42	Tc 43	Ru 44	Rh 45	Pd 46	Ag 47	Cd 48	In 49	Sn 50	Sb 51	Te 52	I 53	Xe 54
Cs 55	Ba 56	La* 57	Hf 72	Ta 73	W 74	Re 75	Os 76	Ir 77	Pt 78	Au 79	Hg 80	Tl 81	Pb 82	Bi 83	Po 84	At 85	Rn 86
Fr 87	Ra 88	Ac† 89	Ku 104	Ha 105													

*	Ce 58	Pr 59	Nd 60	Pm 61	Sm 62	Eu 63	Gd 64	Tb 65	Dy 66	Ho 67	Er 68	Tm 69	Yb 70	Lu 71
†	Th 90	Pa 91	U 92	Np 93	Pu 94	Am 95	Cm 96	Bk 97	Cf 98	Es 99	Fm 100	Md 101	No 102	Lr 103

Figure 5–3
The modern periodic table (with the atomic numbers)

In the long form of the periodic table the rows are called **periods**. The first period contains only hydrogen and helium. The second period consists of the elements lithium ($Z = 3$) through neon ($Z = 10$); the third period contains sodium ($Z = 11$) through argon ($Z = 18$), and so on.

The columns in the periodic table are called **groups** or **families** and are numbered IA through VIIIA and IB through VIIIB. Some of the groups have family names. The elements in Group IA are called the **alkali metals**; those in Group IIA are the **alkaline earth metals**; those in VA, the **pnicogens**; in VIA, the **chalcogens**; and in VIIA, the **halogens**. The elements in Groups IA through VIIA together are called the **representative elements**. In Group VIIIA are found the **noble gases**, also sometimes referred to erroneously as the rare gases or inert gases.

The elements in Groups IB through VIIB are known as the **transition metals**. These include the two rows of elements which for convenience are located below the main body of the table. The elements in the first of these two rows are called the **rare earth** elements, or **lanthanides**, since they follow the element lanthanum ($Z = 57$), and those in the second row are referred to as the **actinides**, since they follow actinium ($Z = 89$).

Notice that hydrogen is not assigned to any family in the periodic table shown. This is because the properties of hydrogen do not resemble those of any group closely enough to warrant its inclusion in a group. In some respects hydrogen reacts as an alkali metal and in other respects as a halogen. For this reason hydrogen is placed in some tables at the head of Group IA, in others at the head of Group VIIA, and in still others in both places. In Figure 5–3 hydrogen has been placed by itself to emphasize its uniqueness.

5.3   The Theoretical Basis for the Periodic Table

In Chapter 4 we saw that each element has a characteristic electronic configuration; that is, the electrons in a particular atom are distributed in a very specific way among the various energy levels and sublevels. In this section we shall see that an element's position in the periodic table and therefore its chemical properties are strongly dependent on the number and distribution of its outer electrons. In addition, the section will demonstrate how the shape of the periodic table reflects the manner in which the sublevels of the atoms are filled.

Let us examine the electronic configurations of the alkali metals, for example. They are as follows:

$$Li = 1s^2 2s^1 \qquad\qquad\qquad\qquad\qquad = [He]2s^1$$

$$Na = 1s^2 2s^2 2p^6 3s^1 \qquad\qquad\qquad\quad = [Ne]3s^1$$

$$K \ = 1s^2 2s^2 2p^6 3s^2 3p^6 4s^1 \qquad\qquad\ = [Ar]4s^1$$

$$Rb = 1s^2 2s^2 2p^6 3s^2 3p^6 4s^2 3d^{10} 4p^6 5s^1 \qquad = [Kr]5s^1$$

$$Cs = 1s^2 2s^2 2p^6 3s^2 3p^6 4s^2 3d^{10} 4p^6 5s^2 4d^{10} 5p^6 6s^1 = [Xe]6s^1$$

Each alkali metal atom has one s electron beyond the closed configuration of the preceding noble gas. Thus, adding the first electron to a major energy level begins a new period in the periodic table. The fact that the alkali metals have similar properties as well as similar outer electronic configurations is strongly suggestive that electronic configuration determines chemical reactivity. We shall find quantitative support for this idea in the next section.

It is true, in general, that the outer electronic configurations of the atoms within a given group are similar, and that these similarities account for the chemical similarities of the elements in the group. The outer electronic configurations for the A groups may be summarized as follows (where n is the number of the period, or major energy level):

IA	IIA	IIIA	IVA	VA	VIA	VIIA	VIIIA
ns^1	ns^2	$ns^2 np^1$	$ns^2 np^2$	$ns^2 np^3$	$ns^2 np^4$	$ns^2 np^5$	$ns^2 np^6$

Figure 5–4
The periodic table according to the subshell occupied by the outer electrons of the elements

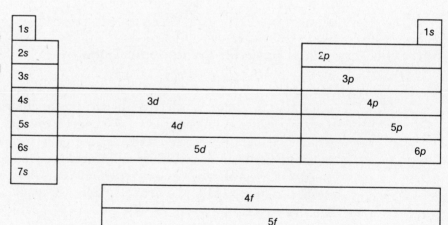

Except for the lanthanides and actinides, whose outer electrons are in the *f* sublevel, the transition elements (the B groups) have their outer electrons in the *d* sublevel. Figure 5–4 shows the periodic table blocked out according to the sublevels occupied by the outer electrons of the elements.

The chemical behavior of elements depends on three properties: ionization potential, electron affinity, and atomic size. We shall see in the following sections that these properties are periodic and depend directly upon electron configuration.

5.4 Ionization Potential

The **ionization potential** is defined as the energy needed to remove an electron from an isolated atom. Thus the first ionization potential is the energy of the following reaction (M represents any element):

$$M(g) + energy \longrightarrow M^+(g) + e^-$$
$$\llcorner \text{ first ionization potential}$$

The second ionization potential is the energy needed to remove the second electron:

$$M^+(g) + energy \longrightarrow M^{2+}(g) + e^-$$
$$\llcorner \text{ second ionization potential}$$

An atom may have as many ionization potentials as it does electrons. The ionization potential, a property of an atom, is usually expressed in eV/atom (1 eV/atom = 23.06 kcal/mole). Figure 5–5 presents the first ionization potentials for the elements.

In looking at the first ionization potentials of the elements in a particular period (Figures 5–5 and 5–6), note that there is a general increase in going from left to right, except for a decrease at Group IIIA. These features can be explained by considering the electronic configurations. In moving across period four, for example, the 4s sublevel is filled first, then the 3d, which is similar in energy to the 4s, and finally the 4p, which is somewhat higher in energy. For each additional 4s or 3d electron, there is an additional proton in the nucleus, giving it a higher positive charge. The nuclear charge is felt almost equally by each of the 4s and 3d electrons, being of similar energy, and this group of electrons is bound a little more tightly to the nucleus each time the charge increases in going

VIIIA							
	He 24.6	Ne 21.6	Ar 15.8	Kr 14.0	Xe 12.1	Rn 10.7	

VIIA
F 17.3
Cl 13.0
Br 11.8
I 10.5
At

VIA
O 13.6
S 10.4
Se 9.8
Te 9.0
Po 8.4

VA
N 14.5
P 11.0
As 9.8
Sb 8.6
Bi 7.3

IVA
C 11.3
Si 8.2
Ge 7.9
Sn 7.3
Pb 7.4

IIIA
B 8.3
Al 6.0
Ga 6.0
In 5.8
Tl 6.1

IIB
Zn 9.4
Cd 9.0
Hg 10.4

IB
Cu 7.7
Ag 7.6
Au 9.2

VIIIB
Ni 7.6
Pd 8.3
Pt 9.1

Co 7.8
Rh 7.5
Ir 8.7

Fe 7.9
Ru 7.4
Os 8.7

VIIB
Mn 7.4
Tc 7.3
Re 7.9

VIB
Cr 6.8
Mo 7.1
W 8.0

VB
V 6.7
Nb 6.9
Ta 7.9
Ha

IVB
Ti 6.9
Zr 6.9
Hf 6.9
Ku

IIIB
Sc 6.6
Y 6.1
La* 5.6
Ac+ 6.9

IIA
Be 9.3
Mg 7.6
Ca 6.1
Sr 5.7
Ba 5.2
Ra 5.3

IA
H 13.6
Li 5.4
Na 5.1
K 4.3
Rb 4.2
Cs 3.9
Fr

Lu 5.0	Lr
Yb 6.2	No
Tm	Md
Er	Fm
Ho	Es
Dy 6.8	Cf
Tb 6.7	Bk
Gd 6.2	Cm
Eu 5.7	Am
Sm 5.6	Pu
Pm	Np
Nd 6.3	U
Pr 5.8	Pa
Ce 6.9	Th
*	+

Figure 5–5
The first ionization
potentials of the elements
(eV/atom)

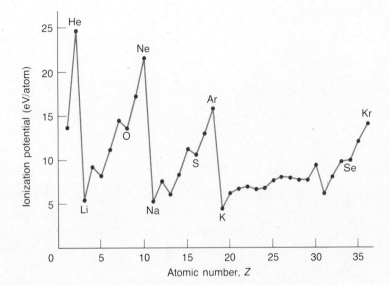

Figure 5–6
A plot of the ionization potentials versus the atomic numbers for elements 1–36

across the period. This makes the first electron more difficult to remove as the period is traversed from K to Zn; in other words, the first ionization potential increases. After Zn, however, the next electron is added to the $4p$ sublevel. An electron in the $4p$ sublevel is farther from the nucleus than those in the $4s$ and $3d$ sublevels and it therefore does not feel a nuclear charge as strongly. Thus the outer electron of Ga is not as tightly bound as those of Zn, and the first ionization potential of Ga is lower. In going from Ga to Kr the first ionization potential increases again, since the electrons are being added to the same sublevel.

   If we pick a family and look at the variation in the first ionization potential, we see that there is generally a decrease in moving down the column (Figure 5–5). This may be attributed to the fact that the successive electrons are in higher major energy levels. For example, in Mg the two outer electrons are in the $3s$ sublevel, whereas in Ca they are in the $4s$ sublevel. Since the $4s$ electrons, being further from the nucleus, are less tightly bound than the $3s$ electrons, the first ionization potential for Ca is less than that of Mg. This decrease in first ionization potential in moving down a group is general for all of the A groups but is less applicable to the transition metals.

   In summary, the first ionization potential increases in going from left to right in a period (except at Group IIIA) and decreases in going down a group. Thus the nonmetals, located in the top right portion of the table, have the highest ionization potentials.

Table 5–2

The First Four Ionization Potentials for Aluminum (in eV/atom)

$$Al \longrightarrow Al^+ + e^- \quad 5.98$$
$$Al^+ \longrightarrow Al^{2+} + e^- \quad 18.8$$
$$Al^{2+} \longrightarrow Al^{3+} + e^- \quad 28.4$$
$$Al^{3+} \longrightarrow Al^{4+} + e^- \quad 120.0$$

The second ionization potential for an element is always greater than the first, since the second electron has to be removed from an ion which is already positively charged. In general, there are regular increases in the successive ionization potentials for a given element until all of the electrons in the outer major energy shell have been removed. Then there is a drastic increase in the energy needed to remove an electron because the electrons in the next inner shell are more tightly bound. Taking aluminum as an example (see Table 5–2), we see that there are regular increases between the first and second and between the second and third ionization potentials. At this point three electrons have been removed (one from the $3p$ and two from the $3s$ sublevels), leaving the stable noble gas configuration of neon ($1s^2 2s^2 2p^6$). The $2p$ electrons are much more tightly bound than the $3s$ and $3p$ electrons were, with the result that the fourth ionization potential for aluminum is drastically higher than the first three. It is for this reason that aluminum appears as an Al^{3+} ion in its compounds.

Similarly, the alkali metals (Group IA) always occur in compounds as M^+ ions, since only one electron (in an s sublevel) is removed before the noble gas configuration is reached. The alkaline earth metals (Group IIA) always occur as M^{2+} ions, since the elements have two electrons beyond

Table 5–3

Successive Ionization Potentials for Sodium and Calcium (in eV/atom)

$$Na \longrightarrow Na^+ + e^- \quad 5.14$$
$$Na^+ \longrightarrow Na^{2+} + e^- \quad 47.3$$

$$Ca \longrightarrow Ca^+ + e^- \quad 7.64$$
$$Ca^+ \longrightarrow Ca^{2+} + e^- \quad 15.0$$
$$Ca^{2+} \longrightarrow Ca^{3+} + e^- \quad 80.1$$

the noble gas configuration. Table 5–3 gives the first few ionization potentials for sodium and calcium, which typify the behavior of alkali metals and alkaline earth metals, respectively. Note the large increase in ionization potential when removing an electron from the noble gas configuration.

We may not carry this rationale into the higher numbered groups, however. As we proceed from left to right into the region of the nonmetals, the compounds formed by these elements cannot be described as containing their positive ions; for example, the ion C^{4+} is not found in compounds. One reason for this is that even the first ionization potential for these elements is too large for the easy removal of an electron. The behavior of their electrons in nonionic compounds will be considered in the next chapter.

Positive ions are called **cations** and are simply named according to the name of the element. For example, Na^+ is the sodium ion, Ca^{2+} is the calcium ion, and so on. Extensions to this rule will be discussed in Chapter 7.

5.5 Electron Affinity

As we have just seen, the ionization potentials for the Group VIIA elements, being nonmetals, are quite high, and therefore these elements have very little tendency to lose an electron in a chemical reaction. On the other hand, since their outer electronic configurations are only one short of attaining a stable noble gas configuration, the halogens do have a large tendency to gain an electron. In doing so, energy is emitted; that is, the process of adding an electron to a halogen atom is exothermic. The energy involved is called the **electron affinity**, which is thus the energy of the following reaction:

$$X(g) + e^- \longrightarrow X^-(g) + energy$$
$$\text{electron affinity} \quad \text{\Large\textuparrow}$$

The electron affinities for some of the elements are listed in Figure 5–7. As expected, the halogens have the highest electron affinities, since their electrons are most tightly bound, and the chalcogens (Group VIA) have the next highest. In general, the magnitude of the electron affinity increases in going across a period, except for the noble gases. In going down the halogen family, the electron affinity generally decreases, since

B	C	N	O	F
0.3	1.24	~0.05	1.47	3.40
Al	Si	P	S	Cl
0.52	1.4	0.78	2.08	3.62
Ga	Ge	As	Se	Br
0.18	1.2	0.60	2.02	3.57
			Te	I
			2.1	3.07
				At
				2.69

Figure 5–7
The electron affinities of several elements (eV/atom)

an outer electron is less tightly bound in the higher energy levels. Using this logic, we would expect fluorine to have the highest electron affinity of any atom, since its added electron in the $2p$ sublevel should be more stable than chlorine's in the $3p$ sublevel. However, the electron affinity of fluorine is anomalously low for an unexplained reason, and thus chlorine has the highest value.

Negative ions are called **anions** and, in the case of monoatomic anions, are given the stem of element's name with the suffix *-ide*. For example, Cl^- is the chloride ion, and S^{2-} is the sulfide ion.

Since the noble gases already have a stable outer electronic configuration (ns^2np^6), they have no tendency to gain extra electrons. In fact, the reaction that forms a negative ion from a noble gas is endothermic. We have also seen that the noble gases have high ionization potentials. The combination of these two properties—high ionization potential and low electron affinity—illustrate the high stability of the ns^2np^6 configuration and suggest why the noble gases are generally unreactive.

5.6 Atomic Size

A third periodic property that contributes to an element's chemical properties is the atomic size of the element. This can be defined in different ways. In each case the atoms are considered to be spheres, and their sizes are reported in terms of their radii. Let us consider the atomic radius and the ionic radius of an atom.

The **atomic radius** of an element is a measure of the atom's size when it exists in a lump of the solid element. Thus the atomic radius of sodium is one-half the distance between two sodium nuclei in a lump of metallic sodium, and the atomic radius of sulfur is one-half of the closest distance between two nuclei in a lump of solid sulfur.

An examination of the atomic radii (Figure 5–8) reveals that in going across a period the radii decrease to a minimum in the transition series, increase to the end of the transition series, and then decrease again to the end of the period. Since electrons in sublevels of similar energy tend to be held more tightly as the nuclear charge increases, the increase in atomic radius after the midpoint of the transition series might seem surprising. It may be explained by electronic repulsions. In order to fill the d sublevel, it is necessary for ten electrons to occupy a certain region of space around the nucleus. After five electrons have been evenly distributed in the five d orbitals, the next five electrons must be paired with them in these relatively small regions. The resulting repulsions among the negatively charged electrons cause the subshell, and thus the atomic radius, to expand slightly as the d sublevel is filled.

The atomic radii increase in going down a family, because the outer electrons of each successive element are in a higher major energy level, which is further from the nucleus. Thus, in summary, there is an overall decrease in atomic radius in going across a period and an increase in going down a group.

The second measure of atomic size is the **ionic radius**. As we have seen, one or more electrons have to be removed from an atom to form a cation. In fact, to form the common metallic cations, the entire outer electronic shell is usually removed. For this reason the common cations are much smaller than their respective neutral atoms. On the other hand, because an anion is formed by adding electrons to an atom, anions are larger than their respective neutral atoms.

Since electrons are removed from atoms in Groups IA, IIA, and IIIA and added to atoms in Groups VA, VIA, and VIIA to give noble gas configurations, some positive and negative ions are **isoelectronic**. Isoelectronic species are those that have the same number of electrons. The ionic radii of the elements in one isoelectronic series are shown in Table 5–4. Because the ions in a given series have the same electronic configuration (that of the corresponding noble gas), the electrons are closer to the nucleus as the nuclear charge (atomic number) increases. Thus the radius decreases in going across the series. In going down a group, the radius of

IA	IIA	IIIB	IVB	VB	VIB	VIIB	VIIIB			IB	IIB	IIIA	IVA	VA	VIA	VIIA	VIIIA
H 0.37																	He
Li 0.23	Be 0.89											B 0.80	C 0.77	N 0.74	O 0.74	F 0.72	Ne
Na 1.57	Mg 1.36											Al 1.25	Si 1.17	P 1.10	S 1.04	Cl 0.99	Ar
K 2.03	Ca 1.74	Sc 1.44	Ti 1.32	V 1.22	Cr 1.17	Mn 1.17	Fe 1.17	Co 1.16	Ni 1.15	Cu 1.17	Zn 1.25	Ga 1.25	Ge 1.22	As 1.21	Se 1.17	Br 1.14	Kr
Rb 2.16	Sr 1.91	Y 1.62	Zr 1.45	Nb 1.34	Mo 1.29	Tc 1.27	Ru 1.24	Rh 1.25	Pd 1.28	Ag 1.34	Cd 1.41	In 1.50	Sn 1.41	Sb 1.41	Te 1.37	I 1.33	Xe
Cs 2.35	Ba 1.98	La* 1.69	Hf 1.44	Ta 1.34	W 1.30	Re 1.28	Os 1.26	Ir 1.27	Pt 1.29	Au 1.34	Hg 1.44	Tl 1.55	Pb 1.54	Bi 1.52	Po 1.53	At	Rn
Fr	Ra	Ac†	Ku	Ha													

*	Ce 1.65	Pr 1.65	Nd 1.65	Pm 1.64	Sm 1.66	Eu 1.85	Gd 1.61	Tb 1.39	Dy 1.59	Ho 1.58	Er 1.57	Tm 1.56	Yb 1.70	Lu 1.56
†	Th 1.65	Pa	U 1.42	Np	Pu	Am	Cm	Bk	Cf	Es	Fm	Md	No	Lr

Figure 5–8
The atomic radii of the elements (in Å)

Table 5–4

Ionic Radii for an Isoelectronic Series (in Ångstroms)

N³⁻	O²⁻	F⁻	Na⁺	Mg²⁺	Al³⁺
1.46	1.40	1.33	0.97	0.72	0.54

ions having like charges increases, since the outer electrons are in a higher major energy level.

   All the information in this chapter is meant to provide an historical and a contemporary perspective on the way in which the elements are organized and classified, and it explains the rationale behind the particular classification. In addition, this chapter, along with the discussion of electronic configuration in Chapter 4, provides a basis for our next topic of study, chemical bonding.

TERMS AND CONCEPTS

- Dobereiner's triads
- Newlands' law of octaves
- Mendeleev's periodic table
- The periodic law
- Metals, nonmetals, and metalloids
   Zintl border
- Groups or families
   alkali metals
   alkaline earth metals
   pnicogens
   chalcogens
   halogens
   noble gases

- Representative elements
- Transition metals
- Rare earth elements or lanthanides
- Actinides
- Outer electronic configuration
- Ionization potential
- Cations
- Electron affinity
- Anions
- Atomic radius
- Ionic radius
- Isoelectronic ions

QUESTIONS

1. What advantage did Mendeleev's periodic table have over the one proposed by Newlands?
2. In Mendeleev's periodic table there was a missing element in the carbon family between silicon and tin. Make predictions as to the properties of the missing element (Ge) based on the properties of the other family members given below. Compare your values with the presently accepted values, which

may be found in the *Handbook of Chemistry and Physics* and which are given in the answer section of this book. (To estimate the atomic mass, the values for Ga and As may also be used.)

	C	Si	Ge	Sn	Pb
atomic mass	12.0	28.1		118.7	207.2
color	black	steel gray		white	blue-white
density	2.25	2.33		7.31	11.4
formula of oxide	CO_2	SiO_2		SnO_2	PbO_2
oxide density	1.56	2.64		6.95	9.38
formula of chloride	CCl_4	$SiCl_4$		$SnCl_4$	$PbCl_4$
chloride density	1.59	1.48		2.23	3.18
boiling point of chloride (°C)	76.8	57.6		114.1	—

3. What was Moseley's contribution to the development of the periodic table?
4. Find the places in the modern periodic table where elements do not fall in sequence according to atomic weight.
5. What are the characteristic properties of metals and of nonmetals?
6. Tell where on the periodic table the following elements are located:
   a. metals
   b. nonmetals
   c. transition elements
   d. alkali metals
   e. halogens
   f. alkaline earth metals
   g. noble gases
   h. lanthanides
   i. chalcogens
   j. metalloids
7. Write the electronic configuration for each of the elements in Group IVA.
8. What would you expect the general trend in ionization potential to be in the series:
   a. Li, Na, K, Rb
   b. I, Br, Cl, F
   c. C, N, O, F
   d. Se, As, Ge, Ga
9. Why is the Na^{2+} ion unlikely to form?
10. Give the charge of the stable ion that you would expect to be formed from each of the elements with the following electronic configurations:
    a. $1s^2 2s^2 2p^6 3s^1$
    b. $1s^2 2s^2 2p^2$
    c. $1s^2 2s^2 2p^5$
    d. $1s^2 2s^2 2p^6 3s^2 3p^4$
    e. $1s^2 2s^2 2p^6 3s^2 3p^1$
    In answering this question, what criterion did you use to determine the stable ion?

11. Define each of the following properties and tell how each varies in the periodic table:
    a. ionization potential
    b. electron affinity
    c. atomic size
12. Explain the observed trend in the ionic radii for the following isoelectronic series:

$$
\begin{array}{ll}
\text{Na}^+ & 0.97 \text{ Å} \\
\text{Mg}^{2+} & 0.72 \text{ Å} \\
\text{Al}^{3+} & 0.54 \text{ Å}
\end{array}
$$

13. Name four ions that have the same electronic configuration as the element krypton (Kr). Arrange them in order of size.
14. Which is larger (explain):
    a. an O atom or an O^{2-} ion?
    b. a Mg atom or a Mg^{2+} ion?
    c. an Fe^{2+} ion or an Fe^{3+} ion?
    d. a Cl atom or a Cl^- ion?
15. Explain the following observations on the basis of electronic configuration:
    a. An atom of Ca is smaller than an atom of Sr.
    b. It requires more energy to remove an electron from a Cl atom than from an S atom.
    c. It requires more energy to remove an electron from an N atom than from an O atom.
    d. An Mg^{2+} ion is smaller than an Na^+ ion.
    e. An atom of Na is larger than an atom of Mg.

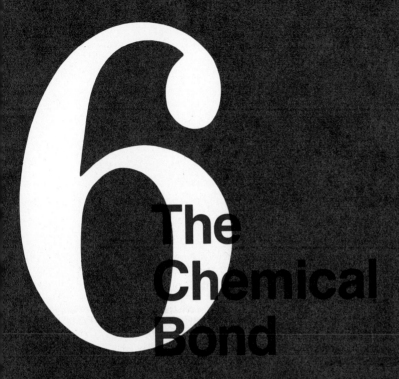

6 The Chemical Bond

Guidelines

After completing this chapter the student should be able to:

- discuss the concepts of Kossel and Lewis which led to the modern ideas of ionic and covalent bonding
- list the energetic factors involved in the formation of an ionic bond
- predict the stoichiometry of an ionic compound
- describe the concept of a covalent bond
- explain how the unequal sharing of electrons results in a bond dipole
- discuss the concept of electronegativity
- write Lewis structures for covalently bonded molecules
- explain the concept of resonance
- predict the effect of lone electron pairs on the molecular geometry of a molecule
- distinguish between polar bonds and polar molecules
- distinguish between intermolecular and intramolecular forces
- describe the nature of weak intermolecular forces in molecular substances and their effect on physical properties
- discuss the concept of hydrogen bonding

6.1 Introduction

The concept of atoms joining together to form molecules is an old one. We have seen that in the early nineteenth century Dalton conceived the idea of atomic "clusters" which he called "compound atoms." Indeed Avogadro, in 1811, was the first to talk about molecules. Then, gradually, as information about molecules and atoms increased, these early concepts evolved into discussions about the nature of the forces between atoms and how they determine the properties of elements and compounds.

In our historical approach to chemical models, the next step is to develop a reasonable theory of chemical bonding—how two or more atoms join together to form a molecule. This theory must give an adequate electronic description of bonding, and it must be able to account for the properties of the molecules that are formed. For example, why does water have the stoichiometry H_2O and not H_4O_3 or HO_2, and why is the shape of a water molecule bent and not linear (the H—O—H bond angle is $104.5°$ rather than $180°$)?

The fact that molecules form from atoms implies that the molecule represents a *lower energy state* than the individual isolated atoms. If we define the state of two hydrogen atoms as having zero potential energy at an infinite separation (so that they do not interact with each other), the formation of a diatomic hydrogen molecule (H_2) involves the release of 4.47 eV (Figure 6–1). That is, the H_2 molecule is 4.47 eV more stable than two isolated hydrogen atoms. Where does this released energy come from? What is the nature of the forces that hold atoms together? These questions must be answered by any proposed theory of bonding.

Even before Thomson's discovery of the electron, many scientists believed that the forces holding matter together were electrical in nature.

153

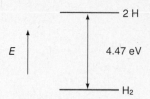

Figure 6–1
The energetics of
the reaction
$2\,H \longrightarrow H_2$

During the nineteenth century, it was observed that solutions of many substances could be decomposed by passing an electric current through them (this process is known as electrolysis and will be discussed more fully in Chapter 13). During this time, Michael Faraday developed a law of electrolysis and Svante Arrhenius put forth a theory of electrolytic dissociation to explain these experimental observations. Arrhenius proposed that an electric current passing through a solution is carried by positively and negatively charged ions. The charges on these ions were eventually found to be equal to simple multiples of the charge on the electron. Thus there seemed to be a relationship between these charged particles and Thomson's electron.

Early Theories

In 1916 two theories which laid the foundations for a modern electronic theory of bonding were proposed, one by Walther Kossel in Germany and the other by Gilbert N. Lewis in the United States. Kossel attached an inherent stability to the electronic configurations of the noble gases. He pointed out, for example, that a noble gas always separates an alkali metal and a halogen in the periodic table and that an alkali metal will easily react with a halogen to form a stable compound. His argument was that by the *transfer* of an electron from the alkali metal atom to the halogen atom, oppositely charged ions, each having a stable **noble gas electronic configuration**, would be formed; these ions would then be bonded together by **electrostatic attraction**, or the interaction between positively and negatively charged species.

Consider the noble gas neon, Ne, with an atomic number of 10 and an electronic configuration of $1s^2 2s^2 2p^6$. The filled $1s$ orbital represents a filled energy level, so we speak of neon as having a total of eight **valence electrons** (outer electrons), each of which is indicated by a dot (or each pair by a pair of dots):

$$:\overset{\cdot\cdot}{\underset{\cdot\cdot}{Ne}}:$$

Note that the alkali metals and the halogens have one more electron and one less electron, respectively, than the noble gases. Taking Na $(Z = 11)$ and F $(Z = 9)$ as examples, the sodium atom can transfer an electron to the fluorine atom to form the sodium and fluoride ions, which can then interact electrostatically to form an **ionic bond**. Schematically, this process can be represented as:

$$Na:\ \ [Ne]3s^1 \qquad F:\ \ [He]2s^22p^5$$

$$Na\cdot + \cdot\overset{\cdot\cdot}{\underset{\cdot\cdot}{F}}: \longrightarrow Na^+ + :\overset{\cdot\cdot}{\underset{\cdot\cdot}{F}}:^-$$

electrostatic
attraction

Kossel's ionic approach was satisfactory for explaining the formation of a large number of compounds, but it was inadequate for many other compounds, including those of carbon (organic compounds). Therefore Lewis proposed that a chemical bond could be formed by the *sharing* of a *pair* of electrons between two atoms. Like Kossel, he considered that the noble gas electronic configuration of eight valence electrons was exceptionally stable. As an example, let us consider the formation of the diatomic Cl_2 molecule:

$$Cl:\ \ [Ne]3s^23p^5$$

$$:\overset{\cdot\cdot}{\underset{\cdot\cdot}{Cl}}\cdot + \cdot\overset{\cdot\cdot}{\underset{\cdot\cdot}{Cl}}: \longrightarrow :\overset{\cdot\cdot}{\underset{\cdot\cdot}{Cl}}:\overset{\cdot\cdot}{\underset{\cdot\cdot}{Cl}}:$$

a shared pair
of electrons

Notice that by sharing a pair of electrons, each atom is surrounded by the eight electrons characteristic of a noble gas electronic configuration. One significant aspect of the Lewis theory of bonding is the concept that a chemical bond is formed from a pair of electrons. To indicate this electron bond, called a **covalent bond**, Lewis used a line in place of the electron dots that represent the shared electron pair:

$$Cl_2 \equiv :\overset{\cdot\cdot}{\underset{\cdot\cdot}{Cl}}:\overset{\cdot\cdot}{\underset{\cdot\cdot}{Cl}}: \equiv :\overset{\cdot\cdot}{\underset{\cdot\cdot}{Cl}}-\overset{\cdot\cdot}{\underset{\cdot\cdot}{Cl}}:$$

The two types of bonding discussed in this section—ionic (electron-transfer) and covalent (shared-pair) bonding—represent two extreme types of chemical bonding. Actually there is no clear-cut break in bonding types; they extend in a continuum from ionic to covalent bonding. Before we consider these intermediate bonds, we will examine the two extreme types in greater detail.

6.2 Ionic Bonding

What is actually involved in the formation of an ionic bond? Let us consider the elements in their atomic states and the process of forming their respective ions. In order to form a positive ion, energy must be added to the system (Ionization Potential, pages 139–143); in order to form a negative ion, energy is usually released (Electron Affinity, pages 143–144). Even in the most favorable case (the metal with the lowest IP is Cs, 3.9 eV, and the nonmetal with the highest EA is Cl, -3.6 eV), the absolute value of the IP is greater than that of the EA. Therefore, the net result of these two operations is that the amount of energy added is always greater than the amount given off. However, there is another source of energy which we have not considered, that of the electrostatic attraction between the positive and negative ions that have been formed (like charges repel each other, unlike charges attract). The energy released by the attraction of the ions is more than enough to compensate for the energy required to form the ions in the first place.

These energy relationships can be shown quantitatively as follows. The ionization of a sodium atom is an endothermic process which requires 5.14 eV:

$$Na \longrightarrow Na^+ + e^- \qquad IP = 5.14 \text{ eV}$$

The formation of a fluoride ion is an exothermic process in which 3.40 eV is given off:

$$F + e^- \longrightarrow F^- \qquad EA = -3.40 \text{ eV}$$

Adding these two equations together, we find that the net reaction representing the transfer of an electron from a sodium atom to a fluorine atom requires 1.74 eV:

$$Na + F \longrightarrow Na^+ + F^- \qquad 1.74 \text{ eV (net cost)}$$

In other words, it "costs" 5.14 eV to ionize a sodium atom and we "get back" 3.40 eV for each fluoride ion formed. Therefore the net energetic cost is 1.74 eV. Since this amount of energy must be added to the system to make the reaction proceed, it would be energetically unfavorable if it were not for the electrostatic attraction between the Na^+ and F^- ions. Once energy has been spent to form equal numbers of positive and negative ions, they are able to attract each other electrostatically. For $Na^+ F^-$ this energy of attraction is -6.26 eV, which more than pays for the 1.74 eV it cost to form the ions:

$$Na^0 + F^0 \longrightarrow Na^+ + F^- \text{ (separated ions)} \quad \Delta E = \quad 1.74 \text{ eV (cost)}$$
$$Na^+ + F^- \longrightarrow Na^+F^- \quad \text{(ion "pair")} \quad \underline{\Delta E = -6.26 \text{ eV (gain)}}$$
$$\Delta E = -4.52 \text{ eV (net gain)}$$

This energy of electrostatic attraction is essential to the formation of an ionic bond, since without it the formation of ions would not be energetically favorable and would not occur. Because of these energy considerations, a strong ionic bond is formed between a metal (low IP) and a nonmetal (high EA). For other types of element pairs, the two atoms will tend to share their electrons in a covalent bond (Section 6.4) or in a partially covalent bond (Section 6.5).

In this discussion we have neglected another important contribution to the stability of ionic compounds. We have been representing the electrostatically interacting Na^+ and F^- ions as an Na^+F^- "molecule," when actually there is absolutely no evidence for the existence of discrete molecular units for any ionic compound in the solid or liquid state. When we write sodium fluoride as NaF we are only writing its empirical formula (page 53). In fact, in the solid state, ionic compounds exist as infinite three-dimensional arrays of positive and negative ions which are characterized by the simplest geometric repeating unit. For the example of NaF, each Na^+ ion is surrounded by six equidistant F^- ions and each F^- ion by six equidistant Na^+ ions in a three-dimensional array. This arrangement provides a greater electrostatic stabilization because each positive ion is attracted to *all* of the negative ions, and each negative ion is attracted to *all* of the positive ions. The magnitude of this additional stabilizing energy depends on the exact nature of the particular compound's crystalline structure.

6.3 Stoichiometry of Ionic Compounds

In the last chapter it was noted that atoms will gain or lose electrons to attain a rare gas configuration and that the periodicity of this property is related to electronic configuration. For example:

$$Ca: \longrightarrow Ca^{2+} + 2e^-$$

$$\cdot \ddot{C}l: + e^- \longrightarrow :\ddot{C}l:^-$$

The stoichiometry of an ionic compound is determined by the charges of the ions in the compound. Since there is no net charge on a neutral compound, we know that equal numbers of electrons are gained and lost when the ions combine. Therefore, in our example, one Ca atom will react with two Cl atoms, forming $CaCl_2$:

$$Ca: + \begin{matrix} \cdot \ddot{C}l: \\ \cdot \ddot{C}l: \end{matrix} \longrightarrow Ca^{2+}(:\ddot{C}l:^-)_2 \equiv CaCl_2$$

From this concept, we can state a general rule that the subscript on one ion has the same magnitude as the absolute value of the charge on the other ion.

EXAMPLE 6.3a   What is the stoichiometry of the ionic compound formed by Al and O? First, what are the charges on the ions?

$$Al: \ [Ne]3s^23p^1 \qquad \cdot Al \cdot \longrightarrow Al^{3+} + 3e^-$$

$$O: \ [He]2s^22p^4 \qquad \cdot \ddot{O} \cdot + 2e^- \longrightarrow :\ddot{O}:^{2-}$$

Since the charge on the Al is $+3$, the subscript on the oxygen in the formula is 3. Similarly, the subscript on the aluminum is 2. Three oxide anions will therefore combine with two aluminum cations to give Al_2O_3. We can verify the formula by checking to see if the total positive charge is equal to the total negative charge:

$$2(+3) = +6 \qquad \text{and} \qquad 3(-2) = -6$$

EXAMPLE 6.3b   What is the stoichiometry of the ionic compound formed by Cs and O?

$$Cs: [Xe]6s^1 \qquad Cs\cdot \longrightarrow Cs^+ + e^-$$

$$O: [He]2s^22p^4 \qquad \cdot\ddot{O}\cdot + 2e^- \longrightarrow :\ddot{O}:^{2-}$$

Because the charge on the Cs is $+1$, the subscript on the O is 1. Similarly, the subscript on the Cs is 2, giving an empirical formula of Cs_2O. We then verify the formula:

$$2(+1) = +2 \quad \text{and} \quad 1(-2) = -2$$

6.4   Covalent Bonding

Let us now turn our attention to covalent bonding, the other extreme form of chemical bonding. We shall first consider a homopolar (sometimes called homonuclear) bond, which joins like atoms: A—A. It is unreasonable to think that one atom of an identical pair should capture an electron from the other, since it is equally probable that its own electron should go to the other. In other words, there is no reason for the following process to occur, since one hydrogen is exactly the same as the other:

$$H\cdot + \cdot H \longrightarrow H^+ + :H^-$$

Instead, the electrons are more likely to be *shared* by both hydrogen nuclei:

$$H\cdot + \cdot H \longrightarrow H:H \quad \text{or} \quad H—H$$

The attraction of the electrons for *two* positive nuclei is greater than the combined repulsion between the electrons and between the two nuclei in the molecular form.

There is a certain amount of **electron exchange** between the atoms. Schematically, this mutual attraction and electron exchange can be indicated as follows:

This representation is simply a more detailed interpretation of the Lewis model of a covalent bond:

$$H\cdot + \cdot H \longrightarrow H{:}H \quad \text{or} \quad H{-}H$$

All homonuclear diatomic molecules can be explained in this manner. For example, the F_2 molecule forms a covalent bond as follows:

$$:\!\ddot{F}\!\cdot + \cdot\ddot{F}\!: \longrightarrow :\!\ddot{F}\!:\!\ddot{F}\!: \quad \text{or} \quad :\!\ddot{F}\!-\!\ddot{F}\!:$$

Each fluorine atom in the molecule attains an **octet of electrons** by sharing a pair of electrons with the other atom.

Thus far, in our brief study of both types of bonding, the discussion has returned to the relative stability of the noble gases, or more exactly, of the noble gas electronic configuration. It is this relative stability of the noble gases that is mirrored in their electronic configuration: ns^2np^6. The electrons in this configuration fill the respective s and p orbitals and are therefore difficult to remove. Interestingly enough, we arrive at the same conclusion about the noble gas configuration whether we are talking about ionic or covalent bonding.

6.5 Polarity of Diatomic Molecules

In the previous sections we have discussed the two extreme types of chemical bonding in considerable detail. With this background, we are now prepared to examine the intermediate bonds that fall in a continuum between the two extremes.

H:H	$\longleftrightarrow$	Na+ :$\ddot{F}$:⁻
equal sharing of electrons (covalent)	(partially covalent/ partially ionic)	complete electron transfer (ionic)

Most molecules have bonds between nonidentical atoms, atoms whose relative attraction for electrons is not so different as to give complete transfer of electrons but will instead result in partial transfer of electrons, or **unequal sharing** of electron pairs.

Hydrogen fluoride, HF, a heteronuclear (containing different atoms) diatomic molecule, is a good example of this intermediate behavior. It turns out that the electrons that make up the bond are attracted more strongly to fluorine than to hydrogen. Consider the Lewis structure for HF:

$$H : \ddot{F} : \quad \text{or, more simply} \quad H : F$$

The pair of shared electrons (the bonding electrons) spend more time about the fluorine end of the molecule than about the hydrogen end. This unequal sharing results in a separation of positive and negative charge, generating an **electric dipole** which has both magnitude and direction. We indicate the dipole with an arrow pointing toward the negative end and crossed at the positive end:

$$\delta+H \quad :F^{\delta-}$$
$$\longmapsto$$

A bond in which electrons are shared unequally is called a **polar bond**. Note, then, that any bond involving dissimilar atoms will be polar to some degree because of the unequal sharing of electrons. An ionic bond may be considered to be the most extreme case of a polar bond, because here we would observe a complete separation of charge, as in $Na^+ + F^-$. For molecules with partially ionic bonds, the magnitude of the dipole is generally less than what one would expect for a completely ionic model, which indicates that the two atoms compete for the electrons involved in the bond. The tendency of an atom to attract the shared electrons in a bond is called **electronegativity**. (This term should not be confused with electron affinity, which is a property of an isolated atom.) Thus the electronegativity of an element (symbolized by χ) is simply the relative pull that the element has on the electron pair involved in a bond.

In the 1930s Linus Pauling developed a self-consistent scale of electronegativities which he determined from bond energies. He assigned the most electronegative element, fluorine, an arbitrary value of $\chi = 4.0$. The least electronegative element, Cs, was found to have a value of $\chi = 0.7$. As we can see from Figure 6–2, which reproduces Pauling's values, electronegativity tends to increase in going from left to right and from bottom to top in the periodic table.

Pauling also related the difference in electronegativity ($\Delta\chi$) of a pair of elements involved in a bond to the amount of ionic character of that bond (Figure 6–3). This relationship occurs since the greater the magnitude of $\Delta\chi$, the greater the separation of charge and the greater the ionic character of the bond. Our example of HF has $\Delta\chi = 1.9$, which corresponds to approximately 50% ionic character. As a further example of

IA	IIA	IIIB	IVB	VB	VIB	VIIB	VIIIB			IB	IIB	IIIA	IVA	VA	VIA	VIIA	VIIIA
H 2.1																	He
Li 1.0	Be 1.5											B 2.0	C 2.5	N 3.0	O 3.5	F 4.0	Ne
Na 0.9	Mg 1.2											Al 1.5	Si 1.8	P 2.1	S 2.5	Cl 3.0	Ar
K 0.8	Ca 1.0	Sc 1.3	Ti 1.5	V 1.6	Cr 1.6	Mn 1.5	Fe 1.8	Co 1.8	Ni 1.8	Cu 1.9	Zn 1.6	Ga 1.6	Ge 1.8	As 2.0	Se 2.4	Br 2.8	Kr
Rb 0.8	Sr 1.0	Y 1.2	Zr 1.4	Nb 1.6	Mo 1.8	Tc 1.9	Ru 2.2	Rh 2.2	Pd 2.2	Ag 1.9	Cd 1.7	In 1.7	Sn 1.8	Sb 1.9	Te 2.1	I 2.5	Xe
Cs 0.7	Ba 0.9	La* 1.0	Hf 1.3	Ta 1.5	W 1.7	Re 1.9	Os 2.2	Ir 2.2	Pt 2.2	Au 2.4	Hg 1.8	Tl 1.8	Pb 1.9	Bi 1.9	Po 2.0	At 2.2	Rn
Fr 0.7	Ra 0.9	Ac†	Ku	Ha													

*Lanthanides: Ce 1.1, Pr 1.1, Nd 1.2, Pm, Sm 1.2, Eu, Gd 1.1, Tb 1.2, Dy, Ho 1.2, Er 1.2, Tm 1.2, Yb, Lu 1.2

†Actinides: Th 1.3, Pa 1.5, U 1.7, Np 1.3, Pu 1.3, Am 1.3, Cm, Bk, Cf, Es, Fm, Md, No, Lr

Figure 6–2
The electronegativities of the elements

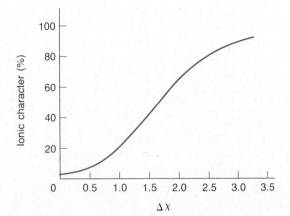

Figure 6–3
The plot of $\Delta\chi$ in relation to the percentage of ionic character of a bond

how electronegativity and ionic character are related, let us examine a series of compounds consisting of elements bonded to fluorine:

Compound	LiF	BeF_2	BF_3	CF_4	NF_3	OF_2	F_2
Bond	Li—F	Be—F	B—F	C—F	N—F	O—F	F—F
$\Delta\chi$	3.0	2.5	2.0	1.5	1.0	0.5	0.0

$\longleftarrow$
increasing ionic character

increasing covalent character
$\longrightarrow$

The bond in LiF is a predominately ionic bond ($\Delta\chi = 3.0$). Going across the row, the bonds become less ionic and more covalent as $\Delta\chi$ decreases. Since the fluorine atoms in F_2 have identical electronegativities ($\Delta\chi = 0.0$), the bond in the F_2 molecule is covalent.

6.6 Lewis Structures

All of the various forms of chemical bonding have now been considered. Before continuing our discussion, we shall return to the topic of covalent bonding and examine it in greater detail. Specifically, we shall learn to write **Lewis structures** (sometimes called **electron-dot structures**), which describe the bonding in simple covalent molecules. To write Lewis structures, we use a set of rules based on the tendency of an atom to attain an eight-electron noble gas configuration (an octet of electrons). These rules are as follows:

1. Draw a skeleton structure in which the central atom is the least electronegative one (the atom farthest to the lower left in the periodic table), exclusive of hydrogen. Hydrogen, since it accepts only one other electron, can bond to only one other atom. It is therefore always on the outside of the molecule.
2. Count up the total number of valence electrons (those outside the closed noble gas configuration). An easy way to determine the number of valence electrons for nontransition-metal elements is to note that this number is equal to the number of the group in which the element occurs. For example, P (in Group V) has 5 valence electrons, S (Group VI) has 6, and Br (Group VII) has 7.
3. Distribute the electrons about the atoms in pairs so as to give an octet about each atom. There must be *at least* two electrons (one bond) between each pair of atoms.

There are several exceptions to rule 3. Hydrogen, of course, will hold only two electrons in its $1s$ orbital and therefore can be bonded to only one other atom. Beryllium and boron are other exceptions, because they typically form "electron-deficient" compounds (those in which the octets are incomplete). Additional exceptions are the heavier nonmetals such as P and S, which sometimes bond to other elements through five or six pairs of electrons in an "expanded" valence shell.

We shall now consider a few examples. First, let us write the Lewis structure for a water molecule, H_2O:

1. We first draw the skeleton for the molecule:

$$H \quad O \quad H$$

2. We then count the number of valence electrons:

$$
\begin{array}{lll}
\text{H:} & 1s^1 & 2 \times 1 = 2 \text{ valence electrons} \\
\text{O:} & [\text{He}]2s^22p^4 & 1 \times 6 = \underline{6} \\
& & 8 \text{ valence electrons}
\end{array}
$$

3. Finally, we place the valence electrons about the atoms so as to

give an octet about the central oxygen atom (the hydrogen atoms can hold only two electrons each):

$$H : \overset{..}{\underset{..}{O}} : H$$

Note that two of the electron pairs about the oxygen atom are bonding to the two hydrogen atoms.

As another example, let us write the structure for NH_3:

1. We draw the skeleton:

$$\begin{array}{c} H \ N \ H \\ H \end{array}$$

2. We then count the valence electrons:

N:	$[He]2s^2 2p^3$	$1 \times 5 = 5$ valence electrons
H:	$1s^1$	$3 \times 1 = \underline{3}$
		8 valence electrons

3. When we distribute these electrons, we have the Lewis structure:

$$\begin{array}{c} H : \overset{..}{N} : H \\ \overset{..}{H} \end{array}$$

Notice the similarity between the electron-dot structures for H_2O and NH_3. Water has two pairs of electrons bonded to hydrogen atoms and two pairs of nonbonding (or "lone-pair") electrons; ammonia has three pairs of electrons bonded to hydrogen atoms and one pair of nonbonding electrons. But more important, H_2O and NH_3 have the same number of valence electrons. In general, species having the same number of valence electrons have similar bonding schemes.

A slightly more complex example is formaldehyde, CH_2O.

1. Since hydrogen can be bonded to only one other atom and since carbon is to the left of oxygen in the periodic table, we put carbon in the center:

$$\begin{array}{c} H \ C \ O \\ H \end{array}$$

2. We then count the number of valence electrons in the molecule:

C: $[He]2s^22p^2$ $1 \times 4 =$ 4 valence electrons
H: $1s^1$ $2 \times 1 =$ 2
O: $[He]2s^22p^4$ $1 \times 6 =$ 6
                                      12 valence electrons

3. We now need to determine the proper distribution of electrons about the atoms:

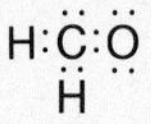

H:C̈:Ö
  H

This distribution accounts for 12 electrons, but there is no octet about O.

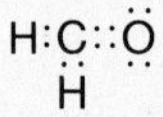

H:C::Ö
  H

This distribution satisfies the octet about both C and O; *two* pairs of electrons are shared by the C and O atoms.

or

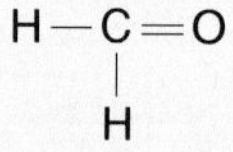

H—C=O
  |
  H

Note the **double bond** between the C and O atoms; it indicates that two pairs of electrons are shared by the pair of atoms.

Formaldehyde has the same number of valence electrons as molecular oxygen, O_2:

O: $[He]2s^22p^4$ $2 \times 6 = 12$ valence electrons

Therefore, according to Lewis structures, O_2 should have a double bond:

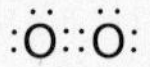

:Ö::Ö:

Experimental evidence shows the presence of unpaired electrons in the O_2 molecule. This is an example of the failure of Lewis structures to completely explain bonding in simple molecules.

As another example of a diatomic molecule, let us consider N_2:

N: $[He]2s^22p^3$ $2 \times 5 = 10$ valence electrons

The only way to put ten electrons about two nuclei to give an octet about both is to share three pairs of electrons, thus forming a **triple bond**:

$$:N:::N:$$

Triple bonds are stronger than double bonds, which in turn are stronger than single bonds, because the sharing of more pairs of electrons leads to greater interaction between the atoms and thus a closer distance between them. Table 6–1 presents the C—C bond distances for three compounds of C and H along with the energy required to break this bond.

Table 6–1

LEWIS STRUCTURE	FORMULA	C—C DISTANCE (Å)	C—C BOND ENERGY (kcal/mol)
H, H H—C—C—H H' H	C_2H_6 (ethane)	1.54	83
H, H C=C H' H	C_2H_4 (ethylene)	1.33	143
H—C≡C—H	C_2H_2 (acetylene)	1.20	196

Note that the triple bond in acetylene is the shortest as well as the strongest (it requires the most energy to break).

Certain polyatomic anions can be represented by Lewis structures. In such cases one must *add* a number of valence electrons equal to the absolute value of the negative charge on the anion. As an example, we shall use SO_4^{2-}, the sulfate anion:

1. We draw the skeleton:

$$\begin{array}{c} O \\ O\ S\ O \\ O \end{array}$$

2. Since the charge on the anion is -2, we need three additional valence electrons:

S: [Ne]$3s^2 3p^4$ $1 \times 6 = $ 6 valence electrons
O: [He]$2s^2 2p^4$ $4 \times 6 = 24$
plus 2 electrons to account
for the -2 charge $\underline{2}$
                                  32 valence electrons

3. We then place the 32 valence electrons about the atoms:

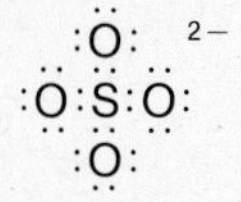

$$\ddot{\underset{..}{O}}\!:^{2-}$$
$$:\!\ddot{O}\!:\!\ddot{S}\!:\!\ddot{O}\!:$$
$$:\!\ddot{\underset{..}{O}}\!:$$

Resonance

It is difficult to describe the electronic structures of certain molecules and polyatomic ions with Lewis structures. Sulfur dioxide, SO_2, for example, has a total of 18 valence electrons:

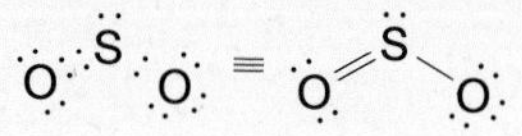

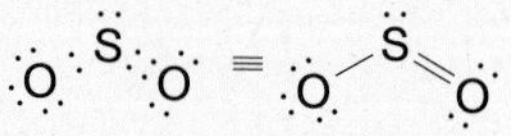

Both of these structures individually satisfy the octet rule; they are said to be **resonant structures**. Resonant structures occur when two or more equally valid Lewis structures can be written for a molecule. There is no reason why one of these Lewis structures should be favored over the other; we then say that the actual structure of SO_2 is a **resonance hybrid** of the resonant structures. This is borne out by the experimental evidence that both of the S—O bond distances in SO_2 are of equal length (and fall between the lengths characteristic of ordinary single and double bonds).

Resonance does *not* mean that the molecule "resonates" between the two or more structures; that is, the molecule is *not* sometimes in one form and sometimes in the other. Resonance does mean that the actual structure cannot be represented by a single Lewis formula but is instead

Kekulé and Benzene

In the mid-nineteenth century a great amount of attention was being given to the rationalization of the seemingly different types of bonding exhibited by the element carbon. It was known at that time that carbon usually formed four bonds to other atoms, but one puzzling aspect of the structural chemistry of carbon was in the compound benzene and its derivatives. The molecular formula of the compound was known to be C_6H_6; thus the atomic ratio of the elements carbon and hydrogen in the benzene molecule was 1:1. None of the then-existing theories of bonding could account for the strange stoichiometry and properties of this compound.

Friedrich August Kekulé, a German chemist concerned with both the chemistry of carbon and the early theories of chemical bonding, was deeply involved in this problem. A possibly apocryphal story is told of his dreaming of a snake-like chain of carbon atoms and realizing that the "head" of the chain (molecule) could grasp the "tail" to give a cyclic structure rather than the commonly assumed open chain. Then, to satisfy the tendency of the carbon atom to form four bonds, Kekulé worked out the bonding to include alternating single and double bonds between the carbon atoms in the cyclic molecule:

I

However, he realized that another possibility existed:

II

Unfortunately, all chemical evidence indicated that only one form of benzene existed. In other words, the two following derivatives should have existed, but only one compound was found:

and

It was not until the concept of resonance was developed in the 1920s that this discrepancy was satisfactorily explained. The benzene molecule is a resonance hybrid of the two resonant forms I and II, which are called Kekulé structures in honor of the scientist who first proposed the correct cyclic structure for this molecule.

an intermediate form, or hybrid, of the resonant structures.

As a last example, both to illustrate Lewis structures for polyatomic ions and to show another case of the existence of both covalent and ionic bonding in a compound, let us consider the carbonate compounds. These compounds contain CO_3^{2-}, an ion composed of more than one covalently bonded atom.

C: $[He]2s^2 2p^2$ $1 \times 4 = 4$ valence electrons

O: $[He]2s^2 2p^4$ $3 \times 6 = 18$

plus 2 electrons to
account for the -2 charge $\underline{2}$

                                              24 valence electrons

The true structure is a resonance hybrid of these three structures. The CO_3^{2-} ion, an example of a negatively charged polyatomic ion, is a perfectly respectable covalently bonded species. It can enter into the formation of an ionic compound by electrostatically interacting with metal cations, such as in $Ca^{2+}CO_3^{2-}$, calcium carbonate. Polyatomic ions in compounds will be dealt with further in Section 7.3.

6.7 Molecular Geometry

In the introduction to this chapter it was stated that any theory of bonding should be able to account for the properties of molecules. One important property of a molecule is its geometry. In this section we shall examine the geometry of several types of molecules and the reasons for the particular shape and bond angles of each type.

In a covalently-bonded molecule, the eight electrons surrounding the central atom may be considered as being a set of four electron pairs $(4 \times 2 = 8)$ which can form a maximum of four bonds. In 1964 J. W. Linnett, in his "double quartet" approach, considered the rationalization of the geometry of simple molecules in this manner. If one simply considers the electrostatic repulsion among the four negatively-charged electron pairs surrounding the central atom's nucleus, it can easily be

Figure 6–4
The tetrahedral array of four pairs of electrons about carbon in the methane molecule, CH_4

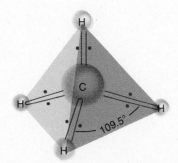

shown that the most stable configuration is a *tetrahedral* arrangement about the central atom. Let us look at methane, CH_4, as an example:

C: [He]$2s^2 2p^2$ $1 \times 4 = 4$ valence electrons
H: $1s^1$ $4 \times 1 = \underline{4}$
                        8 valence electrons

These eight valence electrons surround the carbon atom as four pairs. Figure 6–4 illustrates the tetrahedral arrangement of the four pairs, each of which forms a bond to a hydrogen atom. The observed H—C—H angle in methane is 109.5°, which is the angle between a pair of vertices in a tetrahedron.

The NH_3 and H_2O molecules (page 165) have the same number of valence electrons as CH_4. If we now consider the bonding in these two molecules, we find that we can very simply explain their geometries and rationalize the difference in bond angle. Since they have the same number of electrons as CH_4, there will be four electron pairs in the valence shell of each. However, in NH_3, three pairs of electrons about the central atom are involved in bonds to hydrogen atoms and the fourth pair is a lone pair. The effect of this nonbonding pair on the geometry of the molecule is two-fold. First, the NH_3 molecule is not a planar triangular molecule, as is BF_3 (Figure 6–7), but is rather a *triangular pyramid*. The four electron pairs are oriented tetrahedrally about the nitrogen atom, but only three of the four pairs are bonded to atoms. Since we can experimentally detect only the atoms, we portray the molecule as a triangular pyramid in which the N atom is at one tetrahedral apex (see Figure 6–5). Its nonbonding pair of electrons would be away from the directions of the H atoms, as shown in the figure. The second effect of the lone pair on the geometry of NH_3 is a result of the greater electron-electron repulsion between a lone

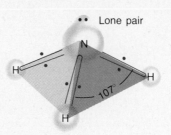

Lone pair

Figure 6–5
The ammonia
molecule, NH_3, a
triangular pyramid

pair and a bonding pair than between two bonding pairs. Therefore the H—N—H angle is squeezed down from the ideal tetrahedral angle (109.5°) to 107°.

In H_2O there are also four pairs of electrons, tetrahedrally arranged about the central oxygen atom. Two corners of the tetrahedron are lone pairs and two are bonding pairs (to the hydrogen atoms). Again, since we "see" only the atoms in the molecule, H_2O is pictured as a *bent* molecule with an H—O—H angle of 104.5° (Figure 6–6). The bond angle is less in H_2O than in NH_3 due to the repulsion of *two* lone pairs of electrons. Note that two apparently distinct Lewis structures for H_2O can be drawn on paper:

$$H:\ddot{O}:H \quad \text{or} \quad H:\ddot{O}: \\ \phantom{H:\ddot{O}:}H$$

Actually, they represent the same structure: they are two-dimensional representations of a three-dimensional molecule.

Let us now consider the shape of the CO_2 molecule. First we shall draw the Lewis structure:

1. We draw the skeleton:

$$O \quad C \quad O$$

Figure 6–6
The water
molecule, H_2O, a
"bent" molecule

Lone pairs

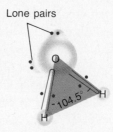

104.5°

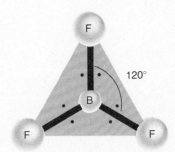

Figure 6–7
The boron
trifluoride molecule,
BF_3, a planar
triangle

2. We count the valence electrons:

C: [He]$2s^2 2p^2$ $1 \times 4 = $ 4 valence electrons
O: [He]$2s^2 2p^4$ $2 \times 6 = \underline{12}$
                          16 valence electrons

3. We place these electrons about the atoms to complete the octets:

$$:\ddot{O}::C::\ddot{O}:$$

Although the central carbon atom has an octet of electrons, they occur in two groups of four electrons each. Each of these "groups" of electrons is located between two atoms, forming double bonds. Thus there are no lone pairs of electrons about the carbon atom. Since the most stable configuration for two groups of negatively charged electrons is at opposite sides of the central atom, CO_2 is a *linear* molecule (bond angle = 180°).

The final case is that of three pairs (or groups) of electrons. Linnett's theory predicts a *plane triangular* arrangement (bond angle = 120°) as is found in BF_3, an electron-deficient compound with three pairs of electrons about the central B atom (Figure 6–7).

Polar Bonds and Molecules

Now that we have considered the geometry of several types of molecules, let us use this background to further examine the concept of electric dipoles (see Section 6.5, page 161).

Molecules that have an electric dipole are known as **polar molecules,** and those that do not are called **nonpolar molecules.** For example, HCl, which is made up of dissimilar atoms and is therefore characterized by a

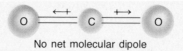

No net molecular dipole

Figure 6–8
The cancellation of bond dipoles in CO_2

dipole, is a polar molecule; Cl_2, which has a completely covalent bond, is nonpolar. To be polar, a molecule must contain polar bonds. However, a molecule may have polar bonds, but because of a symmetric distribution of these bonds in space, it may be a nonpolar molecule. An example of this is carbon dioxide, CO_2. It is a linear molecule, with bond dipoles that are equal and in opposite directions (indicated by the equal but opposite arrows in Figure 6–8). These dipoles cancel each other out, so that there is no *net* molecular dipole. Another example is the symmetric tetrahedral molecule CCl_4 (carbon tetrachloride), illustrated in Figure 6–9. Again the bond dipoles cancel out, and there is no dipole on the molecule. In the unsymmetric molecule $HCCl_3$ (chloroform), where the bond dipoles are unequal, a net molecular dipole results. Figure 6–10 shows the important case of the water molecule, which is known to be nonlinear (bond angle $= 104.5°$) and which therefore has a large molecular dipole resulting from the combination of the substantial bond dipoles. The dipolar nature of water has great effect on its properties as a solvent, a topic that will be discussed in Section 10.2.

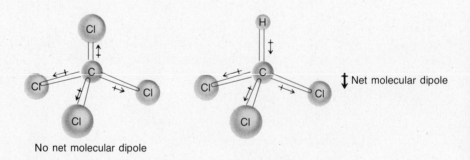

No net molecular dipole

Figure 6–9
The bond dipoles in the carbon tetrachloride and chloroform molecules, CCl_4 and $HCCl_3$

Figure 6–10
The bond dipoles
in the water
molecule, H_2O

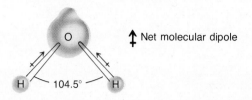

6.8 Classification of Bond Types

Throughout this chapter, we have been considering the chemical bonds that hold atoms within an ion or molecule together. Now, to conclude the chapter, we shall consider the forces that hold these ions and molecules to one another.

Let us begin by looking at the trend in boiling points and melting points of compounds formed by fluorine with the elements in the second row of the periodic table:

	NaF	MgF_2	AlF_3	SiF_4	PF_5	SF_6
Boiling point (K)	1968	2512	1564	187	198	337
Melting point (K)	1261	1539	(sublimes)	183	190	222

Notice that there is a break in the magnitude of both the boiling and melting points between AlF_3 and SiF_4. This is due to a change in the bond type of the compound, and it corresponds to the position of the Zintl border, which divides metals from nonmetals in the periodic table.

The melting point of a compound (the temperature at which the solid transforms to a liquid) and the boiling point (the temperature at which the liquid transforms to a gas) are measures of the strength of the forces holding the molecules (or ions) together in the solid and liquid states, respectively. For the compounds listed above, high melting and boiling points indicate materials that are ionic in nature (NaF, MgF_2, and AlF_3). They form as ionic, three-dimensional structures in the solid state. For example, NaF is composed of Na^+ and F^- ions, with each Na^+ ion being surrounded by six F^- ions and each F^- ion by six Na^+ ions, forming an infinite three-dimensional array. In the liquid state NaF exists as independent Na^+ and F^- ions which are strongly bonded by electrostatic attraction.

When fluorine combines with elements to the right of the Zintl border (SiF_4, PF_5, and SF_6), the compounds exist as covalently bonded *molecules* which are weakly held together in the solid and liquid states. Such compounds are called **molecular substances.** Their molecules are held to one another by weaker forces than ionic or covalent ones. These weaker forces are *inter*molecular forces as opposed to the *intra*molecular forces (covalent bonds) within the molecules. (There are, of course, no intermolecular forces in ionic compounds, such as NaF, because there are no molecules present.)

We can compare the strengths of inter- and intramolecular forces by examining hydrogen, which in the solid and liquid states consists of H_2 molecules bonded internally by an H—H covalent bond (intramolecular force) and externally by very weak intermolecular forces. The very low melting and boiling points of hydrogen (14 K and 20 K, respectively) are indicative of these very weak forces holding the hydrogen molecules together. Energetically, we can compare the intermolecular forces for hydrogen in the solid with the intramolecular forces by comparing the heat of sublimation (ΔH_{subl}) for hydrogen with the heat of dissociation (ΔH_{dissoc}) of the hydrogen molecule. Sublimation is the direct transformation of a solid into a gas; the heat of sublimation is the energy necessary to convert one mole of solid into one mole of gas.

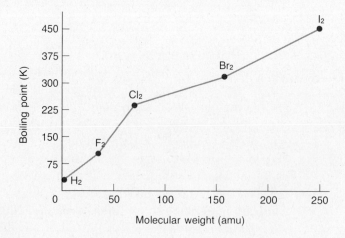

Figure 6–11
A plot of boiling point in relation to molecular weight for halogen molecules

$$\Delta H_{\text{subl}} = 0.122 \text{ kcal/mol; for the process } H_2(s) \longrightarrow H_2(g)$$

$$\Delta H_{\text{dissoc}} = 103 \text{ kcal/mol; for the process } H_2 \longrightarrow 2H$$

Obviously, the intermolecular forces between hydrogen molecules in the solid are very weak, whereas the bond in the hydrogen molecule is quite strong.

In general, we find that both melting and boiling points increase with increasing molecular weight for "similar" molecules. For example, if we consider the trend in boiling points for the nonpolar, diatomic halogen molecules (Figure 6–11), we find a roughly linear increase in boiling point with increasing molecular weight. Thus the intermolecular forces also increase with increasing molecular weight. However, if we consider polar and nonpolar molecules of similar molecular weights, in each case the boiling point for the polar molecule is *higher* than that for the nonpolar molecule of similar weight:

MOLECULE (NONPOLAR)	BOILING POINT (K)	MOLECULAR WEIGHT	MOLECULAR WEIGHT	BOILING POINT (K)	MOLECULE (POLAR)
N_2	77	28	28	81	CO
SiH_4	161	32	34	185	PH_3
GeH_4	185	77	78	218	AsH_3
Br_2	332	160	162	370	ICl

Types of Intermolecular Forces

What is the nature of these intermolecular forces? They fall into two main categories: **dipole-dipole interactions** and so-called **London dispersion forces** We have already noted the effects of a molecular dipole; the molecule behaves as if it had a positive and a negative end. Therefore, in polar molecular compounds, these dipoles can interact with one another in the solid and liquid states to produce a purely electrostatic interaction (Figure 6–12). This interaction is somewhat like an ionic bond, but much weaker, since only a partial charge is developed on the molecular dipole and the resulting electrostatic force of attraction must be less than that found for an ionic bond.

Figure 6–12
Weak interactions
between dipoles

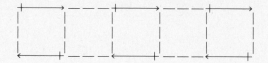

The other type of intermolecular forces, the London forces, are very weak forces between nonpolar molecules. Let us consider the simple case of a spherically symmetric noble gas atom such as argon. Although the electron cloud around the argon atom is symmetric *on the average*, at any instant in time it is possible to have more electron density in one region of the electron orbitals than in another, resulting in intermolecular London forces between argon atoms (Figure 6–13). Thus the very weak interaction between the **instantaneous dipoles** on any two argon atoms is due to the time-dependent nature of the electronic behavior in atomic orbitals. The strength of the London forces is related to the size and shape of the atom or molecule. As we go down the noble gas column in the periodic table (increasing atomic weight and atomic size), the larger electron clouds allow a greater separation of charge and lead to greater London forces. Similarly, if a nonpolar molecule is not spherically symmetrical (such as is the case for homonuclear diatomic molecules), the London forces will be greater in magnitude than for a spherically symmetrical molecule of approximately the same size and shape. To illustrate this, we can compare the boiling points of Cl_2 (molecular weight = 71) and Kr (atomic weight = 84). On the basis of weight alone, Kr should boil at a higher temperature than Cl_2, but in fact, Cl_2 boils at 239 K and Kr at 121 K, due to the stronger London forces found in the diatomic Cl_2 molecule.

There is a third source of significant intermolecular attraction, called **hydrogen bonding.** Figure 6–14, a plot of boiling point versus molecular weight for the simple hydrogen compounds of some elements in Groups VA, VIA, and VIIA, illustrates the effect of hydrogen bonding. Notice that the boiling points of NH_3, HF, and H_2O are anomalously *much higher* than would be expected on the basis of molecular weight alone (boiling

Figure 6–13
London dispersion
forces between two
argon atoms

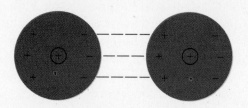

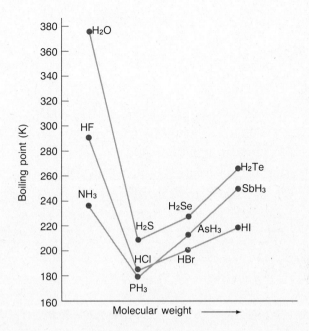

Figure 6–14
A plot of boiling point as a function of molecular weight for HX, H_2X, and XH_3 molecules

point normally decreases with decreasing molecular weight for similar compounds). This behavior is due to the formation of hydrogen bonds between adjacent molecules.

The electronegativity differences ($\Delta\chi$) between H ($\chi = 2.1$) on the one hand and N ($\chi = 3.0$), F ($\chi = 4.0$), and O ($\chi = 3.5$) on the other are great enough to cause the formation of large bond dipoles in NH_3, HF, and H_2O. In other words, these predominantly covalently bonded molecules have a large percentage of ionic character (recall Figure 6–3), with the hydrogen end of each molecule as the positive end of the dipole. Furthermore, the small H atom allows a highly electronegative F, O, or N atom from another molecule to approach closely enough to form a hydrogen bond. This effect is not nearly as great in PH_3, HCl, and H_2S, since the nonhydrogen atom is larger and has lower electronegativity, and since $\Delta\chi$ between these atoms and H is smaller. Figure 6–15 illustrates the hydrogen bonds formed between HF molecules. In solid H_2O (ice) the structure is actually determined by the strong hydrogen bonding; we will discuss this more fully in Section 9.7.

Figure 6–15
Hydrogen bonding
in HF(l)

The material in this chapter, which has focused on chemical bonding within and between molecules and ions, will provide a necessary background for our next topic of study, the naming of inorganic compounds.

TERMS
AND
CONCEPTS

- Noble gas electronic configuration
- Electrostatic attraction
- Valence (outer) electrons
- Ionic bond
- Shared pair of electrons
- Covalent bond
- Electron exchange
- Octet of electrons
- Partial transfer (unequal sharing) of electrons
- Electric dipole
- Polar bond
- Electronegativity
- Lewis electron-dot structures

- Double and triple bonds
- Resonance
    resonant structures
    resonance hybrid
- Lone pair of electrons
- Polar and nonpolar molecules
- Bond type
- Molecular substance
- Intermolecular and intramolecular forces
- Dipole-dipole interactions
- London dispersion forces
    instantaneous dipoles
- Hydrogen bonding

QUESTIONS

1. What did the ideas of Kossel and Lewis concerning chemical bonding have in common?

2. What three processes must be considered in determining whether an ionic bond will form between two elements? Which are endothermic and which are exothermic?

3. There is no such thing as a molecule of table salt (NaCl). Explain.

4. Discuss the difference between an ionic bond and a covalent bond using specific examples.

5. Explain, using the concept of electronegativity, how a bond may be partially ionic and partially covalent at the same time. What determines the degree of ionicity of a bond?

6. Discuss the relationship between the degree of ionicity of a bond and the bond polarity.

7. How would you expect the magnitude of the bond dipole to vary in the series: Al—Cl, Si—Cl, P—Cl, S—Cl?

8. Write the formula for a compound consisting of the following pairs of elements:

    a. Na, O   c. K, I   e. Mg, N   g. Ba, Br
    b. Ca, S   d. Al, S   f. Li, Te   h. Al, P

9. List the compounds formed in Question 8 in order of increasing covalency of the bonds.

10. Which compound of each of the following pairs has the more polar bonds?

    a. $BeCl_2$, $BeBr_2$ e. PCl_3, $AlCl_3$
    b. $BeCl_2$, $MgCl_2$ f. CaO, CaS
    c. NaBr, $MgBr_2$ g. CCl_4, CH_4
    d. LiI, LiCl

11. Write Lewis electron-dot structures for the following molecules and ions:

    a. H_2S d. CO   g. CH_4 j. PH_3
    b. CCl_4 e. CO_2 h. NO_3^- k. $SiCl_4$
    c. ClI   f. $AsCl_3$ i. SO_2 l. $TeBr_2$

12. Arrange the following molecules in order of increasing strength of the C—N bond. Explain the order.

H:C:::N: H:C:N::C::Ö: H:C:N:H
                   H   H H
                  (with H above and below C, H H below N)

13. a. Comment on the fact that H_2O is a nonlinear molecule.

    b. Comment on the fact that NH_3 is not a planar triangular molecule.

14. Arrange the following molecules in order of increasing H—X—H angles: CH_4, NH_3, H_2O

15. Explain the relationship between bond polarity and molecular polarity. Do molecules having polar bonds have to be polar themselves? Explain.

16. Why does CO_2 have no net dipole while CO has a dipole?

17. How do you account for the fact that $SiCl_4$ is a nonpolar molecule while PCl_3 is polar?

18. a. What is the shape of each of the molecules or ions in Question 11?

    b. Which of them are polar?

    c. For which ones can resonance structures be written?

19. The N—N bond in the nitrogen molecule is very strong. However, the boiling point of nitrogen is very low (-195 °C). Explain.

20. List and explain three types of intermolecular forces. Give examples of each.

21. Which has the higher boiling point—a compound composed of nonpolar molecules or a compound of similar molecular weight composed of polar molecules? Explain.

22. At room temperature the halogens chlorine, bromine, and iodine are a gas, a liquid, and a solid, respectively. Explain in terms of intermolecular forces.

23. Both carbon and silicon form oxides with the empirical formula MO_2. CO_2 is a gas at room temperature (boiling point 195 K) but SiO_2 boils at about 2500 K. Explain in terms of bond type.

7

Inorganic Nomenclature

Guidelines

After completing this chapter the student should be able to:

- determine the oxidation state of an element in a particular compound or ion

- name both ionic and covalent compounds by the systematic Stock system

- name oxyacids and the polyatomic anions derived from them

7.1 Oxidation States

Before we can formally consider inorganic nomenclature, the naming of inorganic compounds, the concept of **oxidation state** (also called **oxidation number**) should be introduced. The use of the oxidation state is a "bookkeeping" technique designed to keep track of the electrons in elements undergoing chemical reaction. It is particularly useful in reactions where there is a transfer of electrons, that is, oxidation-reduction reactions, which will be discussed in Chapter 13.

The oxidation state of an element in a particular compound or ion is a positive or negative number assigned to that element according to certain rules. Because all compounds can be treated similarly in assigning oxidation states to the elements in them, only one set of rules is needed. One can always assign oxidation states to elements using the following rules:

1. The oxidation state for any free (uncombined) element is zero.

2. The oxidation state for alkali metals (Group IA) in compounds is always $+1$.

3. The oxidation state for alkaline earth metals (Group IIA) in compounds is always $+2$.

4. The oxidation state for hydrogen in compounds is $+1$ except when it is combined with a metal, in which case it is -1.

5. The oxidation state for oxygen in compounds is -2 with the following exceptions:

      a. In peroxides, it is -1. In hydrogen peroxide, H_2O_2, for example, hydrogen has an oxidation state of $+1$ and oxygen has an oxidation state of -1. (Note that oxygen is still joined to two elements, the other oxygen and a hydrogen atom.)

      b. In the lone compound OF_2, oxygen difluoride, oxygen has an oxidation state of $+2$, since fluorine is more electronegative and must be -1.

6. The oxidation state for halogens (Group VIIA) in halide compounds (compounds in which the halogen is written last) is -1.

7. The oxidation state for sulfur in sulfides (compounds in which the sulfur is written last) is -2.

8. The sum of the oxidation states of the elements in a molecule must equal zero, and the sum of the oxidation states of the elements in a polyatomic ion must equal the charge on the ion.

As an illustration of these rules, let us consider a few examples.

EXAMPLE 7.1a   What is the oxidation state of each of the elements in Hg_2Cl_2, $K_2Cr_2O_7$, and MnO_4^-?

In Hg_2Cl_2 the Cl is -1 by rule 6 and the Hg is $+1$ by rule 8.

In $K_2Cr_2O_7$ each O is -2 by rule 5 and each K is $+1$ by rule 2. The total negative contribution is $7 \times (-2) = -14$ and the positive contribution from K is $2 \times (+1) = +2$. Hence, by rule 8 the contribution from the two Cr is $+12$. The oxidation state of Cr in $K_2Cr_2O_7$ is $+6$.

In MnO_4^- each O is -2 by rule 5, and the total negative contribution is $4 \times (-2) = -8$. By rule 8 Mn must be $+7$ to give a sum of $+7 + (-8) = -1$, the charge on the ion.

EXAMPLE 7.1b   What is the oxidation state of Bi in H_3BiO_3, Se in SeO_4^{2-}, and P in $Ca_2P_4O_{12}$?

In H_3BiO_3 each H is $+1$ by rule 4 and each O is -2 by rule 5. By rule 8 the oxidation state of Bi must balance out $3(+1) + 3(-2) = -3$; therefore, the oxidation state of Bi in H_3BiO_3 is $+3$.

In SeO_4^{2-} each O is -2. Since the net charge on the ion is -2, then by rule 8 Se has an oxidation number of $+6$.

In $Ca_2P_4O_{12}$ each Ca is $+2$ (rule 3); each O is -2. The positive contribution is $2(+2) = +4$ and the negative contribution is $12(-2) = -24$, giving a contribution of $+20$ for the four P (rule 8). Each P, then, has an oxidation state of $+20/4 = +5$.

7.2 Inorganic Nomenclature

There is a very systematic method for naming inorganic compounds called the **Stock system.** However, many trivial names (unsystematic names in common use) still persist. For example, the proper Stock system name for H_2O is dihydrogen oxide; of course, we know H_2O as water. Table 7–1 lists both the common and the systematic names for several commonplace chemicals.

In determining nomenclature, ionic compounds (compounds between metals and nonmetals) are considered separately from covalent

Table 7–1

Common and Systematic Names for Some Inorganic Compounds

FORMULA	COMMON NAME	SYSTEMATIC NAME
$CaCO_3$	chalk, limestone, marble	calcium carbonate
CaO	lime	calcium oxide
$Ca(OH)_2$	slaked lime	calcium hydroxide
$CaSO_4 \cdot \frac{1}{2}H_2O$	plaster of Paris	calcium sulfate hemihydrate
$CaSO_4 \cdot 2H_2O$	gypsum	calcium sulfate dihydrate
$CuSO_4 \cdot 5H_2O$	blue vitriol	copper(II) sulfate pentahydrate
HCl solution	muriatic acid	hydrochloric acid
H_2SO_4 solution	oil of vitriol	sulfuric acid
Hg_2Cl_2	calomel	mercury(I) chloride
K_2CO_3	potash	potassium carbonate
$KHC_4H_4O_6$	cream of tartar	potassium hydrogen tartrate
$Mg(OH)_2$	milk of magnesia	magnesium hydroxide
$MgSO_4 \cdot 7H_2O$	epsom salts	magnesium sulfate heptahydrate
$Na_2B_4O_7 \cdot 10H_2O$	borax	sodium tetraborate decahydrate
$Na_2CO_3 \cdot 10H_2O$	washing soda	sodium carbonate decahydrate
NaCl	common salt	sodium chloride
$NaHCO_3$	baking soda	sodium hydrogen carbonate
$NaNO_3$	Chile saltpeter	sodium nitrate
NaOH	lye	sodium hydroxide
NH_4Cl	sal ammoniac	ammonium chloride

compounds (usually compounds between nonmetals). Ionic compounds are formed between elements on the left of the periodic table (and the transition elements and lanthanide series), which are metals, and elements on the far right of the table, the nonmetals. Their names are derived from the names of the ions of which they are composed.

Naming Cations

In Section 5.4 (page 143) it was noted that monatomic positive ions take the name of the metal atom from which they are formed:

$$Na^+ \quad \text{the sodium ion}$$

$$Sr^{2+} \quad \text{the strontium ion}$$

$$Al^{3+} \quad \text{the aluminum ion}$$

What happens when the metal forms more than one monatomic ion; that is, when there is a possibility of multiple oxidation states? The Stock system uses Roman numerals in parentheses after the name of the metal to indicate the oxidation state:

$$Cu^+ \quad \text{the copper(I) ion}$$

$$Cu^{2+} \quad \text{the copper(II) ion}$$

The older notation, still in common use, is to indicate the *higher* oxidation state by the suffix *-ic* and the *lower* oxidation state by the suffix *-ous* after the Latin name of the metal (see Table 1–3, page 26). Table 7–2 lists several common multivalent cations named in both systems.

Note that the -ous and -ic notation does not indicate the oxidation state; it tells us only whether it is the higher or lower state for that particular metal. This system of notation is further confusing in that, for example, the -ous state for Sn is $+2$ and the -ic state is $+4$, whereas the -ous state for Cu is $+1$ and the -ic state is $+2$. Obviously the Stock system is less confusing.

The $+1$ oxidation state for mercury is written Hg_2^{2+} since the mercury(I) ion occurs as a **dimer** (two ions joined together). The only other common polyatomic cation is NH_4^+, the ammonium ion.

Table 7–2

Some Common Multivalent Cations

ION	STOCK NAME	COMMON NAME
Co^{2+}	cobalt(II)	cobaltous
Co^{3+}	cobalt(III)	cobaltic
Cu^{+}	copper(I)	cuprous
Cu^{2+}	copper(II)	cupric
Fe^{2+}	iron(II)	ferrous
Fe^{3+}	iron(III)	ferric
Mn^{2+}	manganese(II)	manganous
Mn^{3+}	manganese(III)	manganic
Hg_2^{2+}	mercury(I)	mercurous
Hg^{2+}	mercury(II)	mercuric
Sn^{2+}	tin(II)	stannous
Sn^{4+}	tin(IV)	stannic

Naming Anions

In Section 5.5 (page 144) it was stated that monatomic *negative* ions are named by adding the suffix -*ide* to the root of the element from which it is formed:

F^- the fluoride ion

O^- the oxide ion

N^{3-} the nitride ion

H^- the hydride ion
(when bonded to a metal)

The naming of polyatomic anions is more complex. Some simple ones (those that are similar in reactivity to halogenides) are named with the -ide ending:

CN^- the cyanide ion

OH^- the hydroxide ion

HS^- the hydrogen sulfide (or bisulfide) ion

Most polyatomic anions are derived from **oxyacids** (oxygen-containing acids), which are covalently bonded species that contain a nonmetal and hydrogen as well as oxygen. When dissolved in a solvent, oxyacids ionize to give up a hydrogen ion and a polyatomic anion made up of oxygen and the nonmetal:

$$\text{acid} \longrightarrow \text{polyatomic anion} + H^+$$

The names of the anions are derived from the names of the acid. If only one oxidation state exists for the nonmetal (that is, if only one oxyacid and anion can be formed from the nonmetal), the acid has the suffix *-ic* and the corresponding anion has the suffix *-ate:*

$$H_2CO_3 \qquad\qquad CO_3{}^{2-}$$
carbon*ic* acid   carbon*ate* ion

However, if two oxidation states are found for the nonmetal, the -ic/-ate suffixes are given to the higher oxidation state, and an *-ous* and an *-ite* suffix are given to the acid and anion with the lower oxidation state:

oxidation
state of N

+5	HNO_3 nit*ric* acid	$NO_3{}^-$ nit*rate* ion
+3	HNO_2 nit*rous* acid	$NO_2{}^-$ nit*rite* ion

oxidation
state of S

+6	H_2SO_4 sulf*uric* acid	$SO_4{}^{2-}$ sulf*ate* ion
+4	H_2SO_3 sulf*urous* acid	$SO_3{}^{2-}$ sulf*ite* ion

A complication is involved in the oxyacids of chlorine: four are known, with Cl having oxidation states of $+1$, $+3$, $+5$, and $+7$. The prefix *per-* is added to the acid and anion with the highest oxidation state and the prefix *hypo-* to those with the lowest:

oxidation
state of Cl

$+7$	$HClO_4$	*perchloric* acid	ClO_4^-	*perchlorate* ion
$+5$	$HClO_3$	chlor*ic* acid	ClO_3^-	chlor*ate* ion
$+3$	$HClO_2$	chlor*ous* acid	ClO_2^-	chlor*ite* ion
$+1$	$HClO$	*hypo*chlor*ous* acid	ClO^-	*hypo*chlor*ite* ion

One further complication arises when more than one hydrogen is available for removal. The dissociation can occur in steps, as in the following examples:

$$H_2CO_3 \xrightarrow{-H^+} HCO_3^- \xrightarrow{-H^+} CO_3^{2-}$$

carbonic   hydrogen carbonate ion   carbonate
acid   (or bicarbonate ion)   ion

$$H_3PO_4 \xrightarrow{-H^+} H_2PO_4^- \xrightarrow{-H^+} HPO_4^{2-} \xrightarrow{-H^+} PO_4^{3-}$$

phosphoric   dihydrogen   hydrogen   phosphate
acid   phosphate ion   phosphate ion   ion

As a summary, Table 7–3 lists some common polyatomic anions.

Table 7–3

Common Polyatomic Anions

$C_2O_4^{2-}$	oxalate	PO_3^{3-}	phosphite
$C_2H_3O_2^-$	acetate	PO_4^{3-}	phosphate
CO_3^{3-}	carbonate	HPO_4^{2-}	hydrogen phosphate
HCO_3^-	hydrogen carbonate	$H_2PO_4^-$	dihydrogen phosphate
ClO_3^-	chlorate	AsO_4^{3-}	arsenate
ClO_4^-	perchlorate	MnO_4^{2-}	manganate
NO_2^-	nitrite	MnO_4^-	permanganate
NO_3^-	nitrate	CrO_4^{2-}	chromate
SO_3^{2-}	sulfite	$Cr_2O_7^{2-}$	dichromate
SO_4^{2-}	sulfate	UO_4^{2-}	uranate
HSO_4^-	hydrogen sulfate		

Naming Ionic Compounds

As previously mentioned, ionic compounds are formed between elements on the left and central portion of the periodic table, that is, elements which form cations, and elements on the right, which form anions. They are named by first naming the cation, then the anion. To illustrate, let us consider the following compounds: (1) Na_2S, $SrCl_2$; (2) Mn_2O_3, MnO_2; (3) SnO, SnO_2; and (4) $Fe(ClO_3)_3$, $(NH_4)_2SO_4$.

These substances are named as follows: (1) sodium sulfide and strontium are found with a single oxidation state); (2) manganese(III) oxide and manganese(IV) oxide (since manganese is a metal, Roman numerals are used); (3) tin(II) oxide and tin(IV) oxide; and (4) iron(III) chlorate and ammonium sulfate.

Naming Covalent Compounds

Covalent compounds (compounds formed between nonmetals) are named differently according to the Stock system. The most electropositive (that is, the least electronegative) element is named first. If only one binary compound is formed between a pair of nonmetallic elements, it is named in the same manner as a simple binary ionic compound:

HCl hydrogen chloride

H_2S hydrogen sulfide

NF_3 nitrogen fluoride

If more than one covalent compound is formed by a pair of elements, we must use the following Greek prefixes to distinguish among them:

mono	one	hexa	six
di	two	hepta	seven
tri	three	octa	eight
tetra	four	nona	nine
penta	five	deca	ten

The several oxides of nitrogen are the classic example of this nomenclature:

N_2O dinitrogen oxide

NO   nitrogen oxide

N_2O_3 dinitrogen trioxide

NO_2 nitrogen dioxide

N_2O_4 dinitrogen tetroxide

N_2O_5 dinitrogen pentoxide

Note that in the last two names the *a* is dropped from the prefix to the *oxide*.

To illustrate, let us consider BrF_3 and BrF_5. These compounds are named bromine trifluoride and bromine pentafluoride. Since bromine is a nonmetal, prefixes are used instead of Roman numerals.

Lastly, the Zintl border is used in deciding whether to name a compound as ionic or covalent. GeF_2 and GeF_4 are named germanium(II) fluoride and germanium(IV) fluoride, respectively, since Ge is to the left of the Zintl border. However, AsF_3 and AsF_5 are named arsenic trifluoride and arsenic pentafluoride, respectively, since As is to the right of it.

The information in this chapter makes it obvious that the systems for naming chemical compounds were designed to organize and classify our knowledge of these compounds as well as provide names for them. With this background in how chemical compounds are formed and how they are identified and organized, we are ready to turn our attention to the study of how the molecules in compounds interact with one another.

TERMS AND CONCEPTS

- Oxidation state (oxidation number)
- Stock system
- Dimers
- Oxyacids

QUESTIONS

1. Give the oxidation state of nitrogen in each of the following oxides: N_2O, NO, N_2O_3, NO_2, N_2O_5.
2. Give the oxidation state of each of the elements in the following compounds and ions:

   a. CuCl
   b. SnO
   c. SnO_2
   d. TiS_2

   e. Ti_2S_3
   f. K_2PtCl_6
   g. $LiPF_6$
   h. SbF_6^-

   i. AsO_4^{3-}
   j. $HClO_4$
   k. ClO_2^-
   l. $HBrO_3$

   m. HCO_3^-
   n. $CaSO_4$
   o. $(NH_4)_3PO_4$
   p. ClF_3

3. Determine the oxidation state of:
   a. Fe in Ba_2FeO_4
   b. Pt in K_2PtO_4
   c. W in $WO_4{}^{2-}$
   d. Mo in MoO_3
   e. Cr in $Cr_2O_7{}^{2-}$
   f. I in HIO_3
   g. Mo in $Mg_2Mo_3O_8$
   h. Ni in $BaNiO_3$
   i. Te in H_2TeO_4

4. Name the following compounds:
   a. Li_3N
   b. KCN
   c. NH_4NO_3
   d. $CaCO_3$
   e. NaBr
   f. FeF_3
   g. Al_2O_3
   h. $Hg_2(NO_3)_2$
   i. $PbCl_2$
   j. SnI_4
   k. $Ba(ClO_4)_2$
   l. SF_6
   m. $SrCl_2$
   n. $FeSO_4$
   o. $Fe_2(SO_4)_3$
   p. ClF_3
   q. AsF_3
   r. AsF_5
   s. ICl
   t. XeF_4
   u. $Ni(NO_3)_2$
   v. $SiCl_2$
   w. $NaHCO_3$
   x. N_2O_3

5. Write chemical formulas for the following compounds:
   a. mercury(II) nitrate
   b. beryllium chloride
   c. sulfur tetrafluoride
   d. magnesium iodide
   e. calcium carbonate
   f. copper(I) hydroxide
   g. chromium(III) fluoride
   h. potassium permanganate
   i. nickel(II) nitrate
   j. zinc phosphate
   k. copper(I) iodide
   l. manganese(IV) oxide
   m. boron nitride
   n. aluminum hydride

6. On the basis of the information given in Chapters 5 and 6, what oxidation states might you expect to be stable for the following elements?
   a. Be
   b. Y
   c. As
   d. Ti
   e. Se
   f. Ga
   g. I

Gases

Guidelines

After completing this chapter the student should be able to:

- outline the scientific method
- list the general properties of gases
- use Boyle's and Charles' Laws
- convert centigrade temperatures to Kelvin temperatures
- use the combined gas law
- convert the volume of gas at a given temperature and pressure to the volume at STP
- use Avogadro's Principle
- use the ideal gas law
- solve stoichiometry problems involving gases
- use Dalton's Law of Partial Pressures to determine the pressure of a gas collected over water
- state Graham's Law of Diffusion
- list the postulates of the kinetic molecular theory
- define an ideal gas in terms of kinetic theory
- discuss the distribution of kinetic energies within a gas
- explain the behavior of an ideal gas using ideas from the kinetic molecular theory
- cite two reasons why a real gas might deviate from ideal behavior
- discuss the causes of air pollution

8.1 Introduction

Thus far we have discussed the structure of atoms and how atoms combine to form compounds. Now, we will consider how molecules interact in the three states of matter: gas, liquid, and solid. We will consider the gaseous state first because, as we shall see, the gaseous state is the simplest and therefore the best understood state of matter.

In addition, we will use our discussion of the gaseous state to illustrate the **scientific method**. Strictly speaking, the scientific method involves using experimental observations and data to formulate an *hypothesis* about the laws that govern the behavior of something. Experiments are then designed and carried out to test the hypothesis. If, over the years, the hypothesis still holds, it becomes a *scientific law*. A *theory* is a set of unifying concepts designed to explain several laws.

In reality, not all of the theories in science have evolved in exactly this way, although most of them have followed this general pattern. The experimental observations and data about gases, for example, were used to generate *laws* which are nothing more than generalizations based on such empirical data. Then a *theory* was set up to explain and rationalize the various laws. When the laws were found to be invalid in certain cases, they had to be modified along with the theory to account for the new experimental data. We shall follow this course of development of the gas laws and the theory used to explain them in our study of gases in this chapter.

8.2 The General Properties of Gases

All gases have certain characteristic properties which, ideally, should be compared with the general properties of the liquid and solid states when they are introduced. To avoid getting ahead of ourselves, however, we will just list these properties here and then contrast them with the behavior of liquids and solids when we consider the other states of matter in the next chapter.

Relatively speaking, gases are *easily compressed:* if a sample of a gas is "squeezed" (that is, pressure is applied), its volume is easily reduced. The reason this reduction in volume can occur is that gases are mostly empty space and therefore have relatively low densities.

A gas will *expand to fill the available volume,* and when confined in a vessel, it will exert a pressure on all of the walls of the vessel in a uniform manner. We shall see that the uniform expansion of a gas and the uniformity of pressure are due to the completely random rapid movement of gas molecules. Furthermore, gases will mix together in any proportions; they are therefore said to be completely *miscible* (page 28). In fact, in a mixture one gas acts as if the other gases were not present at all.

To describe a sample of a gas, we use the following four variables:

V the *volume* of the container
n the *amount* of gas (number of moles)
P the *pressure* exerted by the gas
T the *temperature*

The value of any one of these variables depends on the values of the other three. For example, V is a function of n, P, and T, or, mathematically stated:

$$V = f(n,P,T)$$

If the value of V depends on the values of n, P, and T, it follows that the value of any of those variables depends on V and the two remaining variables. Thus the equation $V = f(n,P,T)$ implies that knowing any three of the variables completely defines the fourth. It is the general form of an **equation of state**, or an equation that describes the *physical* behavior of a state of matter. The relationships among the four variables, which were determined experimentally, will be described in the following sections.

8.3   Boyle's Law

In the mid-seventeenth century Robert Boyle investigated the relationship between volume and pressure for a given amount of gas at constant

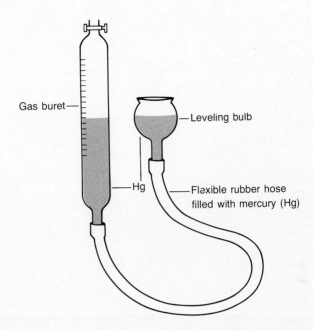

Figure 8–1
A modern version
of the apparatus
used by Robert Boyle

temperature. A modern version of the apparatus he used is shown in Figure 8–1. By trapping a volume of gas in the gas buret and then varying the height of the mercury bulb, the pressure within the calibrated buret can be varied and the changes in volume recorded. Table 8–1 gives some typical data recorded for this experiment, and Figure 8–2 shows a plot of these pressures versus the corresponding volumes.

Table 8–1

Typical Modern Data* for Boyle's Experiment

P (atm)	V (mL)
0.50	500
0.75	333
1.00	250
1.25	200
1.50	167
1.75	143
2.00	125

*For a given sample of a gas at constant T.

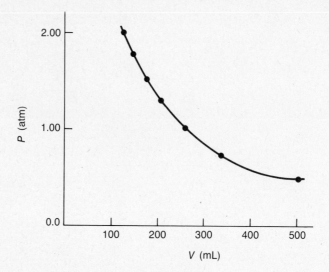

Figure 8–2
A plot of the data in Table 8–1

The shape of the curve is hyperbolic; that is, the curve can be described by an equation for a hyperbola:

$$V = \frac{\text{constant}}{P} \qquad (8\text{–}1)$$

Boyle stated the relationship as what came to be known as **Boyle's Law:**

The volume of a given amount of a gas held at constant temperature is inversely proportional to the pressure exerted by the gas.

$$V \propto \frac{1}{P} \quad \text{(at constant } n \text{ and } T\text{)} \qquad (8\text{–}2)$$

Boyle observed that this relationship applies to gases at relatively low pressures and moderate to high temperatures. At low temperatures and high pressures, deviations from this simple relationship occur. Gases that obey Boyle's Law are said to be **ideal gases.**

We can use Boyle's Law to perform simple calculations if we realize that the product of P and V is constant (by rearrangement of Equation 8–1) for *any values* of P and V for a given amount of gas at constant temperature. Suppose we have a given sample of a gas at constant temperature and at P_1 and V_1. If we then change the pressure to P_2, the volume will become V_2. Since P_1V_1 equals a constant and P_2V_2 equals the same constant (because V varies inversely with P when n and T are constant), we find the following relationship:

$$P_1 V_1 = P_2 V_2 \qquad (8\text{--}3)$$

or, by rearrangement

$$V_2 = V_1 \left(\frac{P_1}{P_2} \right) \qquad (8\text{--}4)$$

Equation 8–4 says that if the pressure of a given amount of gas (at constant temperature) is changed, the new volume is equal to the old volume times a pressure correction. We can think through the problem as follows: If the pressure is raised, the volume will decrease in accordance with Boyle's Law; therefore the pressure correction (or ratio) will be *less than 1*. If the pressure is lowered, the opposite will be true.

EXAMPLE 8.3a   A 2.00 L volume of a gas is at a pressure of 1.25 atm. What volume will it occupy if the pressure is increased to 3.50 atm?
According to Equation 8–4:

$$V_2 = V_1 \left(\frac{P_1}{P_2} \right)$$

$$V_2 = 2.00 \text{ L} \left(\frac{1.25 \text{ atm}}{3.50 \text{ atm}} \right) = 0.714 \text{ L}$$

Note that since the pressure has increased, the new volume is less than the old one and the pressure correction is less than 1.

EXAMPLE 8.3b   A tank of compressed oxygen gas contains 222 ft³ at a pressure of 2.00×10^3 psi (pounds/square inch). If 14.7 psi = 1 atm, how many liters of O_2 gas would this represent at 1 atm pressure?
First we convert 2.00×10^3 psi to atm:

$$2.00 \times 10^3 \text{ psi} \times \frac{1 \text{ atm}}{14.7 \text{ psi}} = 136 \text{ atm}$$

Then, using Equation 8–4, we calculate the new volume in ft³:

$$V_2 = V_1\left(\frac{P_1}{P_2}\right)$$

$$V_2 = 222 \text{ ft}^3\left(\frac{136 \text{ atm}}{1 \text{ atm}}\right)$$

$$V_2 = 3.02 \times 10^4 \text{ ft}^3$$

Alternatively, we could use the ratio of the pressures in *psi* to convert V_1 to V_2 since pressure can be expressed in any units as long as the units are the same for both P_1 and P_2:

$$V_2 = V_1\left(\frac{P_1}{P_2}\right)$$

$$V_2 = 222 \text{ ft}^3\left(\frac{2.00 \times 10^3 \text{ psi}}{14.7 \text{ psi}}\right)$$

$$V_2 = 3.02 \times 10^4 \text{ ft}^3$$

Regardless of which units we use to determine the value of V_2, our next step is to convert ft³ to L (see Example 1.5b):

$$3.02 \times 10^4 \text{ ft}^3 \times \frac{28.4 \text{ L}}{1 \text{ ft}^3} = 8.58 \times 10^5 \text{ L}$$

Just as we use a Boyle's Law calculation to determine the new volume if the pressure of a gas is changed, we can use a similar calculation to determine the new pressure if the volume is changed, assuming that the amount of gas and the temperature are constant.

EXAMPLE 8.3c   A given amount of a gas occupies a volume of 327 cm³ at a pressure of 720. torr. If the volume is allowed to expand to 1.00 L (1 L = 1,000 mL = 1,000 cm³) at constant temperature, what is the new pressure (in torr)?

Let us "think it through": We are told that the volume increases; therefore, by the inverse relationship of Boyle's Law, the pressure must decrease and the volume correction factor is less than 1.

$$\text{new pressure} = 720.\ \text{torr}\left(\frac{327\ \text{cm}^3}{1.00\ \times\ 10^3\ \text{cm}^3}\right) = 235\ \text{torr}$$

or formally, by rearranging Equation 8–4:

$$P_2 = P_1\left(\frac{V_1}{V_2}\right) \qquad\qquad (8\text{–}5)$$

$$P_2 = 720.\ \text{torr}\left(\frac{327\ \text{cm}^3}{1.00\ \times\ 10^3\ \text{cm}^3}\right) = 235\ \text{torr}$$

Both Equations 8–4 and 8–5 are forms of Boyle's Law.

8.4 Charles' Law

In the latter part of the eighteenth century the French physicist J. A. C. Charles found that the volume of a given amount of a gas held at constant pressure was directly proportional to the temperature.

$$V \propto T \text{ (at constant } n \text{ and } P\text{)} \qquad\qquad (8\text{–}6)$$

A simple experimental apparatus that can be used to illustrate Charles' Law is shown in Figure 8–3. Heating the liquid in the beaker heats the gas confined in the flask. The movement of the colored water is used to measure the volume change.

Figure 8–3
An apparatus used
to illustrate
Charles' Law

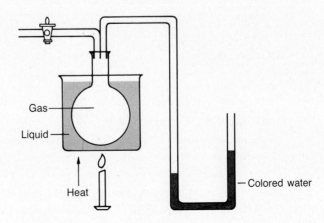

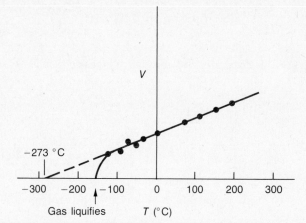

Figure 8–4
An example of a
graphic
representation of
Charles' Law

Plotting volume versus temperature for a typical experiment results in a graph such as the one illustrated in Figure 8–4. The straight line proves that V is directly proportional to T (at constant n and P) for those temperatures of the gas. Two things are evident in this graph. First, as the temperature drops, deviations from linearity are evident until, at the condensation temperature, the gas liquifies and the volume drops drastically. Second, an extrapolation of the straight line intersects the temperature axis at -273 °C. Repeated observations of the behavior of different gases show that all extrapolations to zero volume give a temperature of -273 °C.

We can use this experimental fact to define an *absolute temperature scale* since all gases extrapolate to the same temperature and since that temperature seems to be the lowest one attainable. We do this by shifting the plot in Figure 8–4 along the x axis (the temperature axis) so that the origin is at the lowest temperature: -273 °C. This temperature is redefined as 0 K, or **absolute zero**, and the absolute temperature scale (the Kelvin scale) is defined as:

$$T = 273 \text{ °C} + t$$

where the units of T are K and the units of t are °C.

In effect, we have used the direct dependence of the volume of a gas on temperature to measure the temperature; that is, we have constructed a gas thermometer. By redefining the temperature scale in terms of absolute zero, 0 K, we may now restate Charles' Law properly as:

The volume of a given amount of gas at a constant pressure is directly proportional to the absolute temperature.

Charles' Law is found to hold under the same conditions as Boyle's Law; deviations are found at low temperatures and high pressures.

In accordance with the new definition, we may now rewrite Equation 8–6, a mathematical statement of Charles' Law, as:

$$V = (\text{constant})(T)$$

For the same sample of a gas (at constant P) at two different volumes and temperatures, we have:

$$\frac{V_1}{T_1} = \text{constant}$$

$$\frac{V_2}{T_2} = \text{constant}$$

Since the constant is the same (due to the direct variation of V and T when n and P are constant), we can combine these two expressions:

$$\frac{V_1}{T_1} = \frac{V_2}{T_2}$$

or, by rearrangement:

$$V_2 = V_1\left(\frac{T_2}{T_1}\right) \tag{8-7}$$

This expression can be used to determine the effect of changing the temperature of a fixed amount of a gas at constant pressure by using the temperature correction (or ratio) analogously to the pressure and volume ratios in Boyle's Law calculations. In this case, however, the correction is *greater than 1* when the temperature *increases* because the volume varies directly with temperature.

EXAMPLE 8.4a The temperature of a 400. cm³ volume of a gas is raised from 100. °C to 250. °C at constant pressure. What is the new volume?
First we convert °C to K:

$$T_2 = 273 + 250. = 523 \text{ K} \qquad T_1 = 273 + 100. = 373 \text{ K}$$

Then, according to Equation 8–7:

$$V_2 = V_1 \left(\frac{T_2}{T_1} \right)$$

$$V_2 = 400. \text{ cm}^3 \left(\frac{523 \text{ K}}{373 \text{ K}} \right)$$

$$V_2 = 561 \text{ cm}^3$$

Note that the temperature correction is greater than 1 since increasing the temperature increases the volume.

To determine the new temperature if the volume changes, we simply rearrange Equation 8–7 so that we can solve for T_2:

$$T_2 = T_1 \left(\frac{V_2}{V_1} \right)$$

EXAMPLE 8.4b   A 250. cm³ sample of a gas at an original temperature of 25 °C is allowed to expand to a volume of 300. cm³ at constant pressure. What is the new temperature?
First we must convert °C to K:

$$T_1 = 273 + 25 = 298 \text{ K}$$

Since temperature increases as volume increases, the volume correction factor will be greater than 1.

$$T_2 = 298 \text{ K} \left(\frac{300. \text{ cm}^3}{250. \text{ cm}^3} \right)$$

$$T_2 = 358 \text{ K}$$

8.5 The Combined Gas Law

Boyle's and Charles' Laws may be combined into one equation to calculate the new volume of a fixed amount of gas if both temperature and pressure are varied. The calculation is made by successively applying corrections for the temperature change and for the pressure change. Again, it is much simpler to "think the problem through" than to face the possible confusion with subscripts:

$$V_2 = V_1\left(\frac{T_2}{T_1}\right)\left(\frac{P_1}{P_2}\right) \qquad (8\text{--}8)$$

EXAMPLE 8.5a What volume will 2.50 L of a gas occupy if the pressure goes from 750. torr to 760. torr and the temperature changes from 25 °C to 20. °C?

Since pressure is increasing, the pressure factor will be <1 (volume decreases); the temperature factor will also be <1, since as T decreases, V decreases.

$$V_2 = 2.50 \text{ L}\left(\frac{293 \text{ K}}{298 \text{ K}}\right)\left(\frac{750. \text{ torr}}{760. \text{ torr}}\right)$$

$$V_2 = 2.43 \text{ L}$$

EXAMPLE 8.5b A 4.0×10^3 L balloon is filled with helium to 1.00 atm pressure at sea level, where the temperature is 25 °C. What will the volume of the balloon be when it reaches an altitude where $P = 0.40$ atm and $T = -25$ °C?

The decreasing pressure means that the pressure factor will be >1; the decreasing temperature tells us that the temperature factor will be <1.

$$V_2 = 4.0 \times 10^3 \text{ L}\left(\frac{248 \text{ K}}{298 \text{ K}}\right)\left(\frac{1.00 \text{ atm}}{0.40 \text{ atm}}\right)$$

$$V_2 = 8.3 \times 10^3 \text{ L}$$

For convenience in making calculations involving gases, we may use a **standard temperature and pressure (STP)**, which have been defined as follows:

$$\text{standard temperature} = 273 \text{ K } (0 \text{ °C})$$

$$\text{standard pressure} = 1 \text{ atm } (760 \text{ torr})$$

To convert a given amount of a gas at any temperature and pressure to STP, we use the combined gas law (Equation 8–8).

EXAMPLE 8.5c   A sample of a gas occupies a volume of 1.25 L at 100. °C and 785 torr pressure. What volume does it occupy at standard temperature and pressure?
The temperature is being lowered from 373 K to 273 K; therefore the temperature factor will be <1 (V decreases as T decreases). The pressure is lowered from 785 to 760. torr; thus the pressure factor is >1 (V increases as P decreases).

$$V_2 = 1.25 \text{ L} \left(\frac{273 \text{ K}}{373 \text{ K}}\right)\left(\frac{785 \text{ torr}}{760. \text{ torr}}\right)$$

$$V_2 = 0.945 \text{ L}$$

8.6 Avogadro's Principle

As early as 1809 the French chemist Gay-Lussac observed that one volume of hydrogen, for example, reacts with one volume of chlorine to form two volumes of hydrogen chloride. To account for this observation that gases react in simple proportions by volume, Avogadro proposed that equal volumes of gases at the same temperature and pressure contain equal numbers of molecules (if $V_1 = V_2$ then $n_1 = n_2$, where n is the number of moles, or the *amount,* of a gas). He went on to point out that if this is the case, then the number of molecules must vary directly with the volume of a gas, assuming the temperature and pressure remain constant. Mathematically stated, this becomes:

$$V \propto n \text{ (at constant } T \text{ and } P) \tag{8–9}$$

We can use Avogadro's Principle to show that simple elemental gases are diatomic. Let us take the example of the formation of HCl from its component elements. We know that the HCl molecule contains one atom of H for each atom of Cl. Therefore the molecule must be *at least* diatomic. Let us assume that it is diatomic, that its molecular formula as well as its empirical formula is HCl. If we were to further assume that hydrogen and chlorine are monatomic (H and Cl), then the reaction between hydrogen and chlorine would be as follows:

$$H + Cl \longrightarrow HCl$$

According to this equation one atom of hydrogen reacts with one atom of chlorine to form one molecule of HCl. By Avogadro's Principle this means that one volume of hydrogen reacts with one of chlorine to form one volume of HCl. But this is not observed; Gay-Lussac found that *two* volumes of HCl are produced from one volume each of hydrogen and chlorine. This observation can be explained only by the following reaction:

$$H_2 + Cl_2 \longrightarrow 2\ HCl$$

Therefore hydrogen and chlorine occur as diatomic molecules in the elemental state.

Avogadro's Principle can be applied to problems involving the stoichiometry of equations in what are called volume-volume calculations.

EXAMPLE 8.6a   Butane, C_4H_{10}, burns according to the following reaction:

$$2\ C_4H_{10}(g) + 13\ O_2(g) \longrightarrow 8\ CO_2(g) + 10\ H_2O(g)$$

How many liters of CO_2 are produced by burning 25 L of butane? The stoichiometry of the equation says that 8 mol CO_2 are formed from 2 mol C_4H_{10}, but, at the same temperature and pressure, Avogadro's Principle means that 8 vol CO_2 are formed from 2 vol C_4H_{10}. Therefore:

$$25\text{ L }C_4H_{10} \times \frac{8\text{ vol }CO_2}{2\text{ vol }C_4H_{10}} = 1.0 \times 10^2\text{ L }CO_2$$

EXAMPLE 8.6b　How many liters of NH_3 can be produced from 20. L of N_2 according to the reaction:

$$N_2 + 3H_2 \longrightarrow 2 NH_3$$

In this case, Avogadro's Principle says that 2 vol NH_3 are equivalent to 1 vol N_2.

$$20. \text{ L } N_2 \times \frac{2 \text{ vol } NH_3}{1 \text{ vol } N_2} = 40. \text{ L } NH_3$$

8.7　The Ideal Gas Law

For convenience in calculations, we may now combine Boyle's Law (Equation 8–2), Charles' Law (Equation 8–6), and Avogadro's Principle (Equation 8–9) into one equation:

$$\left.\begin{array}{l} V \propto 1/P \\ V \propto T \\ V \propto n \end{array}\right\} \longrightarrow V \propto (n)(1/P)(T)$$

or

$$V = R \frac{nT}{P} \qquad\qquad (8\text{–}10)$$

where R is the proportionality constant, or the **gas constant**. Equation 8–10 is called the **ideal gas law** and is usually written as:

$$PV = nRT$$

We now need to evaluate the numerical value of the gas constant. It is found by experiment that at STP (1 atm, 273 K) one mole of an ideal gas occupies 22.4 L. Known as the **molar volume of an ideal gas**, this value is the same for any ideal gas at STP. When we plug the appropriate numbers into the ideal gas law, we can solve for R:

$$R = \frac{VP}{nT}$$

$$R = \frac{(22.4 \text{ L})(1 \text{ atm})}{(1 \text{ mol})(273 \text{ K})}$$

$$R = 0.0821 \frac{\text{L atm}}{\text{mol K}}$$

The units of R tell us what unit each of the four variables in the ideal gas law must have: volume is expressed in liters, pressure in atmospheres, amount of material in moles, and temperature in Kelvin.

Let us now take a look at several types of gas law calculations.

EXAMPLE 8.7a   A 50.0 L vessel contains O_2 gas at 100. atm pressure and 25 °C. Calculate the number of moles of O_2 in the tank.

Assuming that the ideal gas law holds in this case:

$$PV = nRT$$

$$n = \frac{PV}{RT} = \frac{(100. \text{ atm})(50.0 \text{ L})}{(0.0821 \text{ L atm/mol K})(298 \text{ K})}$$

$$n = 204 \text{ mol}$$

It is important to ensure that the various units always cancel out against the units of R.

EXAMPLE 8.7b   A 5.00 g sample of XeF_2, a compound of the noble gas xenon, is introduced into a 4.00 L container at 60. °C. What is the resultant pressure (in atm)?

Recalling that $n = g/MW$ (molecular weight), we can substitute this into the ideal gas law:

$$PV = \frac{g}{MW} RT$$

$$P = \frac{gRT}{(MW)V}$$

$$P = \frac{(5.00 \text{ g XeF}_2)(0.0821 \text{ L atm/mol K})(333 \text{ K})}{(169.30 \text{ g/mol XeF}_2)(4.00 \text{ L})}$$

$$P = 0.202 \text{ atm}$$

In Chapter 2 we were shown how to calculate the empirical (or simplest) formula of a compound from analytical data. However, a second experiment must be performed in order to determine the true molecular formula. Experiments with gases give the necessary information.

EXAMPLE 8.7c Chemical analysis shows that a compound contains 24.3% C, 4.1% H, and 71.6% Cl by weight. A 1.50 g sample of this compound fills a volume of 375 cm³ at 25 °C and 752 torr. Calculate the empirical and molecular formulas of this compound.

First, assuming a 100 g sample, we convert g to mol:

$$24.3 \text{ g C} \times \frac{1 \text{ mol C}}{12.01 \text{ g C}} = 2.02 \text{ mol C}$$

$$4.1 \text{ g H} \times \frac{1 \text{ mol H}}{1.008 \text{ g H}} = 4.1 \text{ mol H}$$

$$71.6 \text{ g Cl} \times \frac{1 \text{ mol Cl}}{35.45 \text{ g Cl}} = 2.02 \text{ mol Cl}$$

This gives a formula of $C_{2.02}H_{4.1}Cl_{2.02}$. When we divide through by the smallest subscript, we obtain the empirical formula: CH_2Cl. Then, turning to the gas law data, we can calculate the true molecular weight (MW). To do this, we must first convert torr to atm and cm³ to L:

$$752 \text{ torr} \times \frac{1 \text{ atm}}{760 \text{ torr}} = 0.989 \text{ atm}$$

$$375 \text{ cm}^3 \times \frac{1 \text{ L}}{1,000 \text{ cm}^3} = 0.375 \text{ L}$$

We are now ready to calculate the molecular weight of the compound by plugging the appropriate values into the ideal gas law:

$$PV = \frac{g}{MW}RT$$

$$MW = \frac{gRT}{PV}$$

$$MW = \frac{(1.50 \text{ g})(0.0821 \text{ L atm/mol K})(298 \text{ K})}{(0.989 \text{ atm})(0.375 \text{ L})}$$

$$MW = 99.0 \text{ g/mol}$$

The empirical formula weight is $12.01 + 2(1.008) + 35.45 = 49.48$. The true molecular weight is about double this; therefore the molecular formula is twice the empirical formula, or $C_2H_4Cl_2$.

"Mixed" problems involving reaction stoichiometry with both gases and solids are easily handled using the gas laws.

EXAMPLE 8.7d   Copper oxide (CuO) can be reduced to Cu metal by the action of H_2 gas according to the equation:

$$CuO(s) + H_2(g) \longrightarrow Cu(s) + H_2O(l)$$

How many g of Cu can be produced by reacting 600. cm³ H_2 gas (at 20 °C and 1.15 atm) with CuO?

This problem is most easily attacked by converting the volume of H_2 to STP and then using the knowledge that there are 22.4 L/mol of gas at STP. In the conversion to STP, the temperature is reduced from 293 to 273 K (V decreases), and the pressure is reduced from 1.15 to 1.00 atm (V increases). When we plug these values into the combined gas law formula, we can calculate the new volume:

$$V_2 = V_1 \left(\frac{T_2}{T_1}\right)\left(\frac{P_1}{P_2}\right)$$

$$V_2 = 600. \text{ cm}^3 \left(\frac{273 \text{ K}}{293 \text{ K}}\right)\left(\frac{1.15 \text{ atm}}{1.00 \text{ atm}}\right) = 643 \text{ cm}^3$$

$$V_2 = 0.643 \text{ L } H_2 \text{ at STP}$$

The next step is to convert this volume to moles:

$$0.643 \text{ L H}_2 \text{ at STP} \times \frac{1 \text{ mol H}_2}{22.4 \text{ L H}_2 \text{ at STP}} = 0.0287 \text{ mol H}_2$$

Using the stoichiometry of the equation, we can now convert mol H_2 to mol Cu:

$$0.0287 \text{ mol H}_2 \times \frac{1 \text{ mol Cu}}{1 \text{ mol H}_2} = 0.0287 \text{ mol Cu}$$

Conversion of mol Cu to g Cu gives:

$$0.0287 \text{ mol Cu} \times \frac{63.55 \text{ g Cu}}{1 \text{ mol Cu}} = 1.82 \text{ g Cu}$$

Alternatively, we could use the ideal gas law directly to find the number of moles of hydrogen:

$$PV = nRT$$

$$n = \frac{PV}{RT} = \frac{(1.15 \text{ atm})(0.600 \text{ L})}{(0.0821 \text{ L atm/mol K})(293 \text{ K})}$$

$$n = 0.0287 \text{ mol H}_2$$

EXAMPLE 8.7e   A common laboratory preparation of O_2 is by the thermal decomposition of $KClO_3$ according to the reaction:

$$2 \text{ KClO}_3(s) \longrightarrow 2 \text{ KCl}(s) + 3 \text{ O}_2(g)$$

How many grams of $KClO_3$ must be decomposed to fill a 2.50 L vessel with oxygen at 25 °C and 1.00 atm pressure?
First we convert the volume of O_2 to STP. In making the conversion, the temperature is reduced from 298 K to 273 K, but the pressure does not have to be corrected:

$$V_2 = 2.50 \text{ L} \left(\frac{273 \text{ K}}{298 \text{ K}} \right)$$

$$V_2 = 2.29 \text{ L O}_2 \text{ at STP}$$

Then we convert this volume to moles using the fact that one mole of an ideal gas occupies 22.4 L at STP:

$$2.29 \text{ L O}_2 \text{ at STP} \times \frac{1 \text{ mol O}_2}{22.4 \text{ L O}_2 \text{ at STP}} = 0.102 \text{ mol O}_2$$

Conversion of mol O_2 to mol $KClO_3$ using the balanced chemical equation gives:

$$0.102 \text{ mol O}_2 \times \frac{2 \text{ mol KClO}_3}{3 \text{ mol O}_2} = 0.0680 \text{ mol KClO}_3$$

Finally, we convert mol $KClO_3$ to g $KClO_3$:

$$\text{MW KClO}_3 = 39.10 + 35.45 + 3(16.00) = 122.55 \text{ g/mol}$$

$$0.0680 \text{ mol KClO}_3 \times \frac{122.55 \text{ g KClO}_3}{1 \text{ mol KClO}_3} = 8.33 \text{ g KClO}_3$$

8.8   Dalton's Law of Partial Pressures

Dalton's Law states that if there is a mixture of gases A, B, C, . . . in a closed container, the total pressure in the container is the sum of the *partial pressures* (the pressures exerted by the individual gases):

$$P_{\text{total}} = \Sigma P_i = P_A + P_B + P_C + \cdots$$

The symbol ΣP_i is read "the sum of the partial pressures" (the capital Greek letter sigma means "sum"), and P_A, P_B, P_C, etc., are the pressures that the gases A, B, C, etc., would exert if they were present *alone* in the vessel. In other words, the pressures of the component gases in a mixture are additive; each gas acts as if it were the only gas present.

This phenomenon is particularly important in determining the pressure of a gas "collected over water" in a laboratory experiment. It is quite common in the laboratory to prepare a gas by chemical reaction and then

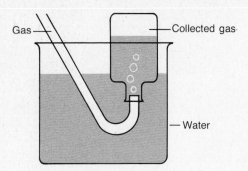

Figure 8–5

Collection of a gas over water

collect it by displacing water from a vessel that is inverted in a tray of water.

Figure 8–5 illustrates a typical experimental apparatus. As a gas is generated by chemical reaction, it enters the tube and bubbles into the inverted flask, displacing the water which originally filled the vessel. When the water level in the flask is the same as the level outside, the pressure in the flask is equal to the prevailing barometric pressure, P_{atm}. However, the collected gas is saturated with water vapor; the pressure exerted by this vapor is given by the **vapor pressure** of water at the temperature of collection. Note from Table 8–2 that the vapor pressure of water increases as temperature increases.

As an example of the relationship among the various pressures in an experiment that involves collecting a gas over water, let us assume that we want to determine the pressure of a sample of hydrogen gas collected in this manner. Once the water level in the flask becomes equal to that in the

Table 8–2

The Vapor Pressures of Water at Several Temperatures

$T(°C)$	$P(torr)$
0	4.6
5	6.5
10	9.2
15	12.8
20	17.5
25	23.8
30	31.8

tray, the total pressure in the flask is equal to the prevailing atmospheric pressure:

$$P_{atm} = P_{total}$$

According to Dalton's Law, $P_{total} = P_{H_2} + P_{H_2O}$. Therefore:

$$P_{atm} = P_{H_2} + P_{H_2O}$$

To determine the pressure of the hydrogen gas, we simply rearrange the equation:

$$P_{H_2} = P_{atm} - P_{H_2O}$$

To determine the pressure of any gas collected over water, the vapor pressure of water is subtracted from the prevailing atmospheric pressure.

EXAMPLE 8.8a   If 15.0 L of O_2 are collected over water at 22 °C when $P_{atm} = 747$ torr, what is the volume of the dry oxygen gas at STP? (At 22 °C the vapor pressure of water is 20. torr.)
First we determine the pressure of the dry oxygen gas (that is, we correct for P_{H_2O}):

$$P_{O_2} = P_{atm} - P_{H_2O}$$

$$P_{O_2} = 747 \text{ torr} - 20. \text{ torr} = 727 \text{ torr}$$

Then we convert the 15.0 L volume to STP. The temperature decreases from 295 to 273 K (V decreases) and the pressure increases from 727 torr to 760 torr (V decreases). Therefore:

$$V_2 = V_1\left(\frac{T_2}{T_1}\right)\left(\frac{P_1}{P_2}\right)$$

$$V_2 = 15.0 \text{ L}\left(\frac{273 \text{ K}}{295 \text{ K}}\right)\left(\frac{727 \text{ torr}}{760. \text{ torr}}\right)$$

$$V_2 = 13.3 \text{ L}$$

EXAMPLE 8.8b   A 0.548 g sample of an unknown gas is collected over water at 25 °C in a volume of 500. cm³. $P_{atm} = 735$ torr. Calculate the molecular weight of this gas.

This problem can be solved by two different methods. The first method involves reducing the volume to STP (after correcting for P_{H_2O}) and then using the knowledge that one mole of an ideal gas occupies 22.4 L. First we correct for P_{H_2O}:

$$P_{unknown\ gas} = P_{atm} - P_{H_2O}$$

$$P_{unknown\ gas} = 735\ torr - 23.8\ torr = 711\ torr$$

Then we reduce the volume to STP:

$$V_2 = 500.\ cm^3 \left(\frac{273\ K}{298\ K}\right)\left(\frac{711\ torr}{760.\ torr}\right)$$

$$V_2 = 429\ cm^3\ at\ STP$$

Using the molar volume of an ideal gas, we can now calculate the molecular weight of the gas:

$$\frac{0.548\ g}{429\ cm^3} \times \frac{22.4\ L}{1\ mol} \times \frac{1,000\ cm^3}{1\ L} = 28.6\ g/mol$$

Note that the conversion factors are set up so that all units except g/mol cancel out.

The second method of solving this problem involves using the ideal gas law (after correcting for P_{H_2O}). We first convert torr to atm and cm³ to L so that we can plug the values of P and V directly into the ideal gas equation:

$$711\ torr \times \frac{1\ atm}{760.\ torr} = 0.936\ atm$$

$$500.\ cm^3 \times \frac{1\ L}{1,000\ cm^3} = 0.500\ L$$

$$PV = \frac{g}{MW} RT$$

$$MW = \frac{gRT}{PV} = \frac{(0.548\ \text{g})(0.0821\ \text{L atm/mol K})(298\ \text{K})}{(0.936\ \text{atm})(0.500\ \text{L})}$$

$$MW = 28.6\ \text{g/mol}$$

EXAMPLE 8.8c   Hydrogen sulfide, H_2S, is an extremely poisonous gas having the odor of rotten eggs. It is commonly produced as sulfur-containing organic matter decomposes. Fortunately, the human nose is very sensitive to the odor of H_2S; it is noticeable at a concentration of 0.002 mg/L. At 23 °C, determine the partial pressure of H_2S at a concentration equal to the detectable level.

Since Dalton's Law of Partial Pressures states that each gas in a mixture ideally acts as if it were the only gas present, this problem is one involving the ideal gas law:

$$PV = nRT$$

We know that there is 0.002 mg (2×10^{-6} g) in a liter of volume, so by substituting $n = g/MW$ and rearranging the equation, we can calculate the partial pressure of H_2S:

$$P_{H_2S} = \frac{gRT}{(MW)V}$$

$$P_{H_2S} = \frac{(2 \times 10^{-6}\ \text{g})(0.0821\ \text{L atm/mol K})(296\ \text{K})}{(34.08\ \text{g/mol})(1\ \text{L})}$$

$$P_{H_2S} = 1 \times 10^{-6}\ \text{atm}$$

8.9   Graham's Law of Diffusion

If some ammonia gas were released in a corner of a room, within a short time the odor of ammonia would be noticeable throughout the room. This is a result of the relatively rapid **diffusion** exhibited by gases. In 1829 Thomas Graham measured this diffusion in relation to the molecular weight of a gas. He observed that the **rate of diffusion (R)** of a gas is in-

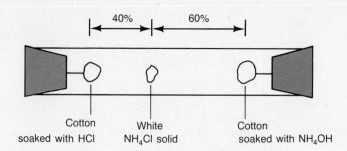

Figure 8–6
An experiment that
illustrates
Graham's Law

40%   60%

Cotton
soaked with HCl

White
NH₄Cl solid

Cotton
soaked with NH₄OH

versely proportional to the square root of its molecular weight, or, mathematically stated:

$$\mathbf{R} \propto \frac{1}{\sqrt{MW}}$$

Figure 8–6 diagrams a simple experiment illustrating Graham's Law. The cotton balls are soaked in solutions of HCl and NH_3 before being placed in the tube. These solutions give off HCl and NH_3 gas, respectively. After a short period of time a white cloud of ammonium chloride, NH_4Cl, appears at the spot indicated in the diagram because of the reaction:

$$NH_3(g) + HCl(g) \longrightarrow NH_4Cl(s)$$

The experiment indicates that the NH_3 gas travels faster (diffuses faster) than the HCl gas. The rates of diffusion are in the ratio:

$$\frac{\mathbf{R}_{NH_3}}{\mathbf{R}_{HCl}} = \frac{60}{40} = 1.5$$

According to Graham's Law, the inverse ratio of the square roots of the molecular weights should be the same:

$$\frac{\sqrt{MW_{HCl}}}{\sqrt{MW_{NH_3}}} = \frac{\sqrt{36.46}}{\sqrt{17.03}} = 1.5$$

Therefore, in general, the following relationship holds for any two gases:

$$\frac{\mathbf{R}_A}{\mathbf{R}_B} = \sqrt{\frac{MW_B}{MW_A}}$$

8.10 The Kinetic Molecular Theory

In the seventeenth century Sir Isaac Newton proposed a model for the gaseous state which was based on gas molecules being fixed in position. The pressure associated with the gas was said to arise from repulsive interactions among these molecules. This erroneous idea persisted until the mid-nineteenth century even though Daniel Bernoulli, in 1738, actually proposed a correct kinetic model, which views the molecules of a gas as being in constant motion.

It was not until 1860 that James Maxwell and Ludwig Boltzmann developed the modern theory of gases, known as the **kinetic molecular theory**. Any theory of gases is aimed, of course, toward accounting for the observed behavior of gases and, in particular, for the ideal gas law. The postulates of the kinetic molecular theory can be outlined in a qualitative manner as follows:

I.   The molecules in a gas are *point masses;* their volume is negligible compared to the volume of the space between them. When describing an ideal gas, the volume we speak of is that of the container holding the gas, not the volume of the gas molecules. The fact that characteristically gases are easily compressed supports this first postulate, which assumes that essentially all of the volume of a gas is empty space.

II.   There are no attractive forces between the molecules of a gas. Therefore the molecules of a gas move about as if they do not "see" one another. The observation that gases completely fill the volume of their container supports this, since in order to do so the intermolecular forces must be low or negligible.

In terms of the kinetic molecular theory, then, an *ideal gas* is defined as a gas in which (1) the molecules are point masses (that is, their volume is negligibly small) and (2) there are no attractive forces between the molecules.

III.   The molecules of a gas are in rapid, random, straight-line motion, and the collisions between these molecules are said to be *elastic.* The motion of gas molecules is considered to be in a straight line because we are assuming that there are no intermolecular forces present to swerve the molecules from a straight path. We know that the motion is rapid; indeed, the calculated value for the velocity of an O_2 molecule at 0 °C is on the order of 5×10^4 cm/sec (over 1,000 miles per hour)!

When we say that collisions between molecules are elastic, we mean that there is no *net* loss of kinetic energy of the molecules undergoing collision. As an analogy, let us imagine a "frictionless" billiard ball table. The billiard balls have no attractive forces between them, and they travel in straight lines. If there were no loss of energy through friction, they would continue to move and collide with no net loss of kinetic energy. If, on collision, one billiard ball (or molecule) loses kinetic energy, then the one it collides with gains that amount of kinetic energy, keeping the total kinetic energy constant. Since there are a very large number of molecules in a mole of gas ($\sim 10^{24}$) and they are moving so rapidly, there are a very large number of collisions per second ($\sim 10^{30}$ at STP). Each collision involves a possible transfer of kinetic energy. On the average, however, the kinetic energy of the whole system is unchanged.

The phenomenon of **Brownian motion** is good evidence for this microscopic behavior. In 1827 Robert Brown made a fundamental observation which was of primary importance in the development of a theory of gases. He observed that particles suspended in a gas (or in a liquid) undergo continuous, random, erratic motion. If the behavior of a smoke particle suspended in air, for example, is examined under a microscope by light scattering, a continuous zig-zag motion can be observed (Figure 8–7). It appears as if the particle is being bombarded by objects— the molecules of the air in which it is suspended. Furthermore, if the temperature of the air is increased, the speed of the particle also increases. These observations suggest that gas is made up of molecules that are in constant, continuous motion, motion which increases and becomes more violent with temperature. The random zig-zag patterns made by minute particles suspended in a gas mirror the random motion that the gas molecules are undergoing. Collisions between the suspended particle and the moving gas molecules cause the particle to move.

Figure 8–7
The Brownian motion of a smoke particle suspended in a gas

IV.   The pressure a gas exerts on its container is due to the collisions of the gas molecules with the walls of the container. Pressure is defined as force per unit area; the average force of each collision times the number of collisions per unit area in one second gives the pressure exerted by the gas on the walls of the container:

$$P = \left(\frac{\text{force}}{\text{collision}}\right)\left(\frac{\text{collisions}}{\text{area}}\right)$$

$$P = \frac{\text{force}}{\text{area}}$$

V. The average kinetic energy of the molecules in a gas (abbreviated $\overline{\text{KE}}$) is directly proportional to the temperature of the gas. Therefore any two gases at the same temperature will have the same average kinetic energy. We have seen that the Brownian motion of a particle suspended in a gas increases with temperature, which implies that the gas molecules move faster when heat is added. Not all of the molecules in a gas move at the same speed (have the same kinetic energy) at any given instant, however, so the kinetic energy of every molecule is not directly proportional to the temperature. But the *average* kinetic energy, if calculated for a large number of molecules, is dependent only on temperature.

It is possible to estimate the percentage of molecules in a gas that have a particular kinetic energy. This can be done for all the possible kinetic energies in a gas at a given temperature. If the percentages of

Figure 8–8
The distribution of kinetic energies for a gas at two temperatures

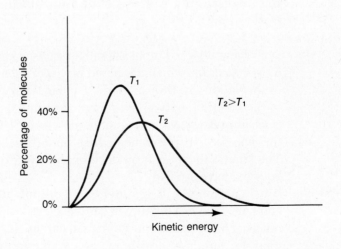

molecules having particular kinetic energies are plotted against the kinetic energies themselves, the result is what is known as a **Maxwell-Boltzmann distribution curve.** Figure 8–8 shows two such curves for a gas at two different temperatures, T_1 and T_2, where $T_2 > T_1$. The top of each distribution curve represents the most *probable* kinetic energy of molecules at that temperature, because it is estimated that there will be more molecules with this kinetic energy than with any other. Note that this top point (and the entire distribution curve) is at higher kinetic energy for T_2 than for T_1. Similarly, the average kinetic energy of a gas increases as temperature increases.

The kinetic molecular theory was developed to explain the various gas laws we have studied in this chapter, including the ideal gas law. We can see, for example, that Boyle's Law, $V \propto 1/P$, is consistent with the kinetic molecular theory. If we were to make a calculation involving Boyle's Law, we would arrive at the same result using the rationale for the law put forth in this theory. As an illustration, let us assume that a gas is contained in a cubic box of edge length l. If we double the lengths of the edges, we increase the volume (l^3) by a factor of $V_2/V_1 = (2\,l)^3/l^3 = 8$. Therefore, the pressure of the gas, which is inversely proportional to the volume according to Boyle's Law, should decrease to $\frac{1}{8}$ of its value. In terms of kinetic theory, doubling the edge length of the box decreases the number of collisions with the wall by $\frac{1}{2}$ (since the molecules have to travel twice as far) and increases the area of the wall (l^2) by a factor equal to the ratio of the areas: $(2\,l)^2/l^2 = 4$. If there are $\frac{1}{2}$ as many collisions, then the total force on the wall is decreased by $\frac{1}{2}$. The pressure ($P = \text{force/area}$) is thus reduced to $\frac{1}{2} \div 4 = \frac{1}{8}$ of its original value, the result indicated by Boyle's Law.

The ability to obtain the same results using either the kinetic theory or the gas laws, which are based on experimental data, gives confidence in the validity of the kinetic molecular theory. However, the postulates of the kinetic theory give us more than just the bulk properties of gases (such as pressure, volume, and temperature). They provide an insight into the *microscopic* phenomena that underlie the macroscopic behavior. The kinetic theory can produce qualitative explanations for each of the laws we have studied.

For example, if gas molecules do not interact (do not "see" one another), then in a mixture of gases each gas will act independently of the others. This is nothing more than a statement of Dalton's Law—that the total pressure of a mixture of gases is the sum of the partial pressures of

Lucretius and Brownian Motion

Consider the following quotation from Lucretius' *On the Nature of the Universe,* Book II (Ronald Latham, translator. London: Penguin Books Ltd., 1951):

"Observe what happens when sunbeams are admitted into a building and shed light on its shadowy places. You will see a multitude of tiny particles mingling in a multitude of ways in the empty space within the light of the beam, as though contending in everlasting conflict, rushing into battle rank upon rank with never a moment's pause in a rapid sequence of unions and disunions. From this you may picture what it is for the atoms to be perpetually tossed about in the illimitable void. To some extent a small thing may afford an illustration and an imperfect image of great things. Besides, there is a further reason why you should give your mind to these particles that are seen dancing in the sunbeam; their dancing is an actual indication of underlying movements of the matter that are hidden from our sight. There you will see many particles under the impact of invisible blows changing their course and driven back upon their tracks, this way and that, in all directions. You must understand that they all derive this restlessness from the atoms. It originates with the atoms, which move of themselves. Then those small compound bodies that are least removed from the impetus of the atoms are set in motion by the impact of their invisible blows and in turn cannon against slightly larger bodies. So the movement mounts up from the atoms and gradually emerges to the level of our senses, so that those bodies are in motion that we see in sunbeams, moved by blows that remain invisible."

This description, written in about 50 B.C., provides an observation of the phenomenon we now know as Brownian motion. It is a tribute to Lucretius that his explanation of this phenomenon presages the modern kinetic molecular theory, that atoms or molecules making up a gas are in constant, random motion. It is this motion of the atoms and molecules that cause the "tiny particles mingling in a multitude of ways" (the dust particles suspended in the air) to move "with never a moment's pause in a rapid sequence of unions and disunions" (a constant and random motion).

the individual gases, where the partial pressure of each gas is the pressure that gas would exert if it were the only one present.

The kinetic molecular theory can be used to derive all of the gas laws as well as explain them. Although the laws were determined experimentally, the fact that they can be derived from the postulates of the kinetic theory gives proof that the theory is accurate, providing the laws are accurate. As an example, let us use the kinetic theory to derive Graham's Law of Diffusion. If we have two gases A and B at the same temperature, then according to kinetic theory their average kinetic energies $\overline{KE}$ (which depend only on temperature) are equal:

$$\overline{KE}_A = \overline{KE}_B$$

In Chapter 1 (page 31) we learned that kinetic energy $= \frac{1}{2} mv^2$, where v is now the average velocity. Therefore:

$$\frac{1}{2} m_A v_A{}^2 = \frac{1}{2} m_B v_B{}^2$$

or

$$\frac{v_A{}^2}{v_B{}^2} = \frac{m_B}{m_A}$$

or

$$\frac{v_A}{v_B} = \frac{\sqrt{m_B}}{\sqrt{m_A}}$$

Since it is reasonable to assume that the rate of diffusion $\mathbf{R}$ is proportional to the average velocity of the molecules, and since the molecular weight of a gas is its mass, we now have:

$$\frac{\mathbf{R}_A}{\mathbf{R}_B} = \frac{\sqrt{MW_B}}{\sqrt{MW_A}}$$

which is Graham's Law of Diffusion.

8.11 Deviations From Ideal Behavior

It was pointed out earlier in this chapter that Boyle's Law and Charles' Law hold well for most gases at relatively low pressures and moderate to high temperatures. This is also true of the ideal gas law; that is, deviations from the relationship $PV = nRT$ are small at these pressures and temperatures. However, deviation from this expression can be extreme for gases at a high pressure or a low temperature.

Let us first consider the behavior of simple gases at high pressures. If we rearrange the ideal gas law, we can write:

$$\frac{PV}{nRT} = 1$$

In regions where a gas does not obey the ideal gas law, the function on the left-hand side of this equation will deviate from 1. Figure 8–9 is a plot of PV/nRT versus pressure for three different gases: H_2, O_2, and CO_2. Notice that at high pressures (hundreds of atmospheres) each of these gases deviates substantially from ideal behavior. Why does this happen?

It happens because gases are never ideal, and at high pressures (and low temperatures) they are far from ideal. Thus the ideal gas law, as well as the other gas laws, is not completely valid, although it works well enough for gases that approach ideality. Similarly, the basic assumptions of the kinetic molecular theory are not completely true. First, kinetic theory assumes that gas molecules are point masses (that is, the volume of the molecules is negligible), and second, it assumes that the intermolecular forces of attraction in gases are completely negligible. But molecules are not quite point masses (even though gases are very dilute and have very low densities), and there are attractive forces between the gas molecules.

In terms of kinetic theory, it is not surprising that deviations from the ideal gas law occur at high pressures and low temperatures. At high pressures, where the molecules are close together, the volume of the molecules is no longer negligible in relation to the volume of the container. Also, if the distance between molecules is deceased, any weak intermolecular forces become more substantial. At low temperatures, where the gas molecules are moving more slowly, the attractive forces between

Figure 8–9
The behavior of three gases at high pressures

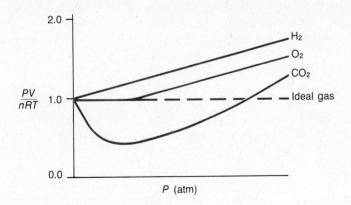

The Chemistry of Air Pollution

The atmosphere which envelops our planet, called *air,* is a mixture of about fifteen different gases. The major components of dry air are N_2 (78.08% by volume), O_2 (20.95%), Ar (0.93%), and CO_2 (0.31%). The remaining components are the noble gases Ne, He, and Kr, along with trace amounts CH_4 (methane), H_2, CO (carbon monoxide), N_2O (nitrous oxide), O_3 (ozone), NH_3 (ammonia), NO_2 (nitrogen dioxide), and SO_2 (sulfur dioxide).

In addition, our atmosphere contains pollutants, which are chemicals not normally found in air or not found in such large concentrations. Usually the term has a derogatory connotation and is taken to mean a material that is harmful. Air pollutants are classified as primary or secondary pollutants. Primary pollutants are produced directly and released into the atmosphere; they include carbon oxides, sulfur oxides, nitrogen oxides, hydrocarbons, and various particulates. Secondary pollutants are produced in the air by chemical reactions of primary pollutants. Although all of the primary pollutants are produced by natural processes, the contribution from man-made sources can increase their concentrations to harmful levels.

Carbon oxides. One of the products of the incomplete combustion of carbon-containing (fossil) fuels is carbon monoxide: $2 C + O_2 \rightarrow 2 CO$. Since most automobile engines depend on gasoline as a fuel, harmful concentrations of carbon monoxide are found in the air above heavily traveled roadways and densely populated cities. The dangerous effect of CO is that it readily combines with the oxygen-carrying component in blood (hemoglobin), interfering with its usual function, since CO binds more strongly to hemoglobin than oxygen. High concentrations of CO in the blood can be fatal.

Another oxide of carbon present in air, carbon dioxide, is a product of the complete combustion of fossil fuels ($C + O_2 \rightarrow CO_2$) and also a normal byproduct of animal respiration. It is consumed in photosynthesis, the process by which plants convert H_2O and CO_2 into glucose ($C_6H_{12}O_6$). Because of the extensive clearing of forests and the increased use of fossil fuels, the concentration of CO_2 in the earth's atmosphere has steadily increased during the last several decades. Molecules of CO_2 absorb infrared radiation (heat), and thus prevent heat from radiating away from the earth's surface and escaping into space. This greenhouse effect could easily increase the average temperature of the atmosphere, which would drastically affect the equilibrium of the oceans and polar ice caps and of plant and animal life.

Sulfur oxides. When any material containing sulfur is burned, oxides of sulfur are formed. For example, if atomic sulfur is burned, the product is sulfur dioxide ($S + O_2 \rightarrow SO_2$), which in turn produces sulfur trioxide ($2 SO_2 + O_2 \rightarrow 2 SO_3$). Both of these oxides are rather noxious, irritating gases that damage the lungs. In addition, a highly corrosive and lethal secondary pollutant, sulfuric acid (H_2SO_4), is produced by the reaction of SO_3 with H_2O. This acid can then further react with ammonia in the atmosphere to form particles of ammonium sulfate, a white solid which clouds the air: $H_2SO_4 + 2 NH_3 \rightarrow (NH_4)_2SO_4$. Because of all the dangers involved in the combustion of sulfur-containing fuels, sulfur impurities are removed from gasoline as part of the refinement process.

Nitrogen oxides. When fossil fuels are burned at high temperatures, a colorless, odorless gas, nitrogen oxide, may be formed: $N_2 + O_2 \rightarrow 2\,NO$. This gas can further react to form a reddish-brown gas with a pungent odor, nitrogen dioxide: $2\,NO + O_2 \rightarrow 2\,NO_2$. The presence of NO_2 in the atmosphere gives rise to the reddish-brown haze present over some cities and industrial areas. Nitrogen oxide can also react with oxygen and water vapor in the air to form nitric acid (HNO_3): $4\,NO + 3\,O_2 + 2\,H_2O \rightarrow 4\,HNO_3$. Both nitric and sulfuric acid can cause rainwater to be acidic, which is harmful to plant and animal life.

Hydrocarbons. Compounds of carbon and hydrogen that are either gases or highly volatile liquids can be found in significant concentrations in air. Aside from methane, which has a natural abundance in air due to leakage of natural gas and to decomposition of vegetable matter, hydrocarbons enter the air by the evaporation and partial combustion of fossil fuels. They are toxic, and many are carcinogenic (cancer-causing).

Particulates. This class of primary pollutants, which includes any finely divided liquid or solid particles suspended in the air, gives rise to the cloudy appearance of polluted air. Particulates include materials such as soot, a by-product of the incomplete combustion of fuel, and various solid byproducts of the melting of ores and refinement of metals. An important effort made by industry has been to use techniques such as filtration to reduce the effluence of particulate matter from flue gases. It is a necessary step, since many of these industrial by-products (such as asbestos and metallic nickel and zinc dust) are carcinogenic.

Smog. Two distinct types of smog exist: industrial (London) smog and photochemical (Los Angeles) smog. **London smog** is formed in the wintertime when unusually large amounts of particulate matter are trapped in a moist air mass. It is characteristic of cities such as London where large amounts of low-grade coal are used for heating. Because soot (coal ash) is a major component (along with SO_2), industrial smog is easily controlled by eliminating coal fires and by precipitating particulates from flue gases. The severe London smogs of the nineteenth and twentieth centuries no longer occur.

Los Angeles smog, on the other hand, is the result of photochemical reactions which occur between sunlight and primary pollutants. The most dangerous secondary pollutants in Los Angeles smog are called **photochemical oxidants.** Ultraviolet radiation from the sun can cause NO_2 to decompose to form NO and atomic oxygen (O), a very reactive oxidant. The atomic oxygen will then combine with diatomic oxygen (O_2) to form another highly reactive oxidant, ozone (O_3). The cycle is completed when O_3 reacts with NO to regenerate NO_2 (and O_2). Both O and O_3 will react with hydrocarbons to form partially oxidized hydrocarbons which are major components of Los Angeles smog. NO_2 and NO can react with hydrocarbons to form organic nitrogen derivatives that are potentially carcinogenic.

Nitrogen oxides and hydrocarbons produce the most dangerous secondary pollutants in Los Angeles smog. Therefore, to control this type of smog, the primary sources of these chemicals must be reduced. Since the automobile is a major contributor, emission controls have been introduced during the past several years to eliminate (as much as possible) the emission of nitrogen oxides.

the molecules become more significant with respect to the kinetic motion which causes the tendency of the molecules to fly about at random. Indeed, as previously discussed, the trends in boiling points reflect the strengths of the attractive forces in the liquid state, and one would expect the relative magnitude of these forces to hold in the gaseous state.

That real gases are not ideal is confirmed by the fact that all gases condense to the liquid state. If there were truly no forces of attraction between gas molecules, then there would be no reason at all for gases to condense. But at high enough pressures (or low enough temperatures), the small intermolecular forces which do exist become dominant over the random kinetic motion, and gaseous molecules coalesce to form liquids. Thus the temperature at which a gas liquifies depends not only on pressure but on the magnitude of the attractive forces. For example, at 1 atm pressure, H_2O gas liquifies at 373 K, whereas at the same pressure N_2 gas liquifies at 77 K. The relatively easy liquefaction of H_2O is due to the large attractive dipole-dipole interactions between the molecules. The attractives forces between N_2 molecules are small, however, and so a very low temperature is required to liquify N_2 gas. As would be expected, the temperature range in which the ideal gas law loses its validity is larger for H_2O than for N_2.

What can be done to remedy the failure of the ideal gas law? In the introduction to this chapter, the scientific method was outlined. According to this method, the ideal gas law (and the kinetic theory) can be modified if new experimental data warrant it. In fact, this is exactly what has been done. More complicated equations of state have been developed to describe the behavior of gases at lower temperatures and higher pressures. The most popular of these is the *van der Waal equation*, which adds terms to the ideal gas equation to account for the volume of the molecules in a gas and the attractive forces between these molecules. The equation is quite successful in extending the usefulness of the ideal gas law to include a greater range of temperatures and pressures.

TERMS AND CONCEPTS		
	• Scientific method	• Standard temperature and pressure (STP)
	• Equations of state	• Avogadro's Principle
	• Boyle's Law	• Ideal gas law
	• Ideal gas	molar volume of an ideal gas
	• Charles' Law	gas constant (R)
	• Absolute zero	• Dalton's Law of Partial Pressures
	• Combined gas law	vapor pressure

- Graham's Law of Diffusion
  diffusion
  rate of diffusion (**R**)
- Kinetic molecular theory
  Brownian motion
  Maxwell-Boltzmann
  distribution curves

- Primary and secondary pollutants
- Greenhouse effect
- Industrial (London) smog
- Photochemical (Los Angeles)
  smog
- Photochemical oxidants

QUESTIONS

1. The volume of a 0.50 L sample of a gas at room temperature and 1.0 atm pressure is reduced to 0.32 L. What is the new pressure on the gas?

2. The temperature of a 0.50 L sample of a gas initially at 25 °C is raised to 192 °C. What is the new volume of the gas?

3. A given amount of an ideal gas occupies 2.50 L at 740. torr and 300. K. What is the volume of the gas at 755 torr and 200. K?

4. An automobile tire is filled to a pressure of 30. psi on a cool morning when the temperature is 18 °C. After the car has been driven for several hours, the temperature of the air in the tire (as a result of friction with the road) is 55 °C. Assuming no change in the tire's volume, calculate the pressure inside the tire.

5. The pressure inside of an aerosol spray can is about 850. torr at 25 °C. The can will rupture at an internal pressure of 2.0 atm. At what temperature (in °C) will this happen if the can is heated?

6. a. A sample of a gas is held in a 0.204 L bulb at 25 °C and 750. torr. The bulb is immersed in a bath at −78 °C. What is the new pressure inside the bulb? (Assume that the gas does not condense to a liquid.)
   b. While the bulb is held at −78 °C, a valve is opened to allow more gas to flow in until a pressure of 750. torr is reached again. What is the percent increase in the number of moles of gas inside the bulb?
   c. If the valve is not reopened and the bulb is warmed to 25 °C, what is the new pressure inside the bulb?

7. Container A and container B have equal volumes and are held at the same temperature and pressure.
   a. If both A and B contain helium, what are the relative numbers of molecules in the two containers?
   b. If A contains helium and B contains oxygen, what are the relative numbers of molecules in the two containers? What are the relative numbers of atoms?
   c. If A contains helium and B contains a mixture of helium and oxygen, what are the relative numbers of molecules in the two containers? What are the relative numbers of atoms?
   d. If A contains SO_2 and B contains CO, what are the relative numbers of molecules? of atoms? of oxygen atoms?

8. The temperature of 2.3 g of an ideal gas occupying 1.2 L is changed from 250 K to 350 K while the pressure remains constant. What is the final volume of the gas?

9. Assuming ideal behavior, calculate the volume occupied by 12.0 g of CO_2 gas at 245 torr and -35 °C.

10. Calculate the volume occupied by 4.62 g of NH_3 gas at STP.

11. What volume will be occupied by 0.16 mol of H_2 gas at 751 torr and 22 °C?

12. In two different experiments, one at STP and the other at 900. °C and 2.20 atm, 30.0 g of Fe_2O_3 were produced by the reaction:

$$2\ Fe_2S_3(s) + 9\ O_2(g) \longrightarrow 2\ Fe_2O_3(s) + 6\ SO_2(g)$$

   a. How many liters of O_2 at STP were used?

   b. How many liters of O_2 at 900. °C and 2.20 atm were used?

13. The chemical reaction between NO_2 and H_2 gas produces NH_3 and H_2O gas according to the equation:

$$2\ NO_2 + 7\ H_2 \longrightarrow 2\ NH_3 + 4\ H_2O$$

How many liters of NO_2 at STP are needed to produce 0.20 mol NH_3?

14. The tank used on an outdoor gas grill contains 20. lb of propane (C_3H_8) stored under high pressure in the liquid state (liquified propane gas, or LPG). It becomes gaseous as it is released. How many liters of propane gas will be released from this tank at 70. °C and 750 torr pressure?

15. At STP 1.26 mol of O_2 are compressed to 4.36 atm and cooled to 86 K. Calculate the new volume.

16. How many moles of ethane, C_2H_6, are in a volume of 16.9 L at STP?

17. A 0.107 g sample of an unknown gas is placed in an evacuated 0.500 L vessel. When the temperature is 82 °C, the pressure is 0.390 atm. Calculate the molecular weight of the gas.

18. a. A gaseous compound containing C, F, and H gives an elemental analysis of 36.4% C, 57.5% F, and 6.10% H. Calculate the empirical formula of this compound.

   b. A 1.50 g sample of this compound, when introduced into a volume of 675 cm³ at 30. °C, exhibits a pressure of 635 torr. Calculate the molecular weight and molecular formula of the compound.

19. a. A gaseous compound of boron and hydrogen gives the following chemical analysis by weight: 78.2% B and 21.9% H. What is its empirical formula?

   b. A 2.00 g sample of this gas contained in a 1500. mL vessel at 25 °C is found to exert a pressure of 900. torr. Calculate the compound's molecular weight and determine its empirical formula.

20. Freon 114, a gaseous compound, is analyzed to consist of 14.0% C, 41.5% Cl, and 44.5% F. When 0.675 g of this compound is enclosed in a container of

110. mL capacity at 100. °C, the pressure is observed to be 835 torr. What is the molecular formula of the compound?

21. How many grams will the steam (H_2O) filling a 150. L container at 100 °C and 1 atm pressure weigh?

22. How many grams of HIO_3 can be produced from 25.0 L of O_3 gas (at 25 °C and 950 torr) according to the following equation?

$$5\ O_3(g) + I_2(s) + H_2O(l) \longrightarrow 5\ O_2(g) + 2\ HIO_3(s)$$

23. Laughing gas, N_2O, which causes hysteria and reduced consciousness when inhaled, is sometimes administered by dentists as an anesthetic. It is made by the decomposition of ammonium nitrate:

$$NH_4NO_3(s) \longrightarrow 2\ H_2O(l) + N_2O(g)$$

To remain happy in a dentist's chair, a patient needs a lungful (300. cm³ at 1 atm and 25 °C) every 10. seconds. If a patient's dental work takes 20. minutes, how many grams of NH_4NO_3 are used to produce the N_2O?

24. The explosive agent in dynamite is nitroglycerine, $C_3H_5(NO_3)_3$. The chemical reaction that occurs when nitroglycerine explodes results in the formation of a large number of moles of gas:

$$4\ C_3H_5(NO_3)_3(l) \longrightarrow 12\ CO_2(g) + 10\ H_2O(g) + 6\ N_2(g) + O_2(g)$$

Calculate the pressure exerted in the closed volume filled by 100. g of nitroglycerine if it is exploded. The density of nitroglycerine is 1.60 g/cm³. Assume that the temperature of the gas immediately after explosion is 500 °C.

25. Gaseous oxygen can be made from water by the process of electrolysis (decomposition by an electric current):

$$2\ H_2O \longrightarrow 2\ H_2 + O_2$$

How many grams of water must be decomposed in order to produce enough oxygen gas to fill a 20.0 L cylinder at a temperature of 25 °C and a pressure of 15.0 atm?

26. Two gases, krypton and fluorine, are reacted in an electric discharge tube. The product, which is also a gas, is admitted to an evacuated and pre-weighed bulb having a volume of 0.263 L. The pressure of the gas is measured to be 740. torr, and then the bulb is reweighed. The gas is found to weigh 1.245 g. The temperature is 27.0 °C. What is the molecular weight of the gas? What is its probable identity?

27. a. How many grams of Zn are needed to produce 0.150 mol of H_2 gas in the following reaction?

$$Zn + 2\ HCl \longrightarrow H_2(g) + ZnCl_2$$

    b. How many grams of Zn are needed to produce 110 mL of H_2 gas at 735 torr and 26 °C?

28. A 6.0 g sample of Zn is reacted with 0.15 mol HCl according to the equation in Question 28.

    a. What volume of H_2 gas is produced at standard conditions?

    b. What volume of H_2 is collected over water at 748 torr and 25 °C?

29. A 0.10 L sample of oxygen gas is collected over water at 15 °C and 747 torr. What volume would the dry O_2 gas occupy at STP?

30. If 47.9 mL of H_2 gas are collected over water at 25 °C and 718 torr, what volume would the dry H_2 occupy at STP?

31. a. A gas at 25 °C and 745 torr has a volume of 0.607 L. What would be its volume under standard conditions?

    b. If the gas had been collected over water, what would be the volume of the dry gas under standard conditions?

    c. How many moles of gas are present in parts a and b?

32. Nitrogen gas is collected over water at 25 °C in a volume of 1.50 L on a day when atmospheric pressure is 745 torr. Calculate the volume of the dry N_2 gas at STP.

33. Oxygen gas is collected over water after generation from $KClO_3$ according to the equation:

$$2\ KClO_3 \longrightarrow 2\ KCl + 3\ O_2$$

How many grams of $KClO_3$ are needed to produce 0.875 L of dry O_2 at 30. °C on a day when atmospheric pressure is 760. torr?

34. A container holding 0.05 mol of helium at a pressure of 250 torr is held at a constant temperature.

    a. A 0.03 mol sample of nitrogen is added. What is the new total pressure? What are the partial pressures of helium and nitrogen?

    b. Next, 0.04 mol of methane (CH_4) is added. What is the total pressure of the three gases? What is the partial pressure of each?

    c. If the temperature is 23 °C, what must the volume of the container be?

    d. If the temperature of the three gases in b is raised to 100 °C with the volume held constant, what is the new total pressure? What is the partial pressure of each gas?

35. The ^{235}U isotope is the form of uranium used in atomic bombs. During the Second World War ^{235}U was separated from the more abundant isotope ^{238}U by a long series of gaseous diffusion processes using the compound UF_6. Calculate the ratio of the rates of diffusion of $^{235}UF_6$ to $^{238}UF_6$ (the isotopic atomic masses are almost exactly equal to their atomic mass numbers).

36. What are the five postulates of the kinetic molecular theory?

37. Define an ideal gas in terms of the kinetic molecular theory.

38. A 0.50 L sample of a gas is at 25 °C and 1.0 atm. The temperature is raised to 192 °C and the pressure is raised to 1.56 atm. What is the new volume of the gas? Explain the answer in terms of kinetic theory.

39. Raising the temperature of a gas causes the molecules to move faster according to the kinetic theory. Does this mean that all of the molecules of a gas will be moving faster at 30 °C than they did at 25 °C? Explain.

40. Under what conditions do real gases approach ideal behavior? Why is this the case?

41. Consider two 22.4 L boxes, each containing one mole of gas at 125 °C. Box A contains Ne and Box B contains H_2O. The pressure is slightly lower in one of the boxes. Which one has the lower pressure and why?

42. What is the difference between primary and secondary air pollutants? Give examples of each.

43. What is a photochemical reaction? What is photochemical smog?

9

Solids, Liquids, and Changes of State

Guidelines

After completing this chapter the student should be able to:

- list the characteristic properties of the solid state
- classify the different types of solids according to bond type
- list the physical properties of compounds having each bond type
- list the characteristic properties of the liquid state
- contrast the physical properties of solids, liquids, and gases
- discuss the phenomenon of evaporation
- define the state of dynamic equilibrium
- discuss the relationship of surface tension and heat of vaporization to the intermolecular forces in a liquid
- describe what happens to the heat that is added to a substance before, during, and after the phase changes of the substance
- discuss the differences in kinetic and potential energy in the various segments of heating and cooling curves
- discuss the phenomenon of supercooling
- interpret the data presented in a phase diagram for a pure substance
- discuss the structure of ice and the probable structure of liquid water

9.1 **The Solid State**

As we look about, most of the things we see are "solid"—tables, chairs, books, and so on. If we view these things scientifically, however, we see them as more than just rigid objects; they are lumps of matter existing in a state that has definite shape and volume—the solid state. But more specifically, most solids are characterized by an orderly internal structure of atoms, molecules, or ions.

In the last chapter we saw that ideally the gaseous state is a totally disordered state with gas molecules constantly moving in rapid, random motion. In contrast, the solid state is generally an ordered state. The atoms, molecules, or ions that make up a crystalline solid are in motion, but only in vibrational motion about an *ordered array* of positions. It can be seen from Figure 9–1, a two-dimensional picture of the gaseous and solid states, that the two physical states are diagrammatically opposite. Each atom or molecule of the gas is in motion and is randomly oriented to the others, whereas in the crystalline solid the atoms and molecules vibrate about fixed points in a specific geometric array.

The bulk (macroscopic) physical properties of solids support this model of the solid state. We shall examine several of these properties and see how they provide evidence for our model.

A noticeable property of most solids is that they have definite *geometric forms*. They occur as crystalline materials with characteristic faces defining the crystal and characteristic angles between the faces. We can account for these geometric forms in terms of the particular orderly arrangement of atoms, molecules, or ions within the crystal. It is logical that this definite order is reflected in the external habit (the shape

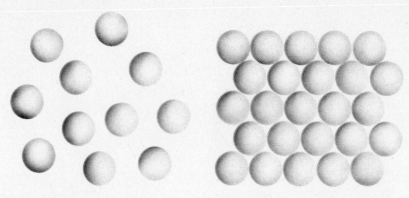

Figure 9–1
Two-dimensional

Gas: Atoms or molecules are
in random motion

Solid: Atoms or molecules are in fixed positions
(they vibrate about fixed points)

or form) of the crystal. A typical packing arrangement in a crystalline solid that contains identical atoms is shown in Figure 9–2a. This type of arrangement will result in the formation of flat planes which then develop into the characteristic faces of the macroscopic crystal. Figure 9–2b presents some typical mineralogical specimens illustrating the varieties of crystalline habit.

Not every solid exhibits a definite external habit because not all solids are **crystalline** (having an ordered internal arrangement). Glasses, for example, are solids that do not have an ordered internal arrangement of atoms or molecules.

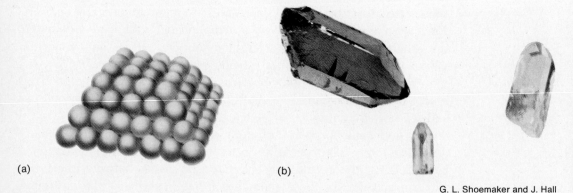

(a)

(b)

G. L. Shoemaker and J. Hall

Figure 9–2
(a) Atoms stacked to show the development of crystal faces (b) Typical mineralogical specimens:
(top left) quartz, SiO_2; (top right) bayerite, $BaSO_4$; (bottom) topaz, $Al_2SiO_4(OH,F)_2$

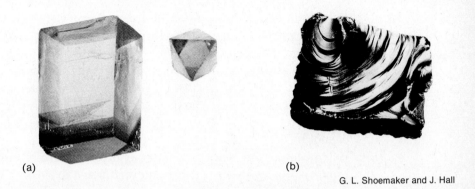

Figure 9–3
(a) Cleavage in crystalline solids: (left) calcite rhomb, $CaCO_3$; (right) fluorite octahedron, CaF_2 (b) Fracture in obsidian, a volcanic glass

A property related to habit is that of **cleavage**. Most crystalline solids, when subjected to external mechanical stress, will *cleave;* that is, they will separate along specific planes to give fragments with extremely flat surfaces (Figure 9–3a). This macroscopic property, which is the stock in trade of gem cutters, is a result of the ordered array of atoms or molecules on planes within the solid. The particular cleavage observed therefore depends on the geometric array and type of bonding within the crystal. Glasses, which lack internal order, do not cleave, but rather break along curved surfaces (Figure 9–3b).

Another property of solids is that they tend to be *rigid,* because the atoms or molecules in a solid occupy *fixed positions,* as we have already discussed. Solids also *maintain their volume,* unlike gases, which expand to fill the available volume. The stronger attractive forces in solids hold the component atoms in fixed positions and give solids their definite volume. Recall from our discussion of gases that it is kinetic energy that causes the randomization of gas molecules, because the intermolecular forces in gases are weak. The strong attractive forces between component molecules in solids, on the other hand, are sufficient to overcome the ever-present thermal randomization. The atoms or molecules in a solid are in motion, but it is only the vibrational motion about fixed points.

Furthermore, since the atoms or molecules occupy fixed positions, solids exhibit *very slow diffusion.* In fact, any appreciable diffusion that does take place in the solid state is the result of defects (mistakes) in the ordered internal arrangement of atoms. These defects sometimes allow atoms or molecules to migrate through the crystalline lattice, leading to some degree of diffusion.

One last property worth mentioning is that under normal laboratory conditions solids are *practically incompressible*. That is, there is little "empty" space between the species making up the solid. Atoms tend to be in contact; there may be holes or channels between them, but these spaces cannot be used for compression. To compress a solid to any great degree, it is necessary to deform electronic orbitals. Strong electron-electron repulsive forces make this extremely difficult to do.

Fortunately, there is a very powerful tool for analyzing the structure of solids, the technique of **x-ray diffraction**. Since the atoms in a solid are in ordered arrays, planes of atoms can be found within the solid which will *diffract* x-ray radiation. The process of diffraction is quite complex, involving the interaction between electrons in atoms and x-rays. It can best be understood by comparing it to the diffraction of optical radiation by a grating (a series of closely spaced parallel lines etched on a piece of glass). The lines in a grating diffract light (break it into its component colors) because the distance between them is on the same order of magnitude as the wavelength of visible light. Similarly, the distance between planes of atoms in a solid has approximately the same magnitude as the wavelength of x-rays (1 Å). The important point is that by careful mathematical analysis of the diffraction pattern obtained by the interaction of x-rays with crystalline solids, the internal structure of solids can be accurately determined. It is due to the widespread use of this powerful tool that the structures of solid state materials are so well understood.

9.2 Types of Solids

We are now in a position to classify the different types of solids according to the type of bonding that occurs and the physical properties that they exhibit. The four broad classifications of solids are ionic, molecular, covalent network, and metallic. We shall briefly examine each of these four general types.

I. Ionic Solids The basic units in ionic solids (page 156) are positively and negatively charged ions which bond together in the solid state through strong electrostatic interactions (ionic bonds). Typically, ionic solids are hard, have high melting and boiling points, and are electrical and thermal **insulators** (they do *not* typically conduct electricity or heat). Ionic compounds are found to form between metallic elements on the left-hand side of the periodic table (those that tend to form cations) and nonmetallic elements on the right-hand side (which tend to form anions). In ionic solids, which include compounds such as NaCl, MgF_2, and $CaCO_3$, the cations and anions are arranged in a fixed geometric array characteristic of the particular compound.

II. Molecular Solids   Molecular solids (which were first introduced on pages 175–79) are composed of molecules that may be either polar or nonpolar. Usually the bonding within these discrete molecular units is predominantly covalent. The intermolecular forces—those holding the separate molecules together in the solid state—are weaker than either covalent bonds or the forces between ions in ionic solids. In polar molecular solids, the intermolecular forces are dipole-dipole in nature (or, if possible, they can include hydrogen bonding). In nonpolar molecular solids, the intermolecular forces are London dispersion forces (page 178). As a result of the weak intermolecular forces, molecular solids tend to be soft, to have moderate or low melting and boiling points, and to be electrical and thermal insulators. Since molecular solids are usually covalent molecular compounds, this class of solids is generally found for compounds between nonmetals (elements on the right-hand side of the periodic table). Examples of molecular solids are CCl_4, SF_6, and O_2.

III. Covalent Network Solids   Certain elements which form strong covalent bonds exist in the solid state as infinite three-dimensional networks of atoms held together by these strong covalent bonds. Figure 9–4 illustrates the structure of diamond, in which each C atom shares a pair of electrons with each of four other C atoms to form an infinite tetrahedral array of covalently bonded atoms. Since the bonds between all of the atoms are strong, covalent network solids are usually hard materials with high melting and boiling points, and they are generally insulators or semiconductors (intermediate conductors of electricity). These solids form from nonmetallic elements in the center of the periodic table; examples are Ge, AlP, and SiC.

IV. Metallic Solids   The solids in this group exhibit various degrees of hardness and have a wide range of melting and boiling points. For ex-

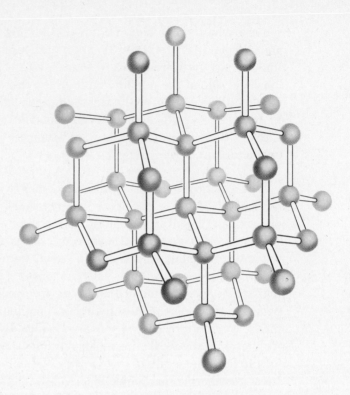

Figure 9–4
The structure of
diamond

ample, mercury is a liquid at room temperature, but iron melts at 1536 °C; sodium can be cut with a knife, whereas titanium is extremely hard. The building blocks of metals are, of course, metal atoms (elements to the left of the Zintl border in the periodic table). The type of bonding found between these atoms is one that we have not yet considered. In a simple theory of metallic bonding known as the **electron-sea model**, the metal atoms are organized in a regular three-dimensional array characteristic of a crystalline solid. However, each atom contributes one or more electrons (depending on the element) to the solid as a whole. Therefore, metals are viewed as positive metallic ions embedded in a "sea" of negative electrons which are free to move. Metallic bonding is relatively strong; even mercury, a liquid metal, has strong interatomic forces, as we shall see in the next section. It is the presence of free electrons that gives metals their characteristic high electrical and thermal conductivity as well as their high metallic luster.

Table 9–1 summarizes these four classifications of solids with reference to their type of bonding and their physical properties.

Table 9–1

Types of Solids

TYPE	BASIC UNITS	BONDING BETWEEN UNITS	PROPERTIES	EXAMPLES
Ionic	positive and negative ions	ionic (electrostatic) bonding	high melting point and boiling point electrical and thermal insulators hard	NaCl MgF_2 $CaCO_3$
Molecular	covalently bonded discrete molecules	dipole-dipole; London forces	moderate to low melting point and boiling point electrical and thermal insulators soft	CCl_4 SF_6 O_2
Covalent network	atoms	covalent (shared pair) bonding	high melting point and boiling point semiconductors or insulators hard	C (diamond) Ge AlP SiC
Metallic	atoms	metallic bonding	variable melting point and boiling point electrical and thermal conductors variable hardness	Hg Fe Na Ti

9.3   The Liquid State

The liquid state of matter is intermediate between the gaseous and solid states. In some properties, liquids are more like solids, but in others they are more like gases. We will examine the characteristic properties of liquids and see what kind of a model can be proposed to account for these properties.

Almost everyone has seen pictures of astronauts in a spacecraft handling suspended droplets of liquid. These large droplets will form in the absence of gravity and can actually be pushed around. This property is due to the fact that liquids, unlike gases, exhibit a **surface tension**; attractive molecular forces are trying to pull the molecules from the surface

Berthollides versus Daltonides

In our discussions of bonding and the solid state we have been making the tacit assumption that compounds are stoichiometric—that they have exactly the mole ratio of their component elements indicated by their formulas. This was first confirmed by Dalton in 1808, and indeed, most of the evidence obtained by x-ray crystallographic investigations seemed to confirm this for solids.

However, a contemporary of Dalton, the French chemist Claude Berthollet, pointed out that *alloys* (solids formed between two or more metals) typically have *variable composition*. As a result, he took the opposite stance to that of Dalton. In support of the Law of Definite Proportions, J. L. Proust, another contemporary, correctly identified most alloys as being solid solutions (solutions of one solid in another) and not compounds. We know now that Berthollet did in fact have a valid point: *some* solid inorganic substances (compounds) can exist with variable composition. Known as nonstoichiometric compounds, these substances do not have definite molar ratios of the component elements, but usually vary over small ranges. Nonstoichiometric compounds are sometimes called berthollides, and stoichiometric ones are then called daltonides. Covalently-bonded molecular compounds are always considered as stoichiometric compounds, while nonstoichiometry is most prevalent in three-dimensional ionic solids.

The most common cause of nonstoichiometry is the presence of vacancies (missing atoms) in the crystalline structure of the compound. For example, iron(II) oxide, FeO, has never been prepared with an exact 1:1 ratio of Fe:O; it is always deficient in Fe. We can show this deficiency by writing $Fe_{1-x}O$, where x, a number between 0 and 0.15, represents the fraction of iron atoms missing from the solid. It turns out that electroneutrality is maintained by a fraction of the iron atoms existing in the 3+ oxidation state: $Fe_{1-3x}^{2+}Fe_{2x}^{3+}O$ for the nominal composition $Fe_{1-x}O$.

Nonstoichiometry plays an important role in determining the electrical and magnetic properties of materials. The semiconductor, microelectronic, and other high-technology industries are based on exotic materials that rely on nonstoichiometry for their unusual properties.

---

of the liquid into its bulk. Figure 9–5 shows the difference in attractive forces surrounding a molecule in the bulk of the liquid and on the surface. Inside the liquid, attractive forces from the surrounding molecules are felt in all directions: up, down, right, left, in, and out. On the surface, there are no molecules in the "up" direction and so there are no attractive forces felt from this direction. The absence of a pull away from the liquid to counteract the pull toward the bulk of the liquid leads to a tendency for

Figure 9–5
Attractive forces
on a molecule in
the bulk of a liquid
and on the surface

the surface to contract so that as few molecules as possible have uncompensated forces. Since a sphere offers the smallest amount of surface area for a given amount of material, the surface will contract so that the droplet becomes a sphere. Beading of water on a smooth surface is a consequence of this, as is the clumping of liquids in the spacecraft. Those of us who have had the experience of trying to recover liquid mercury from a broken thermometer know this phenomenon. Mercury, with its relatively high surface tension, forms almost spherical droplets which rapidly roll over surfaces.

The surface tension of a liquid is therefore a measure of the internal attractive forces in the liquid; it is expressed in dynes/cm, where a dyne is a unit of force. Typical values for liquids are:

He	0.2 dynes/cm	(very weak internal forces)
O_2	16	(weak interaction between diatomic molecules)
CCl_4	27	(a typical nonpolar molecular liquid)
H_2O	73	(a hydrogen-bonded liquid)
Hg	470	(a liquid metal)

The trend is obvious: as the internal intermolecular forces become stronger, the surface tension of the liquid increases.

A second property of liquids is that they are *relatively incompressible*, which indicates that there is very little free volume in the liquid state. In this property liquids are more like solids than gases.

Although liquids maintain relatively definite volumes, they have *no characteristic shape*. Liquids are not rigid like solids; the molecules in a liquid are free to move over one another. Therefore a liquid conforms to the shape of the bottom of a container under the influence of gravity. Removing the force of gravity (as in the spaceship) allows clumping or beading to occur in order to satisfy the intermolecular attractive forces in the liquid.

An additional property found in liquids is that *diffusion occurs at a rather slow rate,* intermediate between the rapid rate in gases and the extremely slow rate in solids. This indicates that the average distance traveled by a molecule between collisions is small; actually, it is on the order of 3 Å in a liquid at room temperature as compared to about 100 Å in a gas. This smaller distance is a result of the denser packing in a liquid. The fact that diffusion occurs very slowly in solids is, of course, due to the fixed positions of the atoms or molecules. Because liquid molecules are free to move, diffusion is more rapid in liquids.

All of these properties lead to a model for a liquid that includes strong attractive forces between molecules, causing a microscopic clustering and a definite volume. However, the attractive forces are not strong enough to hold the molecules in fixed positions (as is found in solids), so the molecules are free to slide over one another. They tend to go to positions of lowest potential energy under the influence of gravity, that is, to the bottom of the container. This relative movement results in a **short-range order** in liquids. The attractive forces are not strong enough to give the **long-range order** characteristic of the solid state, but they are strong enough to overcome the kinetic energy which makes the gaseous state completely random. Figure 9–6 is a two-dimensional illustration of a liquid (compare with Figure 9–1, a gas and a solid).

All of this makes the liquid state the most difficult to understand. Since the intermolecular attractive forces are much larger than in the gaseous state, they cannot be neglected as we did in the case of an ideal gas. In addition, due to the lack of long-range order, techniques such as x-ray diffraction give very limited information about the structure of liquids.

9.4   Evaporation

Liquids exhibit one additional property: they will *evaporate from an open container.* This means that some of the molecules on the surface of the liquid (that is, at the gas-liquid interface) can escape into the gas phase.

Figure 9–6
A two-dimensional
view of a liquid

Atoms or molecules are in motion, but the motion is not completely random.

This phenomenon can be best understood in terms of a distribution of the kinetic energies of the molecules in the liquid. Recall that in our discussion of the kinetic molecular theory we examined the particular distribution of the kinetic energies of molecules in the gas phase (page 223). Since the molecules in a liquid exhibit kinetic motion to some extent, the same statistics apply to molecules in the liquid state. Figure 9–7 illustrates a typical Maxwell-Boltzmann distribution of kinetic energies in a liquid at a particular temperature. Note that a certain number of molecules possess a kinetic energy greater than that needed for a molecule to escape from the surface of the liquid. These escaping molecules must do work against the attractive forces holding the molecules together in the liquid phase because the intermolecular attractive forces are much less in the gas phase.

The molecules with a kinetic energy greater than that necessary to escape are called "hot" molecules. When these molecules escape into the vapor phase, the average kinetic energy of the molecules remaining in the liquid drops and therefore the temperature of the liquid drops. Heat from the surroundings will then enter the liquid. It is this principle that makes it possible to cool fever-stricken patients by an alcohol rub, since heat from the body flows into the liquid to compensate for the heat lost by the rapid evaporation. Normal perspiration cools the body in the same manner.

If a liquid is in an open container that is insulated from its surroundings (such as a thermos bottle), very little heat can flow into the container to replace the energy lost from evaporation. Therefore the heat lost through evaporation of the hot molecules is not easily replaced, causing the process of evaporation to slow and the temperature to drop more slowly.

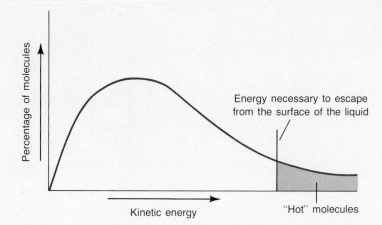

Figure 9–7
The distribution of
kinetic energies in
a liquid

9.5 **Dynamic Equilibrium**

In an open, uninsulated container, evaporation will continue until all of
the liquid has been transformed into the gaseous phase. But what will
happen in a *closed system* where the gas molecules cannot escape into the
atmosphere? Figure 9–8 shows a closed system consisting of a beaker of
water enclosed in a bell jar. Initially the liquid level in the beaker will
drop as water evaporates, but after a while it will remain constant. Why
does this happen? The molecules that escape from the surface of the liquid
are confined to the space above the liquid by the bell jar. As the concentration of H_2O in the gas increases (as P_{H_2O} increases) the probability
of condensation increases. Eventually the state is reached where the rate
of condensation equals the rate of evaporation and an equilibrium is
reached:

$$H_2O(l) \rightleftharpoons H_2O(g)$$

The number of molecules leaving the liquid is exactly compensated by
the number of molecules condensing from the vapor. Therefore the liquid
level remains unchanged.

    This state is known as a **dynamic equilibrium**—a continual evapora-
tion and condensation taking place at the same rate at a particular
constant temperature. There is no net change in liquid level or in partial
pressure of the vapor. The pressure of a vapor in equilibrium with its
liquid is called the **equilibrium vapor pressure**; it depends on the nature

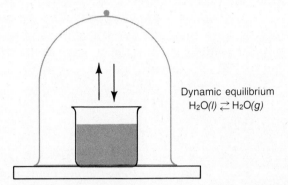

Figure 9–8
A beaker of water
in a closed system

Dynamic equilibrium
$H_2O(l) \rightleftarrows H_2O(g)$

of the liquid but also rather dramatically on temperature. For example, the equilibrium vapor pressures for water at various temperatures are:

T (°C)	0	20	40	60	80	100	120
P (torr)	5	18	55	149	355	760	1,490

These values are plotted in Figure 9–9.

Figure 9–9
A plot of the
equilibrium vapor
pressure of water
versus temperature

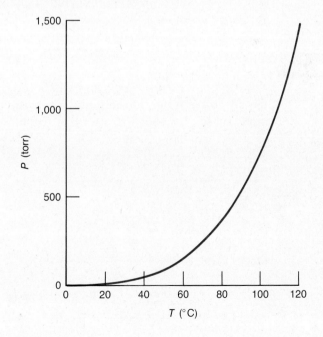

The **boiling point** of a liquid is the temperature at which the vapor pressure equals the prevailing atmospheric pressure. Therefore the boiling point depends on the pressure on the liquid. For example, at a pressure of 760 torr water boils at 100 °C; at 355 torr it boils at 80 °C. If the pressure over a sample of water were reduced until it was equal to 18 torr, the water would boil at 20 °C, slightly below room temperature. Because of this variation of boiling point with pressure, it is necessary to define the **normal boiling point**: it is the temperature at which the vapor pressure of the liquid equals 760 torr (one standard atmosphere). For water, then, the normal boiling point is 100 °C.

What is so special about the boiling point? We have just seen that a liquid can evaporate at temperatures below the boiling point, but this occurs only at the surface. At the boiling point, however, the vapor pressure of the liquid is equal to the prevailing atmospheric pressure. Therefore, the gas formed can "push back" the atmosphere and *bubble* formation will occur below the surface of the liquid. There is then a rapid conversion of liquid to gas not only at the surface of the liquid but also within the liquid; this phenomenon is called boiling.

The amount of heat needed to convert one mole of a liquid into one mole of a gas is called the **heat of vaporization** (ΔH_v). It is equal to the heat content (enthalpy, page 61) of one mole of gas minus the heat content of one mole of liquid:

$$\Delta H_v = H(g) - H(l)$$

The symbol ΔH_v represents an endothermic process and is a measure of the attractive forces in the liquid, since the greater these forces are, the more energy is needed to vaporize the liquid. Typical values are:

	ΔH_v (kcal/mol)
He	0.02
Ne	0.43
Ar	1.59
O_2	1.63
H_2O	10.85
Hg	14.13

The magnitude of ΔH_v parallels the strength of the intermolecular attractive forces. In the series He, Ne, and Ar, these forces are London dispersion forces (page 178), which increase with increasing atomic mass. Because London forces are stronger in a linear molecule than in a spherical atom, ΔH_v is higher for O_2 than for Ar even though O_2 has a lower mass. The strong dipole-dipole and hydrogen bonding interactions in H_2O cause it to have a higher ΔH_v and the strong metallic bonding in mercury gives it an even higher value for ΔH_v.

9.6 Changes of State

In Chapter 1 it was stated that an element or a compound can exist in any of the three states: solid, liquid, or gas. A **phase transition** was also defined as the physical change occurring when a material transforms from one state (phase) into another. We shall now consider this phenomenon in more detail.

Figure 9–10 shows a vessel fitted with a movable piston and completely filled with water. The apparatus is equipped with a means of measuring temperature and a window to observe what is happening to the contents of the vessel. The piston is maintained in such a way that one atmosphere of pressure is constantly applied to the contents.

The procedure in this experiment is as follows. Starting at a very low temperature, heat is added at a constant rate and the temperature and any changes of state are recorded as a function of time. The resultant plot of temperature (T) versus time (t) is known as a **heating curve**. The heating curve shown in Figure 9–11 indicates the changes of state of the material in the container.

Figure 9–10
An experimental apparatus for determining a heating curve

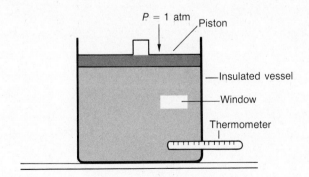

What happens to the heat (energy) that is added to the system along each segment of the heating curve? Because heat is added at a constant rate, we can say that it is being added linearly with time (Figure 9–12). Between phase transitions, this energy is absorbed by the system as kinetic energy (associated with the thermal motion of the molecules); during a phase transition, it is absorbed as potential energy (related to the position of the molecules with respect to other molecules).

Along the line segments labeled s, l, and g, in Figure 9–11, the respective phases (solid, liquid, and gas) are simply warming up. Adding heat increases the temperature, which increases the kinetic energy of the phase. Thus the added heat goes into increasing the molecular motion, which becomes more and more violent until the molecules have enough kinetic energy to change phase, that is, to melt or to evaporate. The slopes of these three line segments are not necessarily the same. They depend on the **heat capacity** of the particular phase, which is defined as the amount of heat necessary to raise the temperature of 1 g of material by 1 °C. The heat capacities for solid, liquid, and gaseous water have different values, leading to different slopes for these three lines.

Along the horizontal lines labeled $s \rightarrow l$ and $l \rightarrow g$, the temperature and therefore the average kinetic energy of the material remains constant. All of the added heat goes into the energy required to carry out the phase change, because the molecules must do work against attractive forces in going into the less ordered phase. This means that the added heat is being converted into potential energy. As a result, the potential energy of a gas is greater than that of a liquid which, in turn, is greater than the potential energy of a solid. In the previous section the energy necessary to transform one mole of liquid to one mole of gas was defined as the heat of vaporization (ΔH_v). Similarly, the heat of fusion (ΔH_f), or the energy

Figure 9–11
A heating curve

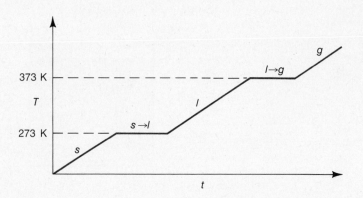

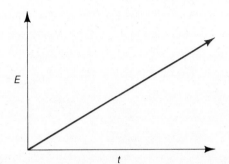

Figure 9–12
Addition of heat
(energy) linearly
with time

associated with melting, is the amount of heat required for the transition from the solid to the liquid state. Both of these enthalpy changes are endothermic (heat is absorbed).

Since the temperature remains constant during a phase transition, both phases involved in the transition have the same temperature. Similarly, since the average kinetic energy (which depends only on temperature) does not change, it is also identical for the two states of matter. For example, both liquid and gaseous water at 100 °C (the boiling point) have the same average kinetic energy. The difference between them is in potential energy; gaseous water, the less ordered phase, has a higher potential energy. Furthermore, the heating curve tells us that we cannot raise the temperature by adding heat faster at the temperature of a phase transition. What will happen is that the *rate* of the phase change will increase. The temperature will always remain constant as long as two phases are present.

It is evident from the heating curve in Figure 9–11 that no vapor phase is observed in our experiment until the normal boiling point is reached. Until that temperature is reached, the vapor pressure is not large enough to overcome the constant one-atmosphere pressure exerted by the piston on the apparatus (Figure 9–10).

A **cooling curve** (Figure 9–13) is just the reverse of a heating curve. Heat is removed at a constant rate and the temperature inside the vessel is recorded and plotted as a function of time. Along the line segments $g \rightarrow l$ and $l \rightarrow s$, the potential energy decreases as the material changes state and the energy released as heat exactly compensates for the heat removed. The enthalpy changes are now exothermic (heat is released) since condensation $(g \rightarrow l)$ is the reverse of vaporization and solidification or crystallization $(l \rightarrow s)$ is the reverse of fusion. Therefore the heat of condensation is numerically equal but opposite in sign to ΔH_v, and the heat of solidification is equal to $-\Delta H_f$.

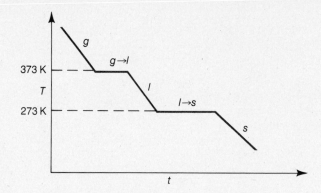

Figure 9–13
A cooling curve

9.7 Phase Diagrams

If we were to repeat the construction of heating or cooling curves at different pressures for a particular substance, we would get a set of curves that would tell us the dependence of temperature on pressure for each of the phase transitions. All of this information can be summarized in a single diagram called a **phase diagram**. Figure 9–14, a plot of the pressure versus the temperature for water, schematically shows the phase diagram for H_2O. We can locate every value of pressure and temperature on the phase diagram. Depending on where that location is in the diagram, we know if we have one, two, or three phases in equilibrium.

Figure 9–14
A schematic phase
diagram for water

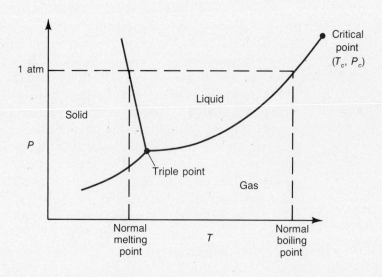

Supercooling and the Glassy State

Supercooling is the phenomenon that occurs when a substance remains liquid at temperatures below the point where it should have become a solid.

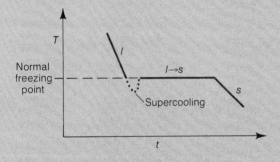

Figure 9–15
The phenomenon of supercooling as illustrated on a portion of a cooling curve

Figure 9–15 is an expanded portion of a cooling curve that shows the region between the liquid and solid phases. The dotted line represents the region of supercooling. When the liquid has cooled to the freezing point, the motion (the kinetic energy) in the liquid is slow enough to form a crystalline solid, but the molecules are still in a disordered arrangement. Before the liquid to solid transition can take place, there must be a cluster of molecules that has the geometric (ordered) arrangement characteristic of the crystal-line phase. The presence of this ordered cluster will happen only by chance and therefore takes time. Because in cooling, heat is still being removed, the temperature may drop below the freezing point before this cluster forms. When the right arrangement does occur, the crystalline solid forms and the heat of crystallization is released, warming the liquid back to the freezing point.

Some substances, usually those with complex crystal structures, seldom if ever hit on the correct geometric arrangement as the liquid is cooled. As the temperature drops further below the freezing point, the motion within the liquid becomes so sluggish that the molecules become locked into a disordered arrangement and the liquid is permanently supercooled. This resulting noncrystalline solid is called a *glass* or an *amorphous solid*.

Silicon dioxide, which forms in several crystalline phases with rather complex structures, melts at 1713 °C to form a very viscous liquid. With proper heat treatment it can be cooled to room temperature as a glassy material called *vitreous silica*. Ordinary glass, which melts at ~650 °C, is a mixture of SiO_2, CaO, and Na_2O. The temperature at which a glass melts can be controlled by varying the amounts of the component oxides.

We can compare a phase diagram to a map, a plot of latitude versus longitude. Figure 9–16 is a schematic map of the New York-Massachu-setts-Connecticut area. At one value of latitude and longitude (pressure and temperature) you are in Massachusetts (one state); at another you

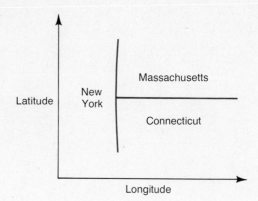

Figure 9–16
A schematic map
analogous to a
phase diagram

may be in Connecticut. At a particular set of values you may be on the border, and at still another you may be exactly between all three states.

In the phase diagram, an *area* represents a *single phase* region: the solid, liquid, or gas region. A *line* in the diagram represents an equilibrium between two phases: solid and liquid, liquid and gas, or solid and gas. The **triple point** is the point at which there is equilibrium between all three phases. For water this occurs at 4.58 torr (0.006 atm) and 273.16 K (0.01 °C).

Note that the solid and gas phases are adjoining regions at low temperatures and pressures. A solid will *sublime* (pass directly into the gas phase) at any temperature less than the temperature of the triple point when the vapor pressure is reduced below the corresponding equilibrium vapor pressure. This is the reason that snow (or ice) will sometimes disappear on a very cold day ($T < 0$ °C) without melting. If the vapor pressure drops below 4.56 torr (the vapor pressure at 0 °C), then the solid will sublime.

The important reference point on the phase diagram is one standard atmosphere (760 torr). The solid-liquid equilibrium at 760 torr is at the normal melting point (273 K), and the liquid-gas equilibrium at 760 torr is at the normal boiling point (373 K).

The liquid-gas equilibrium curve does not continue indefinitely; it stops at the **critical temperature** (T_c), which turns out to be 647 K for water. Above the critical temperature, the thermal motion is so violent that a gas cannot be liquefied, regardless of how high the pressure is raised. The **critical pressure** (P_c) is the pressure that will liquefy the gas at exactly T_c. The critical pressure for water is 218 atm (1.66×10^5 torr).

The Uniqueness of Water

The phase diagram for H_2O differs from those of most other substances, because the solid state of H_2O is less dense than the liquid state. It is this property that causes ice cubes to float in a glass of water. The lower density of ice is due to the significant amount of strong hydrogen bonding between molecules and the consequent structure of H_2O in the solid state. Each oxygen atom in ice is tetrahedrally surrounded by four hydrogen atoms (Figure 9–17): two covalently-bonded H atoms at ~ 1.0 Å (forming the H_2O molecule) and two hydrogen-bonded H atoms (from two other H_2O molecules) at ~ 1.8 Å. The crystal structure of normal ice (Figure 9–18) reflects this tetrahedral arrangement. It is a three-dimensional network held together by pairs of hydrogen bonds. As the figure indicates, it is a very open structure with "holes" or empty channels running through it. When ice melts, this open structure at least partially collapses to give a denser phase (normally liquids are less dense than solids near the melting point). Because the volume change on melting is not as great as one would expect if the open structure entirely disappeared, it appears as though the open structure of ice does not entirely collapse on melting. Thus there may be regions within the liquid that maintain a structure characteristic of the solid state. A current theory pictures liquid water as being composed of clusters of ice-like (solid-like) regions dispersed between relatively few "free" water molecules, molecules which behave as a normal liquid.

As a result of the fact that liquid water is denser than ice, increasing

Figure 9–17
The tetrahedral arrangement of hydrogen atoms in ice

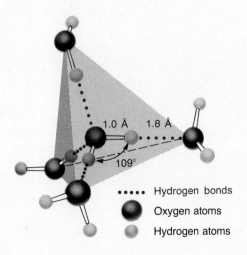

1.0 Å   1.8 Å

109°

•••• Hydrogen bonds

● Oxygen atoms

● Hydrogen atoms

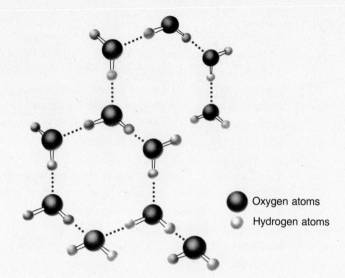

Figure 9–18
The crystal
structure of ice

Oxygen atoms

Hydrogen atoms

the pressure decreases the melting point, because increased pressure favors the denser phase. This gives the negative slope (sloping to the left) to the solid-liquid equilibrium curve for H_2O. For most materials the solid is denser than the liquid and the slope of this curve is positive (sloping to the right). Figure 9–19, the phase diagram of benzene, illustrates the more common case of the solid being denser than the liquid.

This peculiar property of water may be an important factor in the evolution of life on this planet. Since ice floats, lakes freeze from the top downward, not from the bottom up. As ice forms on the top of the lake it

Figure 9–19
A schematic phase
diagram for benzene

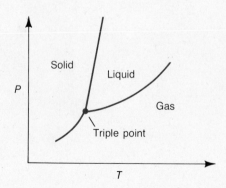

Solid

Liquid

P

Gas

Triple point

T

insulates the bulk of the water from the cold and prevents the lake from freezing solid. Thus the fish and other water-dwelling creatures are able to survive.

It is also this property of water that makes it possible to skate on ice. The increased pressure due to the weight of the skater melts the ice under the skate and consequently provides lubrication for the skate to slide.

TERMS AND CONCEPTS

- Crystalline habit
- Cleavage
- X-ray diffraction
- Ionic, molecular, covalent network, and metallic solids
- Insulator
- Electron-sea model of a metal
- Solid solutions
- Nonstoichiometric compounds
- Berthollide
- Daltonide
- Vacancies
- Surface tension
- Short-range versus long-range order

- Evaporation
- Dynamic equilibrium
- Equilibrium vapor pressure
- Boiling point
- Normal boiling point
- Heat of vaporization (ΔH_v)
- Phase transition
- Heating and cooling curves
- Heat capacity
- Heat of fusion (ΔH_f)
- Supercooling
- Phase diagram
- Triple point
- Critical temperature and pressure

QUESTIONS

1. List the characteristic properties of the solid state.
2. List and give examples of the four types of solids. Briefly describe the type of bonding in each.
3. Classify the following solids as to bond type:
   a. Fe
   b. I_2
   c. CO_2
   d. CaF_2
   e. Na_2O
   f. $SOCl_2$
   g. $CaSO_4$
   h. C (diamond)
   i. GaP
4. Explain why the melting point of Na_2S (1180 °C) is so much higher than that of H_2S (−85.5 °C).
5. List the characteristic properties of the liquid state.
6. Why do liquid droplets tend to assume a spherical shape?
7. Compare and contrast the gaseous, liquid, and solid states with respect to the following properties:
   a. compressibility
   b. rate of diffusion
   c. degree of order
   d. characteristic shape

Table 9Q–1

Vapor Pressures (in atmospheres)

$T(°C)$	Kr	I_2	Hg	Fe
−223	1.4×10^{-7}			
−203	3.5×10^{-4}			
−183	2.6×10^{-2}			
−173	0.12			
−157	0.72			
−153	1.00			
−33		8.7×10^{-7}		
+27		4.7×10^{-4}		
107		8.6×10^{-2}		
127		0.19	1.4×10^{-3}	
147		0.36		
167		0.63		
185		1.00		
227			5.2×10^{-2}	
277			0.19	
327			0.57	
357			1.00	
377			1.42	
827				1.3×10^{-12}
1227				1.5×10^{-7}
1627				1.1×10^{-4}
2327				6.1×10^{-2}
2527				0.20
2727				0.55
2862				1.00
2927				1.31

8. Describe the phenomenon of evaporation of a liquid from an open container.
9. Define and give an example of a dynamic physical equilibrium.
10. What is special about the boiling point of a liquid?
11. Why is it necessary to define a *normal* boiling point?
12. Predict the trend in heats of vaporization for the following series of liquids:
    a. Ne, Ar, Kr
    b. H_2O, H_2S, H_2Se
    c. CH_4, NH_3, H_2O
13. Explain the relationship between the internal forces of a liquid on the one hand and the surface tension, boiling point, and heat of vaporization on the other.

14. Table 9Q–1 lists the vapor pressures of four elements at various temperatures.
    a. What is the normal boiling point for each element?
    b. On a very stormy day atmospheric pressure may drop to 670 torr. What would be the boiling points of these elements on such a day? (For an accurate estimate, temperature versus vapor pressure should be plotted.)
15. Draw a heating curve for water over the temperature range 200–500 K. Label each section of the curve as to the phase or phases present.
16. Explain what happens on a molecular level when changes of state occur as a substance is heated from a very low temperature.
17. A pressure cooker (a closed steel vessel) containing water is heated. At a temperature of 115 °C the pressure inside becomes great enough to open a regulating valve, allowing the water to boil. What is the pressure? If the valve fails to open, what will happen if heating is continued?
18. List the properties of a glass and tell which ones are more characteristic of a solid and which are more characteristic of a liquid.
19. Draw the phase diagram for water. Label each area on the diagram and indicate the normal melting and boiling points.
20. a. Compare the average potential energies of molecules of the same substance in the solid, gaseous, and liquid states at the same temperature (the triple point).
    b. Compare the average kinetic energies of molecules in the solid, liquid, and gaseous states at the same temperature.
21. The solid phase of most substances is denser than the liquid phase, and therefore the solid sinks to the bottom of the liquid when both phases are present. However, ice floats on water. Why?
22. Describe a path on the phase diagram for water by which it can go from the gaseous state to the liquid state without going through a phase change. Describe what happens on a molecular level as this path is traversed.

10 Solutions

Guidelines

After completing this chapter the student should be able to:

- discuss the nature of colloidal suspensions
- discuss the solvent properties of water
- describe the factors involved in the dissolving process
- discuss the factors involved in the solubility of inorganic compounds
- explain Henry's Law
- write net ionic equations for reactions taking place in solution
- express solution concentrations in molarity, molality, and percentage by weight and volume
- perform dilution calculations using molarity
- describe the concept of biological oxygen demand
- perform solution stoichiometry (titration) calculations
- describe colligative properties: vapor pressure lowering, boiling point elevation, freezing point depression, and osmotic pressure
- calculate ΔT_{bp} and ΔT_{fp} for electrolyte and nonelectrolyte solutions
- use ΔT_{bp} and ΔT_{fp} to determine the molecular weight of a nonelectrolyte
- discuss the problem of water pollution and purification

10.1 Introduction

Thus far we have been examining the behavior of atoms, how they bond together to form molecules, and how both atoms and molecules can then exist in the gas, liquid, or solid states. In each case, we have been considering pure substances; now we will consider mixtures.

In Chapter 1 we defined two types of mixtures: homogeneous and heterogeneous. Recall that a homogeneous mixture (a **solution**) consists of only one phase, whereas a heterogeneous mixture is a mixture of two or more different distinct phases. Since one of the phases in a heterogeneous mixture may consist of particles so fine that they are invisible, the apparent heterogeneity or homogeneity of a mixture can depend on the sensitivity with which the observer can detect small particles. Therefore, an arbitrary division is made. In a solution the particles of the lesser phase (the solute) are less than or equal to 1×10^{-7} cm in diameter; in a heterogeneous mixture, the particles of the lesser phase are at least 1×10^{-4} cm in diameter. If the particles are of an intermediate size (between 10^{-7} and 10^{-4} cm in diameter), the mixture is called a **colloidal suspension**, or a **colloid**. These distinctions are summarized in Table 10–1.

Table 10–1

Particle Size Distribution in Mixtures

TYPE OF MIXTURE	PARTICLE SIZE lesser or solute phase
Homogeneous solution	less than or equal to 10^{-7} cm (10 Å)
Colloidal suspension	between 10^{-7} and 10^{-4} cm (10–10,000 Å)
Heterogeneous mixture	greater than or equal to 10^{-4} cm (10,000 Å)

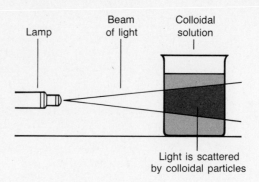

Beam of light

Colloidal solution

Lamp

Light is scattered by colloidal particles

Figure 10–1
A simple experiment that illustrates the Tyndall Effect

Each individual particle in a colloidal suspension may be either a single large molecule (a **macromolecule**) or a collection of atoms or molecules. For example, hemoglobin, the oxygen-carrying component of human blood, is a macromolecule with a molecular weight of about 66,000 amu. The diameter of the hemoglobin molecule is approximately 30 Å, which falls within the size range of the lesser phase of a colloid. Therefore, blood is a colloidal suspension.

If we add a dilute HCl solution to a solution containing sodium thiosulfate ($Na_2S_2O_3$), the thiosulfate anions ($S_2O_3^{2-}$) will decompose into sulfite ions (SO_3^{2-}) and elemental sulfur. On standing, the molecules of sulfur will coalesce to form larger particles. If we then shine a beam of light through this solution (Figure 10–1), the light will be scattered and become visible when the colloidal particles in the solution reach a size comparable to its wavelength (4,000–7,500 Å). This scattering of light, called the **Tyndall effect**, is characteristic of such colloidal suspensions. An automobile headlight beam is visible on a foggy night because the particles of fog (minute droplets of water) form a colloidal suspension which scatters the beam of light.

Solutions

The formation of a solution provides another illustration of the phenomenon of dynamic equilibrium (Section 9.5). As an example let us consider the formation of a solution of sugar ($C_6H_{12}O_6$) in water. As the molecules of solute sugar dissolve, the concentration of solute builds up in the solution:

$$C_6H_{12}O_6(s) \xrightarrow{H_2O} C_6H_{12}O_6(aq)$$

The increasing concentration of solute increases the probability that sugar molecules will precipitate from the solution (recrystallize):

$$C_6H_{12}O_6(aq) \longrightarrow C_6H_{12}O_6(s)$$

When the probability of recrystallization becomes equal to the probability of dissolution, a state of dynamic equilibrium has been reached:

$$C_6H_{12}O_6(s) \rightleftharpoons C_6H_{12}O_6(aq)$$

A solution in which the dissolved solute is in equilibrium with the undissolved solute is known as a **saturated solution**. Because it is in a state of equilibrium, a saturated solution is stable at a particular temperature and contains as much dissolved solute as it can under stable conditions. An **unsaturated solution**, then, contains less than the amount of solute found in the saturated solution at the same temperature; in other words, it can dissolve more solute. Similarly, a **supersaturated solution** contains *more* solute than in the equilibrium state (the saturated solution). As such, it is analogous to a supercooled liquid and is unstable; that is, solute can crystallize out, leaving a saturated solution and excess solute.

As we shall see in the next section, the amount of material that will dissolve in a given amount of solvent is generally temperature dependent. Up to 57 g of KCl, for example, will dissolve in 100 g of H_2O at 100 °C. Figure 10–3 (page 273) shows that decreasing the temperature decreases the solubility of KCl. If we dissolve 50 g of KCl in 100 g of H_2O at 100 °C, the solution will be *unsaturated* (it can hold an additional 7 g KCl). When the solution is cooled to 80 °C it is said to be *saturated* since it now contains the maximum amount of KCl at that temperature. If it is carefully cooled below 80 °C, it may become *supersaturated* (containing more solute than the saturated solution at a given temperature), or solid KCl may precipitate (crystallize), giving a saturated solution in addition to the solid.

10.2 Solubility

Since we will be dealing primarily with the solubility of compounds in *aqueous* solutions (solutions in which water is the solvent), let us consider some of the properties of water that affect its role as a solvent. Note, however, that all of the generalizations we will make about water acting as a solvent more or less hold true for all polar solvents.

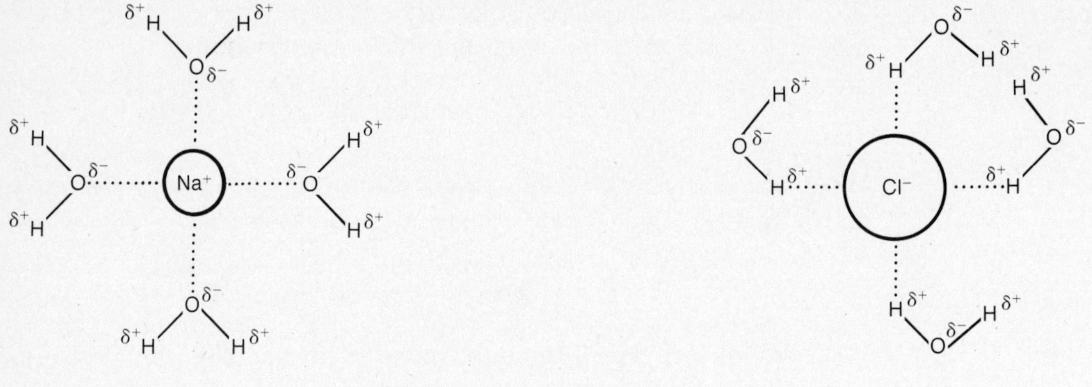

Dotted lines indicate weak electrostatic forces

Figure 10–2
Simple hydration of positive and negative ions in an aqueous solution

We have already examined water in some detail. For example, we know that it is a polar compound whose properties are greatly influenced by the existence of extensive intermolecular hydrogen bonding (page 178). We also know that water exhibits a very unusual property in that its solid state is less dense than its liquid state (pages 259–60). In order to examine the solvent properties of water, we may begin by making two important generalizations.

First, water is a poor solvent for molecular substances, especially nonpolar molecular substances. If a bit of I_2 (a nonpolar solid) is added to a flask containing H_2O and CCl_4 (a nonpolar liquid that does not mix with water), the I_2 will dissolve preferentially in the CCl_4 layer. Thus the nonpolar solute prefers to dissolve in the nonpolar solvent, a phenomenon often referred to as "like dissolves like."

Second, water is the best solvent known for ionic solutes (compounds in which the bonding is predominantly ionic). When dissolved in water, most ionic compounds **dissociate** to form ions, which then become **hydrated** by the solvent water molecules. The process of hydration involves an electrostatic interaction between the charged ions and the water dipoles. Simple hydration (illustrated in Figure 10–2) stabilizes both positive and negative ions in solution and is a great factor in promoting the general solubility of ionic compounds in water.

Unfortunately, as with all generalizations, there are exceptions.

For example, molecular substances that can hydrogen bond usually are soluble in water. Ethyl alcohol (C_2H_5OH) contains a hydroxyl (—OH) group covalently bonded to a carbon atom. The hydrogen in the —OH group can hydrogen bond to a water molecule, as indicated by the dotted line.

This interaction results in the complete miscibility (ability to mix) of ethanol and water.

An exception to the second generalization is that not all ionic solids are soluble. Several factors are involved in the process of converting an ionic solid to a solute in solution. Energetically, the overall process can be broken down into three parts:

(a) Solute-solute attraction must be overcome; the forces bonding the solute species together must be broken.
(b) Solvent-solvent attraction must be partially overcome; it is necessary to make a "hole" in the solvent to accommodate the solute species.
(c) Solute-solvent attractive forces are the energetic driving force for the dissolving process; they will stabilize and thereby promote solution formation.

If the solvent is water, (b) is rather large because of the extensive hydrogen bonding. If the solute is a molecular solid, the attractive forces represented by (c) are usually weak in the absence of a significant dipole on the solute to interact with the water dipole. Energetically, this can be written as follows:

(c) < (a) + (b), leading to low solubility

For ionic solutes, which dissociate into ions when dissolved in water, (c) is normally large because of the relatively strong ion-dipole interactions. In this case (a) is also large, but often not as large as (c) even when added to (b):

$$(c) > (a) + (b), \text{ leading to high solubility}$$

In other words, the attraction between most ions and water molecules is greater than the combined attraction between ions and between water molecules.

Obviously, the competing factors make it rather difficult to predict solubility. On the basis of experimental evidence, the following statements can be made concerning the solubility of common ionic compounds:

Nitrates: all are soluble

Sulfates: all are soluble except those of Ca^{2+}, Sr^{2+}, Ba^{2+}, Pb^{2+}, Hg^{2+}, Hg_2^{2+}, and Ag^+

Chlorides: all are soluble except those of Pb^{2+}, Hg_2^{2+}, and Ag^+

Carbonates: all are insoluble except those of alkali metals and NH_4^+

Hydroxides and Phosphates: all are insoluble except those of alkali metals, NH_4^+, Sr^{2+}, and Ba^{2+}

Sulfides: all are insoluble except those of alkali metals, alkaline earth metals, and NH_4^+

Effects of Temperature and Pressure

Adding to the complexities involved in predicting solubility, we must consider the effects of temperature and pressure. It turns out that solubility can be quite temperature dependent. Usually the solubility of a solid increases with increasing temperature. At 20 °C a saturated solution of KCl contains about 33 g KCl per 100 g H_2O; at 100 °C the solubility is about 57 g per 100 g H_2O. On the other hand, certain substances are less soluble at higher temperatures; they are said to be **retrograde soluble**. For example, 23 g Li_2SO_4 will dissolve in 100 g H_2O at 20 °C, but only 19 g will dissolve at 100 °C. Figure 10–3 is a graph of the solubilities of several inorganic compounds as a function of temperature.

Increasing the pressure by moderate amounts has little effect on the solubility of solids in liquids, but it has a marked effect on the amount of

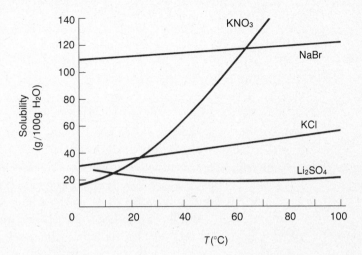

Figure 10–3
Temperature dependence of the solubility of several compounds

a gas that will dissolve in liquids. The concentration, or solubility, of a gas in a solvent (C_g) is directly proportional to the partial pressure of the gas over the solution (P_g). This relationship is known as **Henry's Law:**

$$C_g = kP_g$$

where k, the proportionality constant, is characteristic of a particular gas-liquid system. Decreasing the partial pressure of the gas over the solution will decrease its solubility. For example, bubbles form in champagne (or in any carbonated drink) when the bottle is opened because the solubility of CO_2 gas decreases when the solution is exposed to atmospheric pressure. When manufacturing carbonated drinks, bottling is done under several atmospheres of CO_2. In champagne, the CO_2 is generated in the closed bottle by the fermentation process.

Henry's Law can be used to explain a dangerous condition sometimes experienced by deep-sea divers. Breathing compressed air at higher than normal pressures causes a significant increase in the solubility of nitrogen in the blood. If a diver ascends (moves toward the surface) too rapidly, this dissolved N_2 can form bubbles in the bloodstream, resulting in what is sometimes called the "bends." These bubbles can interrupt blood circulation and cause severe pains in skeletal joints. Therefore, divers are instructed to ascend slowly to avoid the rapid evolution of N_2 in the bloodstream.

10.3 Electrolytes

An additional property of some solutions is that of conductivity, or the ability to conduct electricity. In 1887 Svante Arrhenius postulated that for certain solutions the dissolving process was accompanied by a dissociation of solute species into "fragments" which could then conduct electricity. He classified solutes as being either electrolytes or nonelectrolytes. **Electrolytes** are those solutes that give conducting solutions when dissolved, whereas **nonelectrolytes** are solutes that give nonconducting solutions. Typically, nonelectrolytes are molecular substances that dissolve as molecules because they are hydrated by the water molecules through dipole-dipole interaction. The property of conductivity exhibited by solutions of electrolytes indicates the presence of ions in solution, which are necessary to carry the electrical current.

A simple apparatus for determining the conductive properties of a solution is illustrated in Figure 10–4. Two pieces of metal (electrodes), which are connected to a battery with a light bulb in the circuit, are placed in a beaker containing the liquid. With a nonelectrolyte solution such as ethyl alcohol in water, no current can pass through the liquid and therefore the bulb will not light. However, a solution of NaCl in water will cause the bulb to light, since the ions in solution will complete the electrical circuit and allow current to flow.

Electrolytes may be either completely dissociated ionic compounds or partially or completely ionized molecular species. We may therefore speak of strong and weak electrolytes. A **strong electrolyte** is a solute that

Figure 10–4
An apparatus for testing the conductivity of a solution

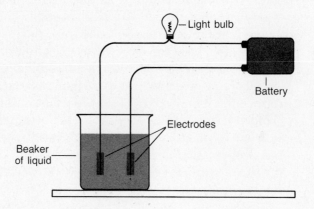

is highly dissociated in solution; that is, there is a high concentration of ions in the solution. A **weak electrolyte**, on the other hand, is a solute that is only slightly or partially ionized in solution. If we were to compare solutions of equal concentrations of hydrochloric acid (HCl) and acetic acid ($HC_2H_3O_2$) in the apparatus illustrated in Figure 10–4, the bulb would glow brightly in the first case but dimly in the second. This indicates that there is a greater ionization of HCl than of $HC_2H_3O_2$ in solution, leading to a higher concentration of ions. Hydrochloric acid is therefore a strong electrolyte. Acetic acid gives a low concentration of ions in solution and is thus a weak electrolyte.

Let us examine the degree of ionization of these two acids in some greater detail. Although we have been considering the bond in the HCl molecule to be essentially covalent, HCl will completely ionize in water, forming a hydrogen ion and a chloride ion:

$$HCl \xrightarrow{H_2O} H^+(aq) + Cl^-(aq)$$

In other words, the bond in the HCl molecule is easily broken in water, allowing HCl to ionize completely.

Now let us look at the ionization of acetic acid, $HC_2H_3O_2$ (abbreviated HOAc):

$$CH_3 - \overset{\overset{\textstyle O}{\|}}{C} - O - H \underset{}{\overset{H_2O}{\rightleftharpoons}} H^+(aq) + [CH_3 - \overset{\overset{\textstyle O}{\|}}{C} - O]^-(aq)$$

This reaction does not go all the way to completion, and in fact only a few percent of the HOAc molecules ionize. Therefore, acetic acid is a weak electrolyte. In comparing these two compounds, we are actually saying that it is more difficult to break the O—H bond in HOAc than the H—Cl bond.

The degree of ionization in a solution is determined by the nature of the solvent as well as by the type of solute. A polar solvent encourages ionization and helps to stabilize the ions once they are formed. In water, a polar solvent, HCl ionizes completely because the HCl bond is easily broken and the water molecules interact with the H^+ and Cl^- ions. In fact, there is no such thing as a free H^+ ion in aqueous solution, as we shall see in Chapter 12. In the nonpolar solvent benzene, HCl dissolves as a molecule and is only very slightly dissociated.

10.4 Net Ionic Equations

When we write equations to describe reactions that take place in solution, we include only those species that actually enter into the reaction. Equations that contain only the reacting species are called **net ionic equations**.

As an example of the way in which we determine the net ionic equation for a reaction, assume we are to mix a solution of NaOH with a solution of $NiCl_2$. We would observe the formation of a pale green precipitate. Since NaCl (a possible product) is soluble, the precipitate would *most likely* be $Ni(OH)_2$. (We say "most likely" because another, more complex salt might precipitate; positive identification by a technique such as x-ray diffraction would be necessary to confirm the identity of the solid.) Let us write an equation for the proposed reaction. Since both NaOH and $NiCl_2$ are strong electrolytes which dissociate completely in aqueous solution, they are present in solution as their component ions:

$$2\ NaOH + NiCl_2 \longrightarrow 2\ NaCl + Ni(OH)_2$$

$$2\ Na^+(aq) + 2\ OH^-(aq) + Ni^{2+}(aq) + 2\ Cl^-(aq) \longrightarrow$$
$$2\ Na^+(aq) + 2\ Cl^-(aq) + Ni(OH)_2(s)$$

Because the $Na^+(aq)$ and $Cl^-(aq)$ ions appear on both sides of the equation, they can be canceled out. Thus the balanced net ionic equation for the reaction is:

$$Ni^{2+}(aq) + 2\ OH^-(aq) \longrightarrow Ni(OH)_2(s)$$

The Na^+ and Cl^- ions, which are not involved in the reaction, are called **spectator ions**.

If two solutions, one containing HCl and the other containing NaOH, are reacted together, the products formed are NaCl and H_2O. Both of the reactants are strong electrolytes and are therefore essentially 100% dissociated in solution. Similarly, the product NaCl is dissociated in solution, but as we shall see in Chapter 12, the H_2O is only very slightly dissociated.

$$H^+(aq) + Cl^-(aq) + Na^+(aq) + OH^-(aq) \longrightarrow$$
$$H_2O(l) + Na^+(aq) + Cl^-(aq)$$

When we cancel out the species that appear on both sides of the equation, we have the net ionic equation:

$$H^+(aq) + OH^-(aq) \longrightarrow H_2O(l)$$

This type of net ionic equation, which will be discussed more fully in Chapter 12, describes the reaction between a strong acid and a strong base.

It is apparent from the equations presented thus far that certain species are written as ions and others as compounds. In general, the species written as compounds in a net ionic equation are (1) solids that precipitate out of solution, (2) gases that are evolved and leave the liquid phase, and (3) weak electrolytes which are only slightly dissociated. The following examples illustrate these three types of compounds:

1. Precipitation of PbS from $PbCl_2$ solution by $(NH_4)_2S$ solution:

$$Pb^{2+}(aq) + 2\,Cl^-(aq) + 2\,NH_4{}^+(aq) + S^{2-}(aq) \longrightarrow$$
$$PbS(s) + 2\,Cl^-(aq) + 2\,NH_4{}^+(aq)$$

Net ionic equation:

$$Pb^{2+}(aq) + S^{2-}(aq) \longrightarrow PbS(s)$$

2. Evolution of CO_2 gas from reaction of Na_2CO_3 and HCl solutions:

$$2\,Na^+(aq) + CO_3{}^{2-}(aq) + 2\,H^+(aq) + 2\,Cl^-(aq) \longrightarrow$$
$$2\,Na^+(aq) + 2\,Cl^-(aq) + H_2O(l) + CO_2(g)$$

Net ionic equation:

$$CO_3{}^{2-}(aq) + 2\,H^+(aq) \longrightarrow H_2O(l) + CO_2(g)$$

3. Formation of the weak electrolyte HOAc from reaction of NH_4OAc and HCl solutions:

$$NH_4{}^+(aq) + OAc^-(aq) + H^+(aq) + Cl^-(aq) \longrightarrow$$
$$HOAc(aq) + NH_4{}^+(aq) + Cl^-(aq)$$

Net ionic equation:

$$OAc^-(aq) + H^+(aq) \longrightarrow HOAc(aq)$$

10.5 Concentration

In chemistry we often speak of dilute and concentrated solutions—solutions containing proportionately small and large amounts of solute, respectively. It is sometimes necessary, however, to have a more quantitative means of expressing concentrations. Among the various ways of stating the concentration of solute in a solution, the most commonly used expression is molarity:

Molarity (M) is defined as the number of moles of solute per liter of solution, where the number of moles of a substance is equal to the number of grams divided by the molecular weight of the substance.

$$M = \frac{\text{no. of mol of solute}}{1 \text{ L of solution}}$$

Because molarity expresses the amount of solute per volume of solution (concentration), it is independent of the amount of solution. The number of moles of solute, however, varies with the amount of solution. To determine the number of moles of solute in V liters of a solution, we simply multiply the molarity of the solution, M, by the number of liters, V:

$$M(\text{in mol/L}) \times V \text{ (in L)} = \text{no. of mol} \tag{10-1}$$

EXAMPLE 10.5a A 220. mL solution of $NiCl_2$ contains 0.165 mol of $NiCl_2$. Calculate the molarity of this solution.

$$M = \frac{\text{no. of mol}}{\text{L}}$$

$$M = \frac{0.165 \text{ mol}}{0.220 \text{ L}}$$

$$M = 0.750 \text{ mol/L}$$

EXAMPLE 10.5b A 450. mL solution of $Ca(NO_3)_2$ contains 38.5 g of $Ca(NO_3)_2$. Calculate the molarity of the solution.

First we need to determine the number of moles of $Ca(NO_3)_2$ present:

$$\text{molecular weight } Ca(NO_3)_2 = 40.08 + 2[14.01 + 3(16.00)]$$
$$= 164.10 \text{ g/mol}$$

$$38.5 \text{ g} \times \frac{1 \text{ mol}}{164.10 \text{ g}} = 0.235 \text{ mol}$$

Then we can calculate the molarity of the solution:

$$M = \frac{0.235 \text{ mol}}{0.450 \text{ L}} = 0.522 \text{ mol/L}$$

EXAMPLE 10.5c How many moles of $(NH_4)_3PO_4$ are in 300. mL of 0.640 M $(NH_4)_3PO_4$ solution? How many grams?

We can calculate the number of moles directly:

$$M \times V = \text{no. of mol}$$

$$(0.640 \text{ mol/L})(0.300 \text{ L}) = 0.192 \text{ mol}$$

To determine the number of grams in 0.192 mol of $(NH_4)_3PO_4$, we first calculate the number of grams per mole and then multiply by the number of moles:

$$\text{molecular weight } (NH_4)_3PO_4 = 3[14.01 + 4(1.008)] + 30.97$$
$$+ 4(16.00)$$
$$= 149.10 \text{ g/mol}$$

$$0.192 \text{ mol} \times 149.10 \text{ g/mol} = 28.6 \text{ g}$$

To prepare a solution with a particular molarity we simply determine the number of moles of solute we need and convert this amount to grams. This weighed amount of material is then put into a volumetric flask, a piece of glassware that is carefully calibrated to contain a volume of solu-

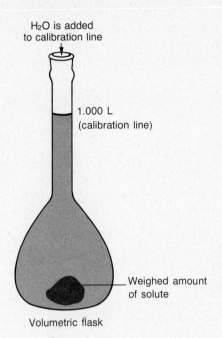

H₂O is added
to calibration line

1.000 L
(calibration line)

Weighed amount
of solute

Figure 10–5
Preparation of a
solution of molarity M

Volumetric flask

tion (see Figure 10–5). Enough water is added to dissolve the compound and the solution is thoroughly mixed. The volumetric flask is then filled to the calibration line (usually 1.000 L).

EXAMPLE 10.5d

How many grams of NaCl are needed to prepare 1.00 L of 0.500 M NaCl solution?
First we determine the number of moles of NaCl that are needed:

$$M \times V = \text{no. of mol}$$

$$(0.500 \text{ mol/L})(1.00 \text{ L}) = 0.500 \text{ mol}$$

We then convert this amount to grams of NaCl:

$$\text{molecular weight NaCl} = 22.99 + 35.45 = 58.44 \text{ g/mol}$$

$$(0.500 \text{ mol})(58.44 \text{ g/mol}) = 29.2 \text{ g}$$

Therefore we would take 29.2 g of NaCl and sufficient water so that the resulting volume of solution was 1.00 L; this would be 1.00 L of 0.500 M NaCl solution.

EXAMPLE 10.5e How many grams of Na_2SO_4 are needed to prepare 2.50 L of 0.780 M Na_2SO_4 solution?

Proceeding as in the previous example, we first determine the number of moles of Na_2SO_4 needed:

$$(0.780 \text{ mol/L})(2.50 \text{ L}) = 1.95 \text{ mol}$$

The molecular weight of Na_2SO_4 is:

$$2(22.99) + 32.06 + 4(16.00) = 142.04 \text{ g/mol}$$

Multiplying no. of mol $\times$ g/mol gives the number of grams needed:

$$(1.95 \text{ mol})(142.04 \text{ g/mol}) = 277 \text{ g}$$

Dilution

It is possible to obtain a new solution (of a particular molarity) simply by diluting the old solution (of known molarity) with pure solvent. Let us examine the relationships between two such solutions.

Equation 10–1 gives us the number of moles of solute in V liters of a solution of molarity M. If pure water (solvent) is added to this volume of solution to dilute it, the number of moles of solute present is not changed; therefore, (no. of mol)$_{concentrated}$ = (no. of mol)$_{dilute}$. If we let M' and V' represent the molarity and volume of the new solution, we have:

$$M \times V \text{ (in L)} = \text{no. of mol}$$
$$M' \times V' \text{ (in L)} = \text{no. of mol}$$

Since the number of moles is the same, we can combine the two equations as follows:

$$M'V' = MV \qquad (10–2)$$

The combined equation involves proportional relationships, so any volume units can be used as long as they are the same for V and V'.

EXAMPLE 10.5f What volume of 0.750 M NaCl solution is needed to prepare 1.50 L of 0.500 M NaCl solution?

$$M'V' = MV$$

$$(0.500\ M)(1.50\ L) = (0.750\ M)(V)$$

$$V = \frac{(0.500\ M)(1.50\ L)}{0.750\ M}$$

$$V = 1.00\ L$$

Thus 1.00 L of the original solution ($M = 0.750$) is needed to make 1.50 L of the diluted solution ($M' = 0.500$). The amount of water that must be added is V' $-$ V = 1.50 L $-$ 1.00 L = 0.50 L.

Molality

The **molality** (m) of a solution is the unit of concentration used in dealing with *colligative* properties (see Section 10.7). It is defined as the number of moles of solute per kilogram of *solvent:*

$$m = \frac{\text{no. of mol of solute}}{\text{kg of solvent}}$$

Since the mass of a material does not change with temperature, this expression of concentration is temperature independent. However, it is generally not very useful in problems that involve molar and volume changes because the dilution factors cannot be calculated easily.

EXAMPLE 10.5g Calculate the molality of a solution made up by dissolving 1.00 g NaNO$_3$ in 75.0 g H$_2$O.

First we determine the number of moles of solute in the solution:

$$\text{molecular weight NaNO}_3 = 22.99 + 14.01 + 3(16.00)$$
$$= 85.00\ \text{g/mol}$$

$$1.00\ \text{g} \times \frac{1\ \text{mol}}{85.00\ \text{g}} = 0.0118\ \text{mol}$$

We then determine the number of kilograms of solvent (H_2O):

$$75.0 \text{ g} \times \frac{1 \text{ kg}}{1,000 \text{ g}} = 0.0750 \text{ kg}$$

We can now calculate the molality:

$$m = \frac{\text{no. of mol of solute}}{\text{kg of solvent}}$$

$$m = \frac{0.0118 \text{ mol solute}}{0.0750 \text{ kg solvent}}$$

$$m = 0.157 \text{ mol solute/kg solvent}$$

Percent Solutions

There are three ways of expressing the concentration of solute as a percentage of solution; these are the weight-weight, weight-volume, and volume-volume percentages.

The weight-weight percentage, or simply the **weight percentage** (wt %), is the mass of the solute divided by the total mass times 100:

$$\text{wt \%} = \frac{\text{wt. of solute}}{\text{wt. of solution}} \times 100\%$$

EXAMPLE 10.5h What is the weight percentage of $NaNO_3$ in the previous example (1.00 g $NaNO_3$ in 75.0 g H_2O)?

$$\text{wt \% NaNO}_3 = \frac{\text{wt. of NaNO}_3}{\text{wt. of NaNO}_3 + \text{wt. of H}_2\text{O}} \times 100\%$$

$$= \frac{1.00 \text{ g NaNO}_3}{1.00 \text{ g NaNO}_3 + 75.0 \text{ g H}_2\text{O}} \times 100\%$$

$$\text{wt \% NaNO}_3 = 1.33\%$$

In the laboratory, it is common to find bottles of solutions whose concentrations are expressed as a weight percentage.

EXAMPLE 10.5i   How would 275 g of a 10% solution of NaCl be prepared?

A 10% solution means that on a weight percentage basis the solution contains 10% solute and 90% solvent. Therefore, in 275 g of this solution, we have:

$$\frac{10}{100} \times 275 \text{ g} = 27.5 \text{ g NaCl}$$

The balance of the solution (247.5 g) is solvent. So to prepare such a solution, we would weigh out 27.5 g of NaCl and dissolve it in 247.5 g of solvent.

A handy way of expressing weight percentage concentration which has become popular in describing dilute amounts of impurity pollutants is **parts per million (ppm)**:

$$1 \text{ ppm} = 1 \text{ part solute per } 10^6 \text{ parts solution}$$

$$= \frac{1}{10^6}$$

$$= 1 \times 10^{-6} \text{ (by weight)}$$

For impurities in very dilute aqueous solutions, ppm by weight is essentially equal to the number of milligrams per liter (mg/L), a weight-volume relationship. A liter of a very dilute aqueous solution weighs about 1 kg (10^3 g), so if an impurity is present at a concentration of 1 mg (10^{-3} g) per liter of solution, we have:

$$\frac{1 \text{ mg impurity}}{1 \text{ kg solution}} = \frac{1 \times 10^{-3} \text{ g}}{1 \times 10^3 \text{ g}}$$

$$= 1 \times 10^{-6} \text{ (or 1 ppm by weight)}$$

Formally, **weight-volume percentage** is the mass of solute divided by the volume of the solution times 100:

$$\text{wt-vol \%} = \frac{\text{wt. of solute}}{\text{vol. of solution}} \times 100\%$$

Dissolved Oxygen in Natural Water Bodies

The presence of dissolved oxygen is necessary for both plant and animal life to exist in aquatic systems. At a partial pressure of about 0.2 atm (the partial pressure of oxygen in the atmosphere), the solubility of O_2 decreases with increasing temperature. For example, at 0 °C there are 15 ppm of dissolved O_2 in water, whereas at 40 °C there are only 6 ppm. (For O_2 in water, 1 ppm $\approx$ 1 g/10^3 L.) This retrograde solubility of O_2 is the reason that the arctic oceans are the primary feeding grounds for fish. Microscopic plankton are found in high concentrations in the colder water because of the higher concentration of oxygen which they need to survive.

The presence of oxygen-consuming wastes in natural water bodies will deplete the oxygen levels. Since these wastes are mostly organic (containing carbon) we can write a schematic equation for this process as:

$$C + O_2 \longrightarrow CO_2$$

From the stoichiometry of this equation we know that 32 g of O_2 are needed to react with 12 g of C. This means that 1 ppm of C present as a hydrocarbon (1 drop of oil mixed with $\sim$3 L of H_2O) will consume nearly 3 ppm of O_2.

The amount of dissolved oxygen consumed during such reactions with oxygen-demanding wastes is called the **biological oxygen demand (BOD)**. It is determined by measuring the dissolved oxygen concentration before and after incubating a particular water sample for 5 days at 20 °C.

$$\text{BOD (in ppm)} = \frac{\text{no. of mg of } O_2 \text{ used}}{\text{no. of liters of sample}}$$

Nearly pure water has a BOD of $\sim$1 ppm; water of doubtful purity has a BOD of greater than 5 ppm. The BOD of raw sewage ranges from 100 to 400 ppm.

What happens in a natural water sample as the dissolved oxygen is depleted by BOD through pollution? The plants and animals that depend on oxygen may die or migrate. The bacteria that decompose wastes by **aerobic** processes (processes involving oxygen consumption) become much less abundant than those using **anaerobic** processes (not involving oxygen). But, more importantly, there are increased amounts of foul-smelling and potentially toxic chemicals, which are products of decomposition in the anaerobic processes. The decomposition products in the aerobic processes are nontoxic.

ELEMENT	PRODUCT	
	Aerobic	Anaerobic
C	CO_2	CH_4, methane
N	NH_3, HNO_3	NH_3, ammonia (poisonous)
S	H_2SO_4	H_2S, hydrogen sulfide (has the odor of rotten eggs and is poisonous)
P	H_3PO_4	PH_3, phosphine (poisonous)

Similarly, the third type of percentage concentration, known as the **volume percentage**, is the volume of solute divided by the volume of the solution times 100:

$$\text{vol \%} = \frac{\text{vol. of solute}}{\text{vol. of solution}} \times 100\%$$

This expression of concentration is used when both the solute and the solvent are liquids.

10.6 Titrations

A sufficient background has now been provided for considering stoichiometry problems involving solutions, which are nothing more than extensions of the types of problems discussed in Chapters 1, 2, and 3. All of the solution stoichiometry problems we examine will be examples of **titrations**: the addition of the exact amount of a reagent required for complete reaction.

EXAMPLE 10.6a How many moles of $CaCl_2$ are needed to react with 150. mL of 0.156 M H_3PO_4 solution? How many grams is this equal to?
The balanced equation is:

$$3\ CaCl_2(s)\ +\ 2\ H_3PO_4(aq) \longrightarrow Ca_3(PO_4)_2(s)\ +\ 6\ HCl(aq)$$

Note that the balanced equation is not written as a net ionic equation, since the number of moles of a compound is called for and not the number of moles of dissociated ions.
Our first step in solving the problem is to determine the number of moles of H_3PO_4 in the solution:

$$M \times V = \text{no. of mol}$$

$$(0.156\ \text{mol/L})(0.150\ \text{L}) = 0.0234\ \text{mol}\ H_3PO_4$$

Using the molar ratio from the balanced equation, we can then determine the number of moles of $CaCl_2$ needed:

$$0.0234\ \text{mol}\ H_3PO_4 \times \frac{3\ \text{mol}\ CaCl_2}{2\ \text{mol}\ H_3PO_4} = 0.0351\ \text{mol}\ CaCl_2$$

To convert moles to grams, we use the molecular weight of $CaCl_2$:

$$\text{molecular weight } CaCl_2 = 40.08 + 2(35.45) = 110.98 \text{ g/mol}$$

$$0.0351 \text{ mol } CaCl_2 \times 110.98 \text{ g/mol } CaCl_2 = 3.90 \text{ g } CaCl_2$$

EXAMPLE 10.6b How many mL of 3.00 M HCl solution are needed to react with 25.0 g of $CaCO_3$ according to the reaction:

$$CaCO_3(s) + 2 \ HCl(aq) \longrightarrow CaCl_2(aq) + H_2O(l) + CO_2(g)$$

We first determine the number of moles of $CaCO_3$ present:

$$\text{molecular weight } CaCO_3 = 40.08 + 12.01 + 3(16.00) = 100.09$$

$$25.0 \text{ g } CaCO_3 \times \frac{1 \text{ mol } CaCO_3}{100.09 \text{ g } CaCO_3} = 0.250 \text{ mol } CaCO_3$$

The balanced equation gives us the molar ratio:

$$0.250 \text{ mol } CaCO_3 \times \frac{2 \text{ mol HCl}}{1 \text{ mol } CaCO_3} = 0.500 \text{ mol HCl}$$

Since the molarity of the solution is given, we calculate the volume of HCl as follows:

$$M \times V = \text{no. of mol}$$

$$V = \frac{\text{no. of mol}}{M}$$

$$V = \frac{0.500 \text{ mol HCl}}{3.00 \text{ mol/L HCl}}$$

$$V = 0.167 \text{ L}$$

$$V = 167 \text{ mL solution}$$

EXAMPLE 10.6c How many mL of 0.754 M NaOH solution are required to completely precipitate $Fe(OH)_3$ from 50.0 mL of 0.425 M $Fe(NO_3)_3$ solution? The balanced equation is:

$$3\ NaOH(aq) + Fe(NO_3)_3(aq) \longrightarrow Fe(OH)_3(s) + 3\ NaNO_3(aq)$$

First we must calculate the number of moles of $Fe(NO_3)_3$ that are present:

$$0.425\ mol/L\ Fe(NO_3)_3 \times 0.050\ L\ Fe(NO_3)_3 = 0.0213\ mol\ Fe(NO_3)_3$$

Using the molar ratio from the equation, we now determine the number of moles of NaOH needed:

$$0.0213\ mol\ Fe(NO_3)_3 \times \frac{3\ mol\ NaOH}{1\ mol\ Fe(NO_3)_3} = 0.0639\ mol\ NaOH$$

The NaOH solution has a concentration of 0.754 mol/L; how many mL do we need to give 0.0639 mol?

$$M \times V = \text{no. of mol}$$

$$V = \frac{\text{no. of mol}}{M}$$

$$V = \frac{0.0639\ mol\ NaOH}{0.754\ mol/L\ NaOH}$$

$$V = 0.0847\ L$$

$$V = 84.7\ mL$$

EXAMPLE 10.6d AgCl is completely precipitated from a solution of NaCl by the addition of 45.8 mL of a 0.500 M solution of $AgNO_3$. What was the original weight of NaCl in solution?

$$NaCl(aq) + AgNO_3(aq) \longrightarrow AgCl(s) + NaNO_3(aq)$$

We first calculate the number of moles of $AgNO_3$ that were added:

$$0.500\ mol/L\ AgNO_3 \times 0.0458\ L = 0.0229\ mol\ AgNO_3$$

The equation states that 1 mol of $AgNO_3$ reacts with 1 mol of NaCl; therefore 0.0229 mol of NaCl was originally in solution.

Our final step is to convert moles to grams:

$$\text{molecular weight NaCl} = 22.99 + 35.45 = 58.44$$

$$0.0229 \text{ mol NaCl} \times 58.44 \text{ g/mol NaCl} = 1.34 \text{ g NaCl}$$

10.7 Properties of Ideal Solutions

The term **ideal solution** means a solution in which there is negligible interaction between solute molecules, a condition that would be most probable in a dilute solution where the solute molecules are far apart. To better explain this concept, a rather imperfect analogy can be made between an ideal gas and an ideal solution. We have seen that the concept of an ideal gas implies that there are no significant attractive forces among the molecules of the gas. This model breaks down at high pressures and/or low temperatures, where the molecules are closer together and, at low temperatures, moving more slowly. Similarly, in an ideal solution—a very dilute solution—the solute molecules are far apart and generally do not interact, but in a more concentrated solution, solute molecules tend to exhibit attractive forces among one another.

A general effect of the presence of a solute on the physical properties of the solvent is to lower the tendency of the solvent to "escape" into the solid or gas phase. As we shall see, this effect results in the expansion of the liquid area in the phase diagram of the pure solvent at the expense of the gas and solid regions.

The properties of solvents resulting from the presence of a solute are called **colligative properties**. These properties depend on the concentration of species in the solution and are independent of the specific solute. They are (1) decreased vapor pressure, (2) an increased boiling point, (3) a decreased freezing point, and (4) creation of osmotic pressure.

One important qualification with regard to these colligative properties is that the solute must be **nonvolatile** (not easily vaporized). For example, ethanol (a volatile material) will dissolve in water and will lower the vapor pressure of water. However, because ethanol will vaporize and thus form its own vapor pressure, the vapor pressure over the solution may actually *increase* as a result of the presence of the solute.

Raoult's Law

The colligative property of **vapor pressure lowering** is given by **Raoult's Law**, which states that the presence of a solute lowers the vapor pressure of the pure solvent; that is, the vapor pressure of the solvent over a solution is less than that over pure solvent at a given temperature. Raoult's Law is an idealization and as such holds better for dilute solutions than for concentrated solutions. Because of this, ideal solutions are usually defined as those which obey Raoult's Law. Figure 10–6 indicates typical behavior of the vapor pressure over solutions plotted against concentration for nonvolatile solutes. The center solid line is the ideal linear relationship given by Raoult's Law. Note that there can be both positive and negative deviations from this relationship and that ideal behavior is found only for dilute solutions.

This vapor pressure lowering is related to another colligative property, that of **boiling point elevation**. Because the vapor pressure of the solvent over a solution is less than that over the pure solvent, a higher temperature is required for the vapor pressure over a solution to equal one atmosphere (the normal boiling point). The solid line in Figure 10–7 represents the liquid-gas equilibrium curve for the pure solvent, and the dashed line represents the curve for the solution. Note that at each temperature the vapor pressure is lower for the solution than for the pure solvent. Similarly, the figure also indicates the increased boiling point for the solvent in solution.

Figure 10–6
A graphic
representation of
Raoult's Law

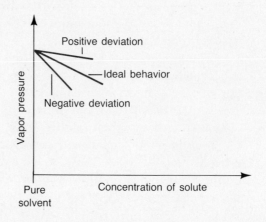

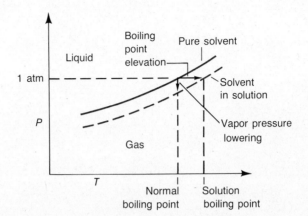

Figure 10–7
Liquid-gas equilibrium curve illustrating the colligative properties of vapor pressure lowering and boiling point elevation

Quantitatively, the boiling point elevation (ΔT_{bp}) is given by

$$\Delta T_{bp} = Bm$$

where B is the boiling point elevation constant characteristic of the solvent and m is the molality of the solute (no. of mol of solute/kg of solvent). To evaluate B, let us look at some data for solutions of sugar in water:

	bp	Δ
pure H$_2$O	100.000 °C	0.512 °C
1 m sugar	100.512 °C	0.512 °C
2 m sugar	101.024 °C	0.512 °C
3 m sugar	101.536 °C	

Since the boiling point is raised 0.512 °C for each 1 m additional solute, for water (the solvent) B is 0.512 °C/m.

EXAMPLE 10.7a A solution of sugar in water gives an observed boiling point of 101.487 °C. What is the molality of this solution?
We determine ΔT_{bp}, the boiling point elevation, by subtracting the normal boiling point of the pure solvent (100.000 °C for water) from the observed boiling point of the solution:

$$101.487 \ °C$$
$$- 100.000 \ °C$$
$$1.487 \ °C = \Delta T_{bp}$$

Using the formula for boiling point elevation, we solve for m:

$$\Delta T_{bp} = Bm$$

$$m = \frac{\Delta T_{bp}}{B}$$

$$= \frac{1.487 \ °C}{0.512 \ °C/m}$$

$$m = 2.90 \ mol/kg \ H_2O$$

The Effect of Dissociation

An experiment would show that 1 m of NaCl in water boils at 101.024 °C. Since we have just seen that for water B is 0.512 °C/m, this is a boiling point characteristic of a 2 m rather than a 1 m solution: 1.024 °C ÷ (0.512 °C/m) = 2.00 m. The boiling point is elevated because NaCl dissociates (page 270) into sodium and chloride ions:

$$NaCl(s) \xrightarrow{H_2O} Na^+(aq) + Cl^-(aq)$$

In this manner, one mole of NaCl gives two moles of particles in solution (ions in this case). It is the number of particles in solution, or the "molality of the particles," that determines the degree of boiling point elevation. The colligative properties depend only on the concentration of particles (solute) in the solution, not on the particular solute.

EXAMPLE 10.7b What is the boiling point of a solution of 24.84 g of $CaCl_2$ in 0.750 kg of H_2O?
We first calculate the molality of the $CaCl_2$ solution:

$$molecular \ weight \ CaCl_2 = 40.08 + 2(35.45) = 110.98 \ g/mol$$

$$\frac{24.84 \ g \ CaCl_2}{110.98 \ g/mol \ CaCl_2} = 0.2238 \ mol \ CaCl_2$$

$$m = \frac{0.2238 \text{ mol } CaCl_2}{0.750 \text{ kg } H_2O}$$

$$m = 0.298 \frac{\text{mol } CaCl_2}{\text{kg } H_2O}$$

Realizing that $CaCl_2$ is a strong electrolyte which completely ionizes in aqueous solution, we know that the following reaction takes place:

$$CaCl_2(s) \xrightarrow{H_2O} Ca^{2+}(aq) + 2 Cl^-(aq)$$

This means that each mole of $CaCl_2$ produces three moles of ions. Therefore, the "molality of the particles" in solution is:

$$3(0.298 \ m) = 0.894 \ m$$

We can now calculate the increase in boiling point, ΔT_{bp}:

$$\Delta T_{bp} = Bm$$
$$= (0.512 \ °C/m)(0.894 \ m)$$
$$= 0.458 \ °C$$

Finally, we add ΔT_{bp} to the boiling point of pure water (100.000 °C) to get a boiling point of 100.458 °C for the solution.

Molecular Weight Determination

The formula $\Delta T_{bp} = Bm$ is also useful in determining the molecular weight of a solute if the boiling point elevation is known. For simplicity, let us consider an example in which the solute dissolves without dissociation.

EXAMPLE 10.7c In an experiment it is determined that nicotine has the empirical formula C_5H_7N. A solution of 2.80 g of nicotine in 500. g of H_2O gives a boiling point of 100.0176 °C. What is the molecular weight and molecular formula of nicotine?
First, we use the boiling point elevation data to calculate the molality of the solution.

$$\Delta T_{bp} = 100.0176 \ ^\circ C - 100.0000 \ ^\circ C = 0.0176 \ ^\circ C$$

$$\Delta T_{bp} = Bm$$

$$m = \frac{\Delta T_{bp}}{B}$$

$$m = \frac{0.0176 \ ^\circ C}{0.512 \ ^\circ C/m}$$

$$m = 0.0344 \ m$$

We are told that there are 2.80 g of nicotine in 0.500 kg of H_2O and we know that the no. of mol = g/MW (since MW is expressed in g/mol). Therefore:

$$m = \frac{\text{no. of mol of solute}}{\text{kg of solvent}}$$

$$0.0344 \ m = \frac{2.80 \ g/MW}{0.500 \ kg}$$

We can now solve for the molecular weight:

$$MW = \frac{2.80 \ g \ \text{nicotine}}{(0.0344 \ \text{mol nicotine/kg} \ H_2O)(0.500 \ kg \ H_2O)}$$

$$MW = 163 \ g/mol$$

The empirical formula weight is $5(12) + 7(1) + 14 = 81$. Since this is almost exactly one-half of the true molecular weight, nicotine has the molecular formula:

$$(C_5H_7N)_2 \quad \text{or} \quad C_{10}H_{14}N_2$$

The colligative property of **freezing point depression** occurs in a similar manner to that of the boiling point elevation. The presence of solute species in solution prevents the solvent from crystallizing and it becomes necessary to go to a lower temperature to transform liquid solvent to a solid. It is almost as if the solute molecules "get in the way" of the crystallizing solvent molecules. The effects of the decreased freez-

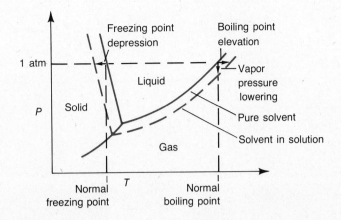

Figure 10–8

A phase diagram illustrating the colligative property of freezing point depression

ing point are summarized in Figure 10–8, which shows the stabilization of the liquid phase in the phase diagram for the solution (dashed lines) relative to that for pure solvent (solid lines). Note that this stabilization is at the expense of both the solid and gas states.

The decrease in freezing point is given quantitatively by the equation

$$\Delta T_{\mathrm{fp}} = \mathrm{F}m$$

where F is the freezing point depression constant ($-1.86\ °\mathrm{C}/m$ for H_2O; $-5.1\ °\mathrm{C}/m$ for benzene). F is constant for dilute solutions and depends only on the solvent.

Osmotic Pressure

The last of the four colligative properties is the phenomenon known as osmotic pressure. If we were to place two beakers under a bell jar, one containing pure water and the other an aqueous solution of a nonvolatile solute (see Figure 10–9), the liquid level in the beaker containing pure water would drop and the liquid level in the beaker containing the solution would increase. This is due to the stabilization of the liquid phase for the water in solution; in other words, because of the presence of solute molecules, more water molecules in the solution stay in the liquid phase

Water Pollution and Purification

We have already discussed the contamination of water by decaying organic matter and its effect on biological oxygen demand (BOD). We shall now consider several additional types of water pollutants, some which occur naturally and some which are man-made.

Hard water. A common phenomenon occurs when water contains relatively large amounts of Ca^{2+} and Mg^{2+}; such water is called **hard water**. When relatively pure water comes into contact with calcium- or magnesium-containing rocks (limestone or dolomite), it picks up enough Ca^{2+} or Mg^{2+} ions to make it unsuitable for household consumption. The most common household soap, sodium stearate, is soluble in water but reacts readily with Ca^{2+} or Mg^{2+} to precipitate insoluble calcium and magnesium stearates, which are the cause of "bathtub rings" and which give household laundry an unsightly gray tinge. A related phenomenon occurs when deposits of iron-containing compounds cause Fe^{3+} to leach into the water supply, resulting in rust-colored deposits of ferric hydroxide.

A more serious consequence of the use of hard water is the precipitation of insoluble calcium and magnesium salts when the water is evaporated by heating. These precipitates are calcium and magnesium carbonates or sulfates and are the cause of deposits in kettles and coffee pots as well as the common boiler scale found in industrial steam boilers.

Several methods are available for "softening" hard water—for removing the offending calcium and magnesium ions. In municipal and industrial treatment plants, the most common technique is a multistep process that involves the addition of calcium hydroxide (slaked lime) and sodium carbonate (soda ash). The sodium carbonate dissolves, acting as a source of carbonate ion which precipitates Ca^{2+} according to the reaction:

$$Ca^{2+}(aq) + CO_3{}^{2-}(aq) \longrightarrow CaCO_3(s)$$

The amount of calcium hydroxide added to the water depends on the concentration of hydrogen carbonate ion ($HCO_3{}^-$). Calcium hydroxide, $Ca(OH)_2$, dissolves with the formation of Ca^{2+} and OH^- ions. The hydroxide ion reacts with $HCO_3{}^-$ to form $CO_3{}^{2-}$ and water:

$$OH^-(aq) + HCO_3{}^-(aq) \longrightarrow \\ CO_3{}^{2-}(aq) + H_2O(l)$$

The carbonate ion then precipitates the Ca^{2+} which had been added. The overall reaction is the removal of $HCO_3{}^-$ by $Ca(OH)_2$:

$$Ca(OH)_2(s) + 2\,HCO_3{}^-(aq) \longrightarrow \\ CaCO_3(s) + CO_3{}^{2-}(aq) + 2\,H_2O(l)$$

It is obvious from this equation that the addition of $Ca(OH)_2$ not only precipitates $CaCO_3$ but releases an additional amount of $CO_3{}^{2-}$ ion, which can then react with Ca^{2+} originally present in the hard water to form more of the insoluble $CaCO_3$.

In a household water softener, a phenomenon known as ion exchange is used to substitute Na^+ for the Ca^{2+} and Mg^{2+} ions. An ion exchange material (called a resin) is one in which either cations or anions are loosely bonded to a larger three-dimensional network structure. The open structure of the resin allows aqueous solutions to easily pass through it. The first step is to "charge" the resin with sodium chloride solution. This binds sodium ions to the material. When hard water is passed over the ion exchange resin, Mg^{2+} (or Ca^{2+}) displaces Na^+ from the resin. This effectively ties up the offending ions and releases Na^+ into the water.

$$Mg^{2+}(aq) + 2\,Na^+(resin) \longrightarrow$$
$$Mg^{2+}(resin) + 2\,Na^+(aq)$$

Particulates. Another type of naturally-occurring pollutant is suspended particulate matter, which occurs when streams and rivers flow through clay-like mineral deposits and pick up silt and other suspended particles. The decay of natural organic material can also contribute suspended particles. Although sometimes particulates are removed by natural filtration through certain types of soil and rocks, it is usually necessary to remove them by passing the water through large sedimentation tanks where the suspended material settles out. Alternatively, large filters can be used to remove the suspended particles.

Detergents. Man-made pollutants include the previously widely used detergents, insecticides, and toxic trace elements. Prior to 1956, synthetic detergents were used in large quantities for washing, since these chemicals do not react with hard water in the same manner as ordinary soaps. Unfortunately, these materials are **nonbiodegradable**; naturally-occurring bacteria are unable to decompose the large synthetic detergent molecule into smaller, simpler pieces. As

a result, water supplies eventually became contaminated with detergents, causing the widespread occurrence of unsightly and unhealthy foam in rivers and other water supplies. By modifying the chemical structure of synthetic detergents, chemists were able to prepare molecules that could be degraded by common bacteria.

Several previously used detergents were also harmful in that they contained inorganic phosphates, which will react with Ca^{2+}, Mg^{2+}, and Fe^{3+} in the water to prevent these ions from interfering with detergent action. However, phosphates are plant nutrients, and high concentrations of phosphates introduced by using large amounts of detergent materials increased the phosphate concentration in rivers and streams. As a result, aquatic plant life bloomed out of control and had a deleterious effect on the ecological balance. Current detergents are non-phosphate: they contain either carbonate or silicate salts which, although they are less effective as cleansing agents, do not react as plant nutrients.

Insecticides and toxic elements. Insecticides (which are man-made) and toxic trace elements (which usually occur as byproducts of refining processes) appear in the water supply when rain-water and ground water pass through watershed areas. In recent years, through the banning of highly toxic insecticides and the environmental control of toxic trace elements, this form of pollution has been drastically reduced. In fact, there is no practical way of removing the minute concentrations of toxic materials from water supplies once they have been introduced. It is only through the careful control of these materials at the source that their presence can be avoided.

Figure 10–9

An illustration of the transfer of pure solvent to a solution in a closed system, which occurs because the vapor pressure over the solution is less than that over pure solvent (arrows indicate the relative magnitudes of the vapor pressures)

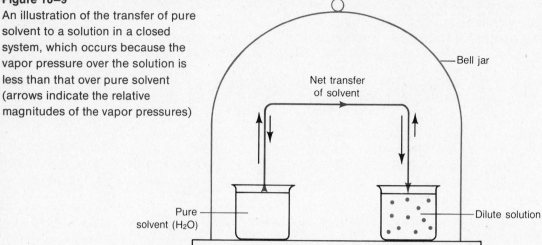

rather than go into the gaseous phase. Thus the vapor pressure of water over the solution is less than that over pure water (Raoult's Law). In an attempt to seek equilibrium between the two vapors, some gaseous H_2O molecules over the pure water join the gaseous H_2O molecules over the solution, which increases the vapor pressure over the solution. Some molecules then go into the liquid phase to reestablish equilibrium between the solution and the vapor pressure over the solution. In actuality this transfer of water molecules from the pure solvent to the solution occurs as one continuous step rather than in the separate steps outlined here for clarity.

In an analogous experiment, a thistle tube filled with a dilute aqueous solution and covered with a membrane is suspended in a beaker of pure water (Figure 10–10). The liquid level will rise within the arm of the thistle tube containing the solution due to osmotic pressure. The membrane is **semipermeable**; that is, the water molecules can pass through it, but the solute molecules cannot. In the previous experiment the air trapped within the bell jar was "permeated" by water molecules, but not by solute molecules; in this experiment it is a membrane that allows only water molecules to pass through. This selectivity toward the passage of molecular (or ionic) species causes the solution level to rise in the thistle tube. The **osmotic pressure** (π) is defined in a rather strange manner. It is equal to the external pressure necessary to *prevent* osmosis—to prevent solvent molecules from passing through the membrane and the level from rising in the thistle tube.

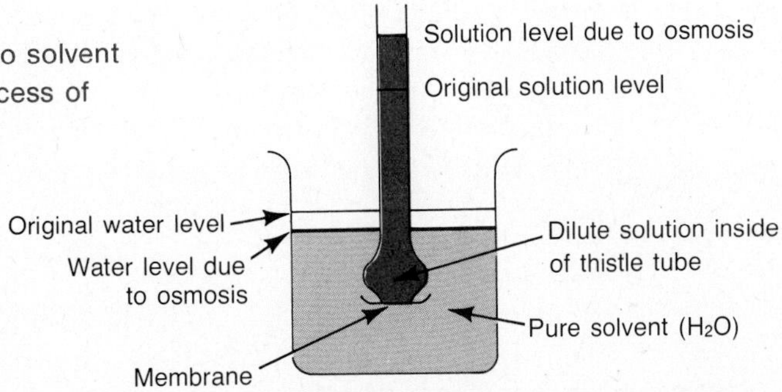

Figure 10–10

The transfer of pure solvent to solvent in a solution through the process of osmosis

Cell walls are excellent examples of semipermeable membranes through which various components of biological solutions can selectively pass. The selectivity of these cell walls helps to maintain the various chemical equilibria in the body. It is important to consider the process of osmosis when, for example, a liquid is injected into the bloodstream. Red blood cells, which have a high concentration of dissolved components, will allow water to enter through the cell walls. If the osmotic pressure of an injected liquid is not the same as that of the blood (0.12 atm), water will enter the red blood cells until the pressure inside the cells causes them to burst. Solutions that have equal osmotic pressures are said to be **isotonic**.

TERMS AND CONCEPTS

- Colloidal suspension (colloid)
- Macromolecule
- Tyndall Effect
- Saturated, unsaturated, and supersaturated solutions
- Dissociation
- Hydration
- Retrograde soluble
- Henry's Law
- Electrolytes and nonelectrolytes
- Strong and weak electrolytes
- Net ionic equations
- Spectator ions
- Molarity (M)
- Dilution
- Molality (m)
- Weight, weight-volume, and volume percentages

- Parts per million (ppm)
- Biological oxygen demand (BOD)
- Aerobic and anaerobic processes
- Titration
- Ideal solution
- Colligative properties
- Nonvolatile solutes
- Vapor pressure lowering
- Raoult's Law
- Boiling point elevation
- Freezing point depression
- Osmotic pressure
- Semipermeable membrane
- Isotonic
- Hard water
- Nonbiodegradable

1. How is a colloid different from a solution or a heterogeneous mixture? Why can the Tyndall Effect not be observed for a solution?
2. Explain how a solution may become supersaturated.
3. Explain why water is a poor solvent for substances composed of nonpolar molecules but a good solvent for substances composed of polar molecules.
4. Why won't all ionic solids dissolve to an appreciable extent in water?
5. Explain what happens to cause a bottle of soda to "fizz" when opened.
6. Explain the difference between a strong electrolyte and a weak electrolyte.
7. Write the net ionic equation for each of the following reactions in *aqueous* solution (watch out for the formation of insoluble compounds!):

   a. $NiCl_2 + Na_2S \rightarrow$ c. $NaCl + Ba(OH)_2 \rightarrow$
   b. $CaCl_2 + NH_4H_2PO_4 \rightarrow$ d. $Co(NO_3)_2 + NH_4OH \rightarrow$

8. Determine the molarity of each of the following solutions:

   a. 0.15 mol of NaCl dissolved in enough water to give 1.0 L of solution
   b. 0.20 mol of $MgCl_2$ dissolved in enough water to give 0.35 L of solution
   c. 0.097 mol of HCl dissolved in enough water to give 487 mL of solution
   d. 0.0021 mol of Na_2SO_4 dissolved in enough water to give 50.0 mL of solution
   e. 5.16 g of KCl dissolved in enough water to make 1.00 L of solution
   f. 31.7 g of $AgNO_3$ dissolved in enough water to make 1.00 L of solution
   g. 6.75 g of H_5IO_6 dissolved in enough water to make 75 mL of solution
   h. 12.81 g of $C_4H_7O_2N_2$ dissolved in enough alcohol to make 2.0 L of solution
   i. 3.66 g of H_2PtCl_6 dissolved in enough water to make 0.100 L of solution

9. A vinegar solution contains 25.0 g of acetic acid, $HC_2H_3O_2$, in 525 mL of solution. Calculate the molarity of the acetic acid in solution.
10. How many grams of NaCl are needed to prepare 275 mL of a 2.50 *M* NaCl solution?
11. How many grams of $NiCl_2$ are dissolved in 0.250 L of a 1.12 *M* $NiCl_2$ solution?
12. How many grams of $AgNO_3$ are needed to prepare 150 mL of 0.125 *M* $AgNO_3$ solution?
13. Chloral hydrate, $C_2Cl_3O_2H_3$, was one of the first synthetic anesthetic drugs. "Knockout drops" containing chloral hydrate can be added to alcohol to make the alcoholic drink known as a "Mickey Finn."

    a. Calculate the molarity of $C_2Cl_3O_2H_3$ in knockout drops containing 5.00 g of chloral hydrate in 100. mL of solution.
    b. Calculate the molarity of $C_2Cl_3O_2H_3$ in a shot of whiskey (45 mL) to which 5 drops (1.0 mL) of the solution described in part a has been added. Assume additivity of the volumes.
    c. How many grams of $C_2Cl_3O_2H_3$ are there in the answer to part b?

14. A solution is prepared by dissolving 5.11 g of K_2CrO_4 in 150 mL of water and then diluting to exactly 250 mL. Calculate the solution's molarity.
15. How many mL of 18 *M* sulfuric acid solution are required to prepare 1.50 L of 1.0 *M* sulfuric acid solution by dilution?

16. a. How many grams of $NaNO_3$ are needed to prepare 2.00 L of a 2.50 M $NaNO_3$ solution?
    b. How many liters of this 2.50 M $NaNO_3$ solution are needed to prepare 1.50 L of 1.00 M $NaNO_3$ solution (by dilution)?

17. Describe how to prepare:
    a. 1.0 L of 1.0 M HCl from concentrated HCl solution (12 M)
    b. 500 mL of 6.0 M ammonia from concentrated NH_3 solution (15 M)
    c. 250 mL of 0.15 M $AgNO_3$ from 0.95 M $AgNO_3$
    d. 100 mL of 0.0050 M $HC_2H_3O_2$ from 0.10 M $HC_2H_3O_2$

18. Determine the molality and weight percentage of each of the following solutions:
    a. 1.76 g of $C_6H_{12}O_6$ (glucose) dissolved in 95.0 g of water
    b. 2.35 g of $C_{10}H_8$ (naphthalene) dissolved in 200. g of benzene
    c. 6.37 g of $C_{12}H_{22}O_{11}$ (sucrose) dissolved in 240. mL of water
    d. 12.1 g of C_6H_5COOH (benzoic acid) dissolved in 990.0 g of acetone
    e. 9.75 g of C_6H_5COOH dissolved in 475 mL of acetone (density of acetone = 0.790 g/mL)
    f. 0.761 g of $C_6H_4Br_2$ dissolved in 25.0 mL of benzene (density of benzene = 0.879 g/mL)

19. A solution is prepared by dissolving 12.8 g of $CaCl_2$ in 335 g of H_2O.
    a. Calculate the molality of the $CaCl_2$ solution.
    b. Calculate the weight percentage of $CaCl_2$ in the solution.

20. 90 proof vodka contains 45 vol % of ethyl alcohol. If 1 gal = 3.79 L, how many liters of ethyl alcohol are in one gallon of vodka (assume additivity of volumes)?

21. How many mL of 0.555 M NaF solution must be added to completely precipitate PbF_2 from 0.278 L of 0.877 M $Pb(NO_3)_2$ solution according to the reaction:

$$Pb(NO_3)_2(aq) + 2\ NaF(aq) \longrightarrow PbF_2(s) + 2\ NaNO_3(aq)$$

22. When 186 mL of a 0.875 M $(NH_4)_2S$ solution is added to 275 mL of a solution of $NiCl_2$ of unknown molarity, it will completely precipitate all of the nickel as NiS according to the reaction:

$$NiCl_2(aq) + (NH_4)_2S(aq) \longrightarrow NiS(s) + 2\ NH_4Cl(aq)$$

Calculate the molarity of the $NiCl_2$ solution.

23. The concentration of sulfate ion (SO_4^{2-}) in a sample of water is found to be 350 ppm. Calculate the amount of 2.5 M $BaCl_2$ solution necessary to precipitate all of the SO_4^{2-} in a 250 L sample of this water, assuming that the reaction goes to completion:

$$BaCl_2(aq) + SO_4^{2-}(aq) \longrightarrow BaSO_4(s) + 2\ Cl^-(aq)$$

24. How many mL of 1.52 M H_3PO_4 solution must be added to 0.875 L of 0.248 M $BaCl_2$ solution to completely precipitate $Ba_3(PO_4)_2$?

25. You find that 38.5 mL of 0.548 M $CaCl_2$ solution are needed to completely precipitate all of the silver ion in 50.0 mL of $AgNO_3$ solution as insoluble AgCl. What was the original concentration of the $AgNO_3$ solution?

26. Cr^{3+} is quantitatively precipitated from solution as Cr_2S_3 by the sulfide ion. If the addition of 245 mL of 0.530 M Na_2S solution to 365 mL of a solution of $CrCl_3$ is required to precipitate all of the Cr^{3+}, how many grams of $CrCl_3$ were present in the original solution?

27. Calculate the boiling point (at 1 atm) of a solution containing 64.5 g of glucose ($C_6H_{12}O_6$) in 550.0 g of water.

28. Why does the presence of a nonvolatile solute lower the vapor pressure of a solvent? Why does it raise the boiling point and lower the freezing point?

29. When 18.5 g of an unknown nonelectrolyte is dissolved in 250. g of water, it gives an experimentally determined freezing point of -1.04 °C. Calculate the molecular weight of this compound.

30. The freezing point of nitrobenzene is 5.67 °C. The molal freezing point depression constant is 8.1 °C/m. It is found that 45.0 g of a nonelectrolyte called Y dissolved in exactly 500 g of nitrobenzene lowers its freezing point to 3.65 °C. What is the molecular weight of Y?

31. Ethylene glycol, $C_2H_6O_2$, is used extensively as an antifreeze for aqueous solutions.

    a. Calculate the molality of a solution of ethylene glycol in water that will not freeze above -15 °F.

    b. If the density of $C_2H_6O_2$ is 1.11 g/cm³, how many liters of $C_2H_6O_2$ must be added per liter of water to protect an automobile's cooling system to this temperature?

    c. Express the answer to part b in quarts/gallon.

11

Chemical
Equilibrium

Guidelines

After completing this chapter the student should be able to:

- describe the process of dynamic chemical equilibrium
- write the equilibrium expression for a chemical reaction
- calculate the value of K from experimental data
- relate the magnitude of K to the position of equilibrium
- use Le Châtelier's Principle to predict the effect of disturbing a system in equilibrium
- write the equilibrium expression for a heterogeneous equilibrium
- write the solubility product expression for partially soluble compounds
- determine K_{sp} from solution concentration data
- discuss the common ion effect
- describe the concept of activation energy as applied to the rate of a chemical reaction
- discuss the effect of a catalyst on the rate of reaction

11.1 Introduction

In Chapter 9 we saw that at a particular temperature a state of dynamic equilibrium exists between the liquid phase of a substance and the vapor phase which fills the space above it in a closed container. This state of dynamic equilibrium was defined as the condition where the rate of evaporation is equal to the rate of condensation, resulting in no net change in the amounts of material in the liquid and gas phases. Since the liquid and the vapor phases were composed of the same substance, we were dealing with a **physical equilibrium**—an equilibrium between two different physical states. In this chapter we will examine **chemical equilibria**, which exist (often within the same phase) between different substances under conditions of chemical reaction.

If 1.50 mol of PCl_5 gas are put into a 0.750 L container at 546 K, the PCl_5 immediately begins to decompose according to the equation:

$$PCl_5(g) \longrightarrow PCl_3(g) + Cl_2(g)$$

Thus, as PCl_5 decomposes into PCl_3 and Cl_2, the quantity of PCl_5 decreases and the quantities of PCl_3 and Cl_2 increase. The PCl_3 and Cl_2, however, begin to recombine in the reverse reaction to form PCl_5 at an ever increasing rate as greater amounts of them are formed:

$$PCl_3(g) + Cl_2(g) \longrightarrow PCl_5(g)$$

Eventually the rate of the reverse reaction becomes equal to the rate of the forward reaction. At this point, although the chemical reactions continue, the quantities of all three gases remain constant. In this condition the system is in a state of **dynamic chemical equilibrium.** The equation describing a system in chemical equilibrium is often written with double arrows to indicate that at a given temperature the reaction is occurring in both directions at the same rate:

$$PCl_5(g) \rightleftharpoons PCl_3(g) + Cl_2(g)$$

11.2 The Equilibrium Constant

In order to assess the quantitative aspects of equilibria, it is necessary to deal with concentrations of substances rather than with their absolute masses. The concentration units normally used are moles per liter (mol/L), or molarity, M (page 278). For example, in the previous section 1.50 mol of PCl_5 were placed into a 0.750 L container. Thus the initial concentration of the gas was:

$$\frac{1.50 \text{ mol}}{0.750 \text{ L}} = 2.00 \ M$$

If we start with a concentration of 2.00 M PCl_5 in an otherwise empty container, the experimentally determined constant concentration after equilibrium is reached is found to be 1.65 M. In this case, the concentrations of PCl_3 and Cl_2 are found to be 0.347 M each (see Figure 11–1).

Suppose that instead of beginning with PCl_5, we place 2.00 M PCl_3 and 2.00 M Cl_2 in a container with no PCl_5 present initially. The PCl_3 and

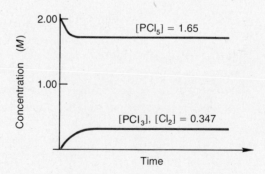

Figure 11–1

Equilibrium concentrations for the reaction $PCl_5 \rightleftharpoons PCl_3 + Cl_2$

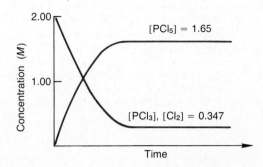

Figure 11–2
Equilibrium concentrations for the reaction $PCl_5 \rightleftarrows PCl_3 + Cl_2$

Cl_2 combine to form PCl_5, and eventually the same state of equilibrium is reached as in the first case (see Figure 11–2). At equilibrium, we find that the concentrations of PCl_3 and Cl_2 are equal to 0.347 M each and that the concentration of PCl_5 is 1.65 M.

Now let us consider a third and more complicated experiment in which we begin with 2.20 M PCl_5, 3.30 M PCl_3, and 4.40 M Cl_2. As the reactions proceed, the concentrations vary as shown in Figure 11–3 until the final equilibrium values are reached: 5.223 M PCl_5, 0.277 M PCl_3, and 1.377 M Cl_2.

It turns out that a relationship can be found among the equilibrium concentrations of the three components in all such experiments, regard-

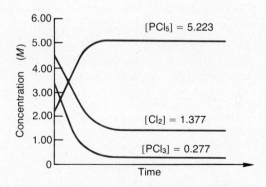

Figure 11–3
Equilibrium concentrations for the reaction $PCl_5 \rightleftarrows PCl_3 + Cl_2$

less of what the starting concentrations are. This relationship is expressed as follows:

$$\frac{[PCl_3][Cl_2]}{[PCl_5]} = \text{constant}$$

where $[PCl_3]$ is the concentration of PCl_3 in mol/L, and so on. For the first two cases we had $[PCl_3] = 0.347\,M$, $[Cl_2] = 0.347\,M$, and $[PCl_5] = 1.65\,M$. Therefore:

$$\frac{[PCl_3][Cl_2]}{[PCl_5]} = \frac{(0.347)(0.347)}{(1.65)} = 0.0730$$

For the third experiment, then, we have:

$$\frac{[PCl_3][Cl_2]}{[PCl_5]} = \frac{(0.277)(1.377)}{(5.223)} = 0.0730$$

In any system in which these three gases are in equilibrium at 546 K (the particular temperature of these experiments), their concentrations will be such as to satisfy the expression:

$$\frac{[PCl_3][Cl_2]}{[PCl_5]} = 0.0730 \tag{11–1}$$

The experimentally determined value 0.0730 is called the **equilibrium constant** (*K*) for the system. As we have seen, this constant is a number that is independent of the initial and final concentrations of the individual components.

The result expressed in Equation 11–1, when generalized, can be applied to any system at equilibrium. The balanced equation for such a system can be represented as follows:

$$nA + mB + \cdots \rightleftharpoons pC + qD + \cdots$$

The upper-case letters, A, B, C, D, . . . , represent the symbols of elements or compounds; the lower-case letters represent the coefficients in the balanced equation. The equilibrium constant, *K*, is given by

$$K = \frac{[C]^p[D]^q \ldots}{[A]^n[B]^m \ldots} \qquad (11\text{-}2)$$

Thus the concentrations of the substances on the right-hand side of the chemical equation, called the products for convenience, appear as factors in the numerator, with each concentration raised to a power equal to the coefficient in the chemical equation. The concentrations of the substances on the left-hand side of the chemical equation, called the reactants, appear in a similar way in the denominator.

As an example, let us consider the reaction of N_2 and H_2 at equilibrium:

$$N_2(g) + 3\ H_2(g) \rightleftharpoons 2\ NH_3(g)$$

When we plug the appropriate values from this balanced equation into equation 11-2, we have:

$$K = \frac{[NH_3]^2}{[N_2][H_2]^3}$$

The general equation for the equilibrium constant (Equation 11-2) expresses the **Law of Chemical Equilibrium.** The right-hand side of the equilibrium equation, called the **mass action expression**, is equal to the equilibrium constant, K, if—and only if—the system is at equilibrium. If the mass action expression is not equal to K, either the forward or the reverse reaction will predominate to bring the system to equilibrium concentrations. For example, in the experiment in which we began with 2.20 M PCl_5, 3.30 M PCl_3, and 4.40 M Cl_2, the initial value of the mass action expression was:

$$\frac{[PCl_3][Cl_2]}{[PCl_5]} = \frac{(3.30)(4.40)}{(2.20)} = 6.60$$

Since 6.60 is greater than K, 0.0730, the numerator, or product concentrations, must decrease relative to the denominator in order to attain equilibrium. Therefore, the reverse reaction proceeds at a faster rate than the forward reaction until the equilibrium concentrations are reached.

EXAMPLE 11.2a   HI dissociates according to the reaction:

$$2 \; HI \rightleftharpoons H_2 + I_2$$

At 400 °C an equilibrium mixture was found to contain 0.123 M HI, 0.0204 M H_2, and 0.0110 M I_2. Calculate K for this equilibrium at 400 °C. We first write the equilibrium expression for the reaction:

$$K = \frac{[H_2][I_2]}{[HI]^2}$$

Since the concentrations given are equilibrium concentrations, we can substitute them into this expression:

$$K = \frac{(0.0204)(0.0110)}{(0.123)^2}$$

$$K = 0.0148$$

In general, the value of K for any given reaction is characteristic of that reaction and depends only on the temperature and the units of concentration used (usually mol/L).

The Law of Chemical Equilibrium was first proposed in 1867 by Cato Maximilian Guldberg and Peter Waage, who inferred it from experimental observations. In fact, the term "mass action expression," which describes the right-hand side of the Law of Chemical Equilibrium, comes from their description of equilibrium as an "action force" between reactants and products that is proportional to the "active masses." The Law can now be derived from kinetic theory, although the value of K for a given reaction at a given temperature must be determined experimentally.

11.3   The Magnitude of *K*

The magnitude of the equilibrium constant K for a reaction gives information on the tendency of the reaction to occur. If K is very small, say 10^{-5} or less, the numerator of the mass action expression at equilibrium is small compared to the denominator; that is, the product concentrations are much smaller than the reactant concentrations at equilibrium. This means that the forward reaction is unfavorable compared to the reverse reaction. If a reaction having a small K is begun with only the reactants present, only small amounts of products are formed before equilibrium is reached.

Similarly, if K is very large, say 10^5 or greater, the product concentrations at equilibrium are greater than the reactant concentrations. In this case the forward reaction is more favorable than the reverse reaction. Thus if a reaction having a large K is begun with only the reactants present, most of the material is converted to products by the time equilibrium is reached, and only small amounts of the reactants remain.

If K is neither very large nor very small, the numerator and the denominator of the mass action expression are more balanced at equilibrium. The forward and the reverse reactions are about equally favored, and significant concentrations of all components (reactants and products) are present at equilibrium. This was the case with the example reaction used in the preceding section, $PCl_5 \rightleftarrows PCl_3 + Cl_2$, for which $K = 0.0730$.

11.4 Le Châtelier's Principle

The equilibrium state of a system represents its most stable energetic configuration; therefore, when a system reaches equilibrium, it tends to remain that way. However, an equilibrium can be disturbed in a number of ways, such as by adding or subtracting a component or by changing the temperature or pressure. In 1888 Le Châtelier proposed a "law of reaction" which considered what happens to a system at equilibrium when it is disturbed. **Le Châtelier's Principle** may be stated as follows:

When a system at equilibrium is disturbed by some stress, the position of the equilibrium will *shift* in such a way as to relieve that stress.

In illustration, we shall consider the principal stresses that may be placed on a system in chemical equilibrium and use Le Châtelier's Principle to predict how the stress will be relieved. When applicable, we will also show that the prediction is consistent with the Law of Chemical Equilibrium.

The Effect of Adding or Removing a Component

Let us begin by considering the following reaction at equilibrium:

$$N_2(g) + 3 H_2(g) \rightleftharpoons 2 NH_3(g) \qquad (11\text{--}3)$$

If a stress is introduced by adding N_2 to the system, Le Châtelier's Principle says that the system will act in such a manner that the amount of N_2 will be decreased, that is, that the forward reaction will predominate until equilibrium has been reestablished.

This result could also have been predicted from the Law of Chemical Equilibrium as follows. Initially, the mass action expression is equal to the equilibrium constant, since the system is at equilibrium:

$$\frac{[NH_3]^2}{[N_2][H_2]^3} = K \qquad (11\text{--}4)$$

However, when N_2 is added to the system, the mass action expression becomes smaller than K, since its denominator increases. In order for the mass action expression to reassume its equilibrium value, the numerator must increase and the denominator must decrease; that is, N_2 and H_2 must react to give more NH_3, and the reaction proceeds in the forward direction. The end result is that there is more N_2 and NH_3 but less H_2 in the system than in the beginning.

By similar reasoning, using either Le Châtelier's Principle or the Law of Chemical Equilibrium, we could show that if NH_3 is removed from the system, the forward reaction will predominate until equilibrium is restored. Since the forward process does not readily occur (K is small for this reaction), during the industrial process of manufacturing ammonia (NH_3), H_2 and N_2 are continuously added to the system and NH_3 is continuously removed so that the forward reaction will always predominate.

The Effect of Temperature

If we write the reaction we have been considering to include the heat of reaction, we have:

$$N_2(g) + 3 H_2(g) \rightleftharpoons 2 NH_3(g) + 22 \text{ kcal}$$

Thus the forward reaction is exothermic ($\Delta H = -22$ kcal), while the reverse reaction is endothermic. Suppose the system is at equilibrium, and we decide to raise the temperature. This means that we are adding thermal energy to the system. According to Le Châtelier's Principle, the equilibrium will shift in a way to absorb the added energy. Thus raising the temperature causes the endothermic reaction (the reverse reaction) to predominate until equilibrium is reestablished. Since the concentration of NH_3 decreases during the shift to the new equilibrium, K itself will decrease. From this we may conclude that for equilibrium equations in which the forward reaction is exothermic, K will *decrease* if the temperature is increased. If the forward reaction is endothermic, K will *increase* when the temperature is increased.

The Effect of Pressure

If the pressure on a gaseous system at equilibrium is increased, Le Châtelier's Principle predicts that the equilibrium will be altered in such a way that the pressure will decrease again, if possible. Here we must recall from Chapter 8 that pressure is the result of collisions of molecules with the walls of the container. Therefore, the greater the number of molecules there are in a given volume, the higher the pressure. In order to relieve a stress of increased pressure, then, the equilibrium state of a gaseous system must shift so that fewer molecules are produced. Again using the system described by Equation 11–3 as an example, we see that four molecules on the left-hand side of the equation (one of N_2 and three of H_2) will combine to produce only two molecules of NH_3. Hence, if the pressures of all of the components in this system are increased by decreasing the volume of the container, the forward reaction will predominate until a new state of equilibrium is reached. For this reason the production of ammonia is carried out at relatively high pressures.

This result could also have been arrived at by considering Equation 11–4. If the pressure of each component is doubled, for example, by halving the volume of the container, the concentration of each component is also doubled. Hence the denominator of the mass action expression increases by a factor of 16 (2×2^3), whereas the numerator increases only by a factor of 4 (2^2). In order for equilibrium to be restored, the numerator (the concentration of NH_3) must increase, so the forward reaction predominates.

Thus it is clear that when the pressure in a system is increased by a decrease in the volume of the system, the equilibrium will adjust accordingly. However, if increased pressure results from the addition of a gas that does not enter into the reaction, the position of the equilibrium is unaffected. The concentration of a gas is directly proportional to the partial pressure of the gas, which is independent of the partial pressures of other gases (Dalton's Law, page 215). Thus the concentrations of the individual species at equilibrium are not disturbed when an inert gas is added to the system. This concept can also be illustrated by noting that the concentration of the particular inert gas does not occur in the mass action expression since it does not enter into the reaction. Therefore, the equilibrium expression is undisturbed.

11.5 Heterogeneous Equilibrium

In Section 10.2 we saw that the terms soluble and insoluble are very qualitative. A compound that dissolves to an appreciable extent is considered to be soluble; one that dissolves to a very limited extent or not at all is said to be insoluble. Although these terms are useful, it is often necessary to give a more quantitative description of solubility by relating the dissolving process to an equilibrium constant.

Since the process of dissolution is an equilibrium process, we can write an equilibrium expression for it. Consider the dissolution of $BaSO_4$, a relatively insoluble salt:

$$BaSO_4(s) \rightleftharpoons Ba^{2+}(aq) + SO_4{}^{2-}(aq) \tag{11-5}$$

In accordance with Equation 11–2, the Law of Chemical Equilibrium, the equilibrium expression for this reaction is:

$$K' = \frac{[Ba^{2+}(aq)][SO_4{}^{2-}(aq)]}{[BaSO_4(s)]}$$

The concentration of solid $BaSO_4$ is a constant since it is fixed by the density (m/V) of the solid. Therefore, $[BaSO_4(s)]$ can be combined with K', which of course is also a constant:

$$K'[BaSO_4(s)] = [Ba^{2+}(aq)][SO_4{}^{2-}(aq)]$$

Since the product of two constants is a constant, the equilibrium expression can be written as:

$$K = [Ba^{2+}(aq)][SO_4^{2-}(aq)] \qquad (11\text{--}6)$$

This expression is usually called the **solubility product constant** (K_{sp}).

The solubility of compounds in **heterogeneous equilibria**—equilibria involving two or more phases—can generally be expressed in this manner. In writing the mass action expression for a heterogeneous equilibrium, we include only those concentrations that can be varied, that is, the concentrations of solute species in gas, liquid, or solid solutions. We *omit* the concentrations of all pure liquid and solid phases, since these phases have fixed concentrations.

EXAMPLE 11.5a Write the equilibrium expression for the following reaction, assuming it takes place in a blast furnace at 1000 °C:

$$Fe_2O_3(s) + 3\ CO(g) \rightleftharpoons 2\ Fe(l) + 3\ CO_2(g)$$

Since Fe_2O_3 and Fe are pure solid and liquid phases, respectively, their concentrations are constant. Therefore:

$$K = \frac{[CO_2]^3}{[CO]^3}$$

EXAMPLE 11.5b In a saturated solution of AgCl, the concentrations of Ag^+ and Cl^- are found to be $1.0 \times 10^{-5}\ M$ each. Write the solubility product expression and determine the numerical value of K_{sp}.

The equilibrium equation is:

$$AgCl(s) \rightleftharpoons Ag^+(aq) + Cl^-(aq)$$

Therefore the corresponding equilibrium expression must be:

$$K_{sp} = K = [Ag^+(aq)][Cl^-(aq)]$$

When we plug in the numerical values given in the example, we have:

$$K_{sp} = (1.0 \times 10^{-5})(1.0 \times 10^{-5})$$

$$K_{sp} = 1.0 \times 10^{-10}$$

In writing mass action expressions, care must be taken to observe the stoichiometry of the reaction. If a solution is made up by dissolving 1.0 mol of $AlCl_3$ in enough water to make 1.0 L of solution, the equilibrium equation is:

$$AlCl_3(s) \rightleftharpoons Al^{3+}(aq) + 3\ Cl^-(aq)$$

Thus one Al^{3+} and *three* Cl^- ions are formed in solution by this dissociation reaction.

EXAMPLE 11.5c Chemical analysis of a saturated solution of BaF_2 at 20 °C gives $[Ba^{2+}(aq)]$ = 7.5×10^{-3} M. Calculate K_{sp} for BaF_2.
The equilibrium equation is:

$$BaF_2(s) \rightleftharpoons Ba^{2+}(aq) + 2\ F^-(aq)$$

We know the concentration of $Ba^{2+}(aq)$; the $F^-(aq)$ concentration is:

$$7.5 \times 10^{-3}\ M\ Ba^{2+}(aq) \times \frac{2\ mol\ F^-(aq)}{1\ mol\ Ba^{2+}(aq)} = 1.5 \times 10^{-2}\ M\ F^-(aq)$$

When the concentration values are substituted into the mass action expression, we can solve for K_{sp}:

$$K_{sp} = [Ba^{2+}(aq)][F^-(aq)]^2$$
$$= (7.5 \times 10^{-3})(1.5 \times 10^{-2})^2$$

$$K_{sp} = 1.7 \times 10^{-6}$$

For insoluble compounds the value of K_{sp} is very small (on the order of 10^{-5} or less), whereas for very soluble compounds the value of K_{sp} is large.

We can use the concept of equilibrium to describe an interesting effect on the solubility of ionic compounds. Consider the equilibrium described by Equation 11–5. If we were to add more Ba^{2+} ion (as a soluble salt such as $BaCl_2$), according to Le Châtelier's Principle we would cause more $BaSO_4$ to precipitate from solution to relieve the stress imposed on the equilibrium. Similarly, in terms of the equilibrium expression (Equation 11–6), increasing $[Ba^{2+}(aq)]$ will cause $[SO_4^{2-}(aq)]$ to decrease (by removing SO_4^{2-} as $BaSO_4$) in order to keep the mass action expression equal to K. We may summarize this effect, called the **common ion effect**, by stating that the addition of an ion that is *common* to an ion of the insoluble salt in the solution will cause the solubility of that salt to decrease drastically.

11.6 Activation Energy

We have stated that reactions which have high equilibrium constants have a great tendency to proceed in the forward direction to attain equilibrium. It should be understood, however, that the value of K says nothing about the *rate* at which the system will approach equilibrium. A reaction for which K is large may, in fact, proceed so slowly toward equilibrium that for all practical purposes the reaction may be said not to proceed at all.

An excellent example of this is the relative stability of two forms of elemental carbon—diamond and graphite.

$$C \text{ (diamond)} \rightleftharpoons C \text{ (graphite)}$$

At room temperature graphite is the stable form of carbon; K for the equilibrium has a value of 3.2. As we have seen (page 311), this means that there should be significant conversion of diamond into graphite at this temperature. However, the *rate* of this reaction is extremely slow, and although diamonds are not eternally lasting, for all practical purposes they are stable.

To explain how rate enters into consideration, let us look at the following hypothetical reaction for which K is large:

$$A_2(g) + B_2(g) \rightleftharpoons 2\ AB(g)$$

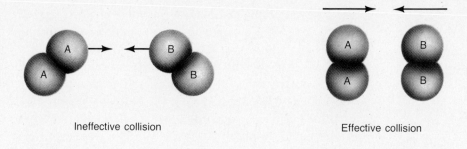

Ineffective collision   Effective collision

Figure 11–4
Two possible collisions for the reaction $A_2 + B_2 \rightarrow 2\,AB$

In order for the gaseous molecules A_2 and B_2 to react with each other, they must collide. The collision of two of the different molecules, however, does not necessarily mean that they will react. Two primary criteria must be met first. One of these is that the two molecules must collide in the proper geometric orientation. If the molecules approach each other "end-on" (see Figure 11–4), they will tend to simply bounce apart, but if they approach each other laterally, they are more likely to react. The geometric factor is most important for large molecules that have irregular shapes.

The second criterion for a collision of A_2 and B_2 to result in a reaction is that they must collide with sufficient energy to break the bonds joining the like atoms. If either the A—A or the B—B bond energy is very high, the necessary collision energy is likely to be high. The minimum collision energy that is necessary for the reaction to be carried forward is called the **activation energy.**

The concept of activation energy is shown graphically in Figure 11–5. The energy stored in the reacting species (the potential energy represented by the chemical bonds) is plotted against a "reaction co-ordinate" on which the course of the reaction may be followed from left to right. Note that since the potential energy of the reactants is higher than that of the products, the reaction as shown is exothermic (ΔH in the figure) in going from reactants to products. However, there is not a direct "downhill" path from reactants to products. Instead there is an energy barrier represented by the peak in the graph, the height of which is the activation energy. Thus, in order for the reaction to proceed from left to right, the energy stored in the reactants must be raised by a collision to a

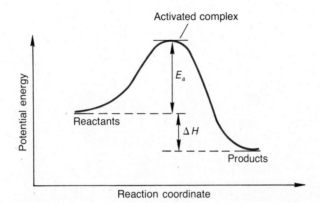

Activated complex

E_a

Reactants

ΔH

Products

Potential energy

Reaction coordinate

Figure 11–5
A potential energy
diagram for a
chemical reaction

value equal to the height of the peak. After this point the reaction proceeds "downhill" to the products.

An analogy that illustrates the concept of activation energy may be drawn by comparing the position of a marble in a bowl that is set on a table with a position on the floor beside the table. The position on the floor is lower in energy and therefore is much more favored than the position in the bowl. However, the "reaction" (marble in bowl → marble on floor) cannot proceed until the marble is given enough activation energy to reach the edge of the bowl, from where it may fall to the floor.

The nature of the chemical entities present at the energy barrier (the peak of the curve) is of interest because they are neither reactants nor products. These intermediates are often said to be in a "transition state" and may be referred to as the **activated complex**. A possible activated complex for our example is represented as:

$$A \dashrightarrow B$$
$$A \dashrightarrow B$$

where the dashed lines represent the bonds which are forming. The branch of physical chemistry that includes the study of equilibria, reaction rates, and activated complexes is called **chemical kinetics**.

Previously we saw that increasing the temperature for an exothermic reaction will decrease the equilibrium constant and thus render the reaction less favorable. However, if the activation energy for such a reaction is high, it may be necessary to raise the temperature in order for the reaction to proceed at all. This is true for the synthesis of ammonia (Equation 11–3). In this case the activation energy is very high due to the strength of

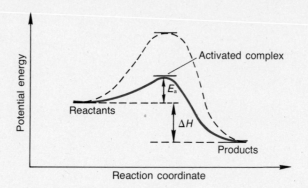

Figure 11–6
A potential
energy diagram for
a catalyzed
reaction

the triple bond in the nitrogen molecule, which must be broken before the reaction may proceed. Raising the temperature ensures that a significant fraction of the molecules will acquire the kinetic energy necessary for successful collisions.

In many cases, including the synthesis of ammonia, the rate of a reaction can be increased by the use of a **catalyst**, which is a material that alters the rate of a chemical reaction without being consumed. The catalyst usually lowers the energy barrier by providing an alternative path for the reaction so that the formation of the activated complex is enhanced. The path of a catalyzed versus an uncatalyzed reaction is shown in Figure 11–6. Note that since the energies of the reactants and the products are unchanged for the catalyzed reaction, ΔH for the reaction is unchanged. Correspondingly, the equilibrium constant is also unchanged.

Many reactions carried out in the chemical industry are catalyzed, as are hundreds of natural biochemical reactions. The very specific catalysts that speed up biochemical reactions are called *enzymes*. These biological molecules provide the geometry necessary for certain reactions to occur. It appears that the enzyme operates by bringing together the reactants in a geometric arrangement that is favorable to the formation of the activated complex, thus enabling the reaction to take place efficiently.

In summary, there are many factors that must be considered in any discussion of reactions and chemical equilibria. The goal of this chapter has been to provide a basic introduction to these factors and to lay the groundwork for subsequent chapters, which rely on the concepts presented here.

TERMS
AND
CONCEPTS

- Physical and chemical equilibria
- Dynamic chemical equilibrium
- Equilibrium constant (K)
- Law of Chemical Equilibrium
- Mass action expression
- Le Châtelier's Principle
- Solubility product constant (K_{sp})

- Heterogeneous equilibrium
- Common ion effect
- Activation energy
- Activated complex
- Chemical kinetics
- Catalyst

QUESTIONS

1. Write the equilibrium expression (Law of Chemical Equilibrium) for each of the following gaseous reactions:
   a. $CO(g) + Cl_2(g) \rightleftarrows COCl_2(g)$
   b. $N_2(g) + O_2(g) \rightleftarrows 2\,NO(g)$
   c. $2\,H_2S(g) \rightleftarrows 2\,H_2(g) + S_2(g)$
   d. $CH_4(g) + 2\,H_2S(g) \rightleftarrows CS_2(g) + 4\,H_2(g)$
   e. $CO(g) + H_2O(g) \rightleftarrows CO_2(g) + H_2(g)$
   f. $2\,SO_2(g) + O_2(g) \rightleftarrows 2\,SO_3(g)$
   g. $2\,NO(g) + O_2(g) \rightleftarrows 2\,NO_2(g)$
   h. $N_2O_4(g) \rightleftarrows 2\,NO_2(g)$

2. At 750 °C the equilibrium constant for the following reaction is 1.1×10^{-6}, and at 830 °C it is 4.2×10^{-6}:

$$2\,H_2S(g) \rightleftarrows 2\,H_2(g) + S_2(g)$$

   Is the reaction endothermic or exothermic?

3. Bromine is introduced into a container which is then heated to 900 °C. The concentration of $Br_2(g)$ is found to be 0.100 M, and the concentration of $Br(g)$ is 1.20×10^{-3} M at this temperature.
   a. What is the equilibrium constant at 900 °C for the reaction?

$$Br_2(g) \rightleftarrows 2\,Br(g)$$

   b. When the temperature is raised to 950 °C, $[Br_2] = 0.100$ M and $[Br] = 1.81 \times 10^{-3}$ M. What is the value of K at 950 °C?
   c. Is K larger or smaller for the higher temperature? Is the reaction endothermic or exothermic?
   d. If the temperature is lowered to room temperature, will K increase or decrease? What does this say about the relative amounts of Br_2 and Br in bromine vapor at room temperature?

4. The equilibrium constant for the following reaction at 900 °C is 1.71×10^{-4}:

$$4\,CuO(s) \rightleftarrows 2\,Cu_2O(s) + O_2(g)$$

    a. Write the Law of Chemical Equilibrium for the reaction.

    b. What is the equilibrium partial pressure of O_2 above solid CuO at 900 °C?

    c. At 1060 °C the equilibrium constant is 3.35×10^{-3}. Is the reaction endothermic or exothermic?

5. The equilibrium constant for the following reaction at 1009 °C is 5.60:

$$C(s) + S_2(g) \rightleftharpoons CS_2(g)$$

    a. Write the Law of Chemical Equilibrium for the reaction.

    b. If $S_2(g)$ and an equal number of moles of $CS_2(g)$ are introduced into a closed vessel containing carbon at 1009 °C, which reaction (forward or reverse) will predominate until equilibrium is attained? Explain.

    c. If $[S_2(g)]$ at equilibrium is 0.10 M, what is $[CS_2(g)]$?

    d. If the pressure in the reaction vessel is increased by decreasing its volume, how is the equilibrium affected? Explain.

6. Ammonium hydrogen sulfide decomposes at room temperature (25 °C) into ammonia and hydrogen sulfide:

$$NH_4HS(s) \rightleftharpoons NH_3(g) + H_2S(g)$$

The equilibrium constant is 1.81×10^{-4}. Which reaction (forward or reverse) will predominate until equilibrium is reached if:

    a. $[NH_3] = 0.00310$ M and $[H_2S] = 6.00 \times 10^{-3}$ M

    b. $[NH_3] = 0.0516$ M and $[H_2S] = 6.00 \times 10^{-3}$ M

    c. $[NH_3] = 8.11 \times 10^{-3}$ M and $[H_2S] = 0.0223$ M

    d. If $NH_4HS(s)$ alone is placed in a closed container at 25 °C, what will $[NH_3]$ and $[H_2S]$ be when equilibrium is established? What are the partial pressures of these two gases? (Hint: Under these conditions $[NH_3] = [H_2S]$. Explain.)

7. At 713 K the following equilibrium can be established:

$$Sb_2S_3(s) + 3 H_2(g) \rightleftharpoons 2 Sb(s) + 3 H_2S(g)$$

    a. If at equilibrium $[H_2]$ is found to be 0.149 M and $[H_2S]$ is 0.112 M, what is the equilibrium constant K?

    b. What are the partial pressures of H_2 and H_2S at the concentrations in part a?

    c. If the volume of the container is 0.745 L, how many moles of each of the gases are present?

8. a. At 248 °C $[SbCl_5] = 0.093$ M, $[SbCl_3] = 0.063$ M, and $[Cl_2] = 0.037$ M. What is the equilibrium constant for the following reaction?

$$SbCl_5(g) \rightleftharpoons SbCl_3(g) + Cl_2(g)$$

   b. If $[SbCl_5] = 0.16\ M$, $[SbCl_3] = 0.052\ M$, and $[Cl_2] = 0.095\ M$, is the mass action expression larger or smaller than the equilibrium constant? Will the forward or reverse reaction predominate until the system attains equilibrium?

9. Consider the following reaction at equilibrium:

$$CO(g) + 2\ H_2(g) \rightleftharpoons CH_3OH(g) + heat$$

State the effect on the reaction and on the concentration of each component in the reaction if:

   a. H_2 is added to the system

   b. CH_3OH is added to the system

   c. CO is removed from the system

   d. the pressure is increased by decreasing the volume

   e. the temperature is lowered

   f. the pressure is increased by adding argon gas

10. The equilibrium constant for the following reaction at 395 °C is 1.23×10^3:

$$CO(g) + Cl_2(g) \rightleftharpoons COCl_2(g)$$

   a. If the initial concentration of each of the components is $0.05\ M$, will the forward or reverse reaction predominate until equilibrium is attained? Why?

   b. If $[CO] = [Cl_2] = 0.01\ M$ and $[COCl_2] = 0.2\ M$, which reaction will predominate? Why?

11. Write the equilibrium expression (Law of Chemical Equilibrium) for each of the following heterogeneous equilibria:

   a. $C(s) + H_2O(g) \rightleftharpoons CO(g) + H_2(g)$

   b. $2\ Mg(s) + O_2(g) \rightleftharpoons 2\ MgO(s)$

   c. $FeO(s) + CO(g) \rightleftharpoons Fe(s) + CO_2(g)$

   d. $AgCl(s) \rightleftharpoons Ag^+(aq) + Cl^-(aq)$

   e. $PbF_2(s) \rightleftharpoons Pb^{2+}(aq) + 2\ F^-(aq)$

   f. $Ca_3(PO_4)_2(s) \rightleftharpoons 3\ Ca^{2+}(aq) + 2\ PO_4^{3-}(aq)$

12. A saturated solution of $AgIO_3$ consists of 0.049 g of $AgIO_3$ dissolved in 1.00 L of solution. What are the concentrations of Ag^+ and IO_3^- for the solution? What is K_{sp} for $AgIO_3$?

13. A saturated solution of $SrSO_4$ is found to have $[Sr^{2+}] = 5.29 \times 10^{-4}\ M$. Calculate K_{sp} for this sparingly soluble salt.

14. A saturated solution of PbF_2 is found to contain 2.4×10^{-3} mol/L of F^-. Calculate K_{sp} for PbF_2.

15. K_{sp} for $MgCO_3$ is 1×10^{-5}.

   a. What are the concentrations of Mg^{2+} and CO_3^{2-} in a saturated solution of $MgCO_3$?

    b. How many moles of $MgCO_3$ are present in 1.00 L of saturated solution? How many grams?

    c. How many grams of Mg^{2+} are present in 250 mL of saturated $MgCO_3$ solution?

16. CuCl has a K_{sp} of 3.2×10^{-7}. How many grams of CuCl are in 180 mL of saturated CuCl solution? How many grams of Cl^-?

17. It is found that there is 0.0891 g of $Ba(IO_3)_2$ in 250 mL of a saturated solution of that salt.

    a. What is the concentration of Ba^{2+} in saturated $Ba(IO_3)_2$ solution?

    b. What is the concentration of IO_3^- in saturated $Ba(IO_3)_2$ solution?

    c. What is K_{sp} for $Ba(IO_3)_2$?

18. K_{sp} for Ag_2S is 1.6×10^{-49}. If $[S^{2-}]$ in a given solution is 0.10 M, what is the maximum concentration of Ag^+ that can be present? What is the maximum weight of Ag^+ that can be present in 150 mL of this solution?

19. The Pb^{2+} concentration of a solution is 0.10 M. Will $PbCl_2$ ($K_{sp} = 1 \times 10^{-4}$) precipitate from this solution if enough NaCl is added to raise $[Cl^-]$ to 0.003 M? Explain. What if $[Cl^-]$ is raised to 0.020 M?

20. What is the effect on each of the components and on the position of the equilibrium in Question 2 if:

    a. H_2 is removed from the system

    b. S_2 is added to the system

    c. H_2S is removed from the system

    d. the pressure is decreased by increasing the volume

    e. the pressure is increased by adding helium gas

    f. the temperature is raised

21. It is always necessary to know the precise chemical equation for which an equilibrium constant is given. To illustrate this, first calculate K for the following equation at 400 °C if $[N_2] = 0.020$ M, $[H_2] = 0.136$ M, and $[NH_3] = 0.0050$ M at equilibrium.

$$N_2(g) + 3\,H_2(g) \rightleftharpoons 2\,NH_3(g)$$

Now calculate K using the same concentrations for:

$$\tfrac{1}{2}N_2(g) + \tfrac{3}{2}H_2(g) \rightleftharpoons NH_3(g)$$

(Note that $x^{1/2} = \sqrt{x}$ and $x^{3/2} = (\sqrt{x})^3$.)

Can you determine the relationship between the two equilibrium constants which you calculated?

22. Discuss the role of the activated complex in reaction rate theory.

23. Explain how a catalyst affects the rate of a chemical reaction.

24. a. The equilibrium constant for the following reaction at 25 °C is 7.1×10^{25}.

$$2 SO_2(g) + O_2(g) \rightleftharpoons 2 SO_3(g)$$

If $[SO_3]$ is 0.0050 M and $[O_2]$ is 0.010 M, what is $[SO_2]$ at equilibrium?

b. What are the partial pressures of SO_2 and SO_3? (Hint: Use the ideal gas law.)

c. If SO_2 were introduced into a container with excess oxygen and a suitable catalyst, what would be the relative amounts of SO_2 and SO_3 at equilibrium? Would only a little or most of the SO_2 be used up?

12

Acids and Bases

Guidelines

After completing this chapter the student should be able to:

- list the properties of acids and bases
- describe the process of neutralization
- define an Arrhenius acid and base
- identify acid and basic anhydrides
- discuss the Brønsted-Lowry concept of acids and bases
- predict the direction of proton transfer between Brønsted-Lowry acid-base pairs
- write an equilibrium expression for the proton transfer of an acid to the solvent
- calculate K_a for an acid from the appropriate experimental data
- discuss the dissociation of water
- discuss the concept of pH
- state the relative acidities of solutions, given their pHs
- calculate the pH of a solution from $[H_3O^+]$ and vice versa
- write net ionic equations for neutralization reactions
- perform calculations involving acid-base titrations
- describe the way in which a buffer solution works
- identify Lewis acids and bases

12.1 Introduction

Acids, bases, and salts are three classes of compounds which were recognized to have distinguishing properties early in the history of chemistry. **Acids** are sour tasting, feel prickly on the skin, turn the organic dye litmus red, and react with certain metals to produce hydrogen gas. **Bases** have a bitter taste, feel slippery, and turn litmus blue. Acids and bases are sometimes thought of as being "opposites," since they **neutralize** each other when mixed in proper proportions; that is, they lose their respective acidic and basic properties. The result of a neutralization reaction in aqueous solution is the production of molecules of the solvent water and a neutral compound (neither acidic nor basic) called a **salt**. An example of a neutralization reaction is the reaction of nitric acid with sodium hydroxide (a base):

$$HNO_3(aq) + NaOH(aq) \longrightarrow H_2O(l) + NaNO_3(aq)$$

The products in this reaction are water and the salt sodium nitrate, $NaNO_3$. Since nearly any ionic compound hypothetically can be made by combining the proper acid and base, an ionic compound may be referred to as a salt.

Because the degree of acidity (or basicity) of a chemical system very often plays an important role in determining the reactions that can take place in the system, an adequate model of acid-base behavior is necessary for sound chemical theory and practice. This chapter introduces the most generally employed concepts, terms, and calculations concerning acids and bases.

12.2   The Arrhenius Concept of Acids and Bases

There are currently three ways of approaching acid-base behavior in aqueous systems, none of which is radically different from the others. The first of these modern acid-base theories was proposed in 1887 by Svante Arrhenius as a part of his general theory of electrolytes (page 274). According to Arrhenius, an **acid** is a compound that ionizes in aqueous solution to give H^+ ions, and a **base** is a compound that ionizes in aqueous solution to give OH^- (hydroxide) ions.

$$\text{acid} \quad HCl(g) \xrightarrow{\text{H}_2\text{O}} H^+(aq) \ + \ Cl^-(aq)$$

$$\text{base} \quad NaOH(s) \xrightarrow{\text{H}_2\text{O}} Na^+(aq) + OH^-(aq)$$

In his study of acids Arrhenius considered the fact that the compounds with the most pronounced acidic properties, the **strong acids**, are also strong electrolytes, and that weakly acidic compounds, or **weak acids**, are invariably weak electrolytes. According to his general theory, strong electrolytes must have a high concentration of ions. Thus Arrhenius proposed that a strong acid must be completely ionized in solution and a weak acid must be partially or incompletely ionized. Since HCl is a strong acid, the reaction for the solution of HCl in water must proceed completely to the right. In other words, when HCl is dissolved in water, it completely ionizes, so that there are no HCl molecules left in the solution.

On the other hand, acetic acid, $HC_2H_3O_2$ (abbreviated HOAc), which is a weak acid, must ionize only slightly in aqueous solution, and, in fact, an equilibrium must exist between the acetic acid molecules and the corresponding ions:

$$HOAc(aq) \xrightleftharpoons{\text{H}_2\text{O}} H^+(aq) + OAc^-(aq)$$

After HOAc is ionized in water, most of the HOAc molecules still exist in the solution. Only a small percentage of them ionize to give H^+ ions and acetate ions (abbreviated OAc^-).

We now know that since H^+ is a very small ion, it will be immediately hydrated by x number of water molecules to form a species of $H(H_2O)_x{}^+$. Experimentally, it has been found that approximately four H_2O molecules solvate each H^+ ion, giving the species $H_9O_4{}^+$. For convenience, however, we write the hydrated proton as the **hydronium ion**, H_3O^+, realizing that more than one molecule of water is associated with each ion.

Acid-Base Anhydrides and Acid Rain

The cation M^{n+} of the Arrhenius base $M(OH)_n$ is, of course, always a metallic ion, since nonmetals do not form monatomic positive ions. Similarly, the anion of an Arrhenius acid is usually composed of a nonmetallic element or elements. For example, in HCl and HNO_3, the anions Cl^- and NO_3^- are composed of nonmetallic elements.

For these reasons metals, especially the alkali and alkaline earth metals, are often associated with bases, and the nonmetals with acids. In fact, many Arrhenius bases can be prepared by reacting the appropriate metal oxide with water:

$$Na_2O(s) + H_2O(l) \longrightarrow 2\,NaOH(aq)$$
$$BaO(s) + H_2O(l) \longrightarrow Ba(OH)_2(aq)$$

Hence metal oxides are sometimes referred to as **basic anhydrides** ("bases without water"); Na_2O and BaO are basic anhydrides.

Similarly, the Arrhenius oxyacids can be prepared by reacting the appropriate nonmetal oxides with water:

$$N_2O_3(g) + H_2O(l) \longrightarrow 2\,HNO_2(aq)$$

$$P_2O_5(s) + 3\,H_2O(l) \longrightarrow 2\,H_3PO_4(aq)$$

Thus nonmetal oxides such as N_2O_3 and P_2O_5 can be referred to as **acid anhydrides** ("acids without water").

An unfortunate example of this type of reaction occurs in the atmosphere as a result of pollution. As we have seen (pages 60 and 228), sulfur occurs as an impurity in certain types of coal, and when coal is burned to produce energy, the sulfur reacts to form SO_2 gas, which escapes into the atmosphere. The SO_2 further reacts to form SO_3, which behaves as an acid anhydride with the moisture in the air to give sulfuric acid:

$$SO_3(g) + H_2O(l) \rightleftharpoons H_2SO_4(aq)$$

For this reason the rain that falls in most industrial areas is acidic and thus very damaging to buildings, both ancient and modern, and in some cases to vegetation and wildlife. To prevent this type of pollution, efforts are being made in this country to ban the use of coal that has a high sulfur content and to require the use of "scrubbers" to remove SO_2 from flue gases before it can escape.

12.3 The Brønsted-Lowry Concept of Acids and Bases

The Arrhenius definition of a base includes only those compounds that contain OH^- ions. There are many other chemical species, however, that exhibit properties characteristic of a base and that will react readily with H^+ ions to neutralize acids. The Danish chemist J. N. Brønsted and the

British chemist T. M. Lowry took this fact into account when in 1923 they independently proposed an expanded concept of acids and bases.

According to the Brønsted-Lowry definition, an acid is a species that can *donate* a proton, and a base is a species that can *accept* a proton. (Recall that a proton is simply an H^+ ion.) Thus the Brønsted-Lowry definition of an acid is similar to but broader than that of Arrhenius. Similarly, Brønsted-Lowry bases include not only OH^-, but also OAc^-, CN^-, F^-, NH_3, and many other species, since each of these can accept a proton.

Let us examine the relationship between Brønsted-Lowry acids and bases by considering the following equation:

$$HCl(aq) + OAc^-(aq) \longrightarrow HOAc(aq) + Cl^-(aq)$$

In the reaction HCl is an acid because it donates a proton to the acetate ion, which is acting as a base (accepting the proton). However, in accepting the proton from the acid HCl, the base OAc^- forms an acid, HOAc, and HCl forms a base, the Cl^- ion. In summary, every Brønsted-Lowry acid is paired with a base. These pairs are called **conjugate acid-base pairs:**

HX is the conjugate acid of the base X^-
X^- is the conjugate base of the acid HX.
HX and X^- are a conjugate acid-base pair.

According to the Brønsted-Lowry definition, the hydronium ion, H_3O^+, is an acid because it can donate a proton (H^+). When it does this, it forms H_2O, its conjugate base. Thus H_3O^+ and H_2O are an acid-base pair. The H_2O, however, can also act as an acid, forming its conjugate base, OH^-. Substances such as water which can act as both an acid and a base (in different reactions) are said to be **amphoteric.**

Using this concept of acid-base behavior, dissolving HX in water is not simply represented by the reaction:

$$HX(aq) \longrightarrow H^+(aq) + X^-(aq)$$

Rather, it involves proton transfer (to the solvent):

$$HX(aq) + H_2O(l) \longrightarrow H_3O^+(aq) + X^-(aq)$$

The relative strengths of Brønsted-Lowry acids are determined by the extent of proton transfer of the acid in water. By comparing the tendencies

Table 12–1

Conjugate Acid-Base Pairs in the Solvent Water

Strong acid	$HClO_4 + H_2O \rightleftharpoons H_3O^+ + ClO_4^-$	Weak base
	$H_2SO_4 + H_2O \rightleftharpoons H_3O^+ + HSO_4^-$	
	$HCl + H_2O \rightleftharpoons H_3O^+ + Cl^-$	
	$HNO_3 + H_2O \rightleftharpoons H_3O^+ + NO_3^-$	
	$H_3O^+ + H_2O \rightleftharpoons H_3O^+ + H_2O$	
	$HSO_4^- + H_2O \rightleftharpoons H_3O^+ + SO_4^{2-}$	
	$HF + H_2O \rightleftharpoons H_3O^+ + F^-$	
	$HOAc + H_2O \rightleftharpoons H_3O^+ + OAc^-$	
	$H_2CO_3 + H_2O \rightleftharpoons H_3O^+ + HCO_3^-$	
	$H_2S + H_2O \rightleftharpoons H_3O^+ + HS^-$	
	$NH_4^+ + H_2O \rightleftharpoons H_3O^+ + NH_3$	
	$HCN + H_2O \rightleftharpoons H_3O^+ + CN^-$	
	$HCO_3^- + H_2O \rightleftharpoons H_3O^+ + CO_3^{2-}$	
	$H_2O + H_2O \rightleftharpoons H_3O^+ + OH^-$	
	$HS^- + H_2O \rightleftharpoons H_3O^+ + S^{2-}$	
Weak acid	$OH^- + H_2O \rightleftharpoons H_3O^+ + O^{2-}$	Strong base

of compounds to transfer protons, a table of relative strengths in the solvent water can be constructed.

This table of acids (Table 12–1) lists the acids in order of decreasing acid strength, that is, in order of decreasing degree of ionization in water. As we go down the table, we are in effect considering these acids in order of their increasing *stability* in aqueous solution, because it becomes more difficult for the species to dissociate (give up a proton). Notice that the conjugate base (Cl^-) of the strong acid HCl is a weak base (the reverse reaction has a low tendency to occur), but that the conjugate base (OAc^-) of the relatively weak acid HOAc is a fairly strong base. This can be made into a general rule that the conjugate base of a strong acid is always a weak base, and the conjugate base of a weak acid is always a strong base. We can infer this intuitively by considering that in a weak acid such as HOAc, the H^+ ion has great affinity for the conjugate base (the anion OAc^-); therefore the base must be strong. In a strong acid such as HCl, however, the proton has a very weak affinity for the conjugate base (Cl^-); thus Cl^- is a weak base. The strongest base in our table is the O^{2-} anion, which has the weakest conjugate acid, the OH^- ion.

Knowing the relationships in the table of relative acid strengths allows one to predict the direction in which proton transfer occurs. For example, if some acetic acid is added to a solution containing both Cl^-

and NH_3, the proton on HOAc will be transferred to NH_3, since NH_3 is a stronger base (has a greater proton affinity) than OAc^-. (HOAc is a stronger acid than $NH_4{}^+$.) The proton will not be transferred to Cl^- or to H_2O because both of these are also weaker bases than NH_3. (Their conjugate acids are stronger than $NH_4{}^+$.) If HCN is also added to this solution, however, its protons are not transferred, since CN^- would be the strongest base present. In general, then, since protons tend to be associated with the strongest base present, the weakest acid will tend to be formed first.

In this table of acids only $HClO_4$, H_2SO_4, HCl, and HNO_3 are strong acids in water (essentially 100% transfer of the protons to H_2O). Note that the conjugate base of H_2SO_4 is $HSO_4{}^-$, which is also listed as a weak acid and which therefore does not exhibit complete transfer of protons to H_2O. Thus the predominant species in a solution of H_2SO_4 are $HSO_4{}^-$ and H_3O^+.

Let us now apply our knowledge of strong and weak acids and bases to a very practical example: the use of baking soda, $NaHCO_3$, in making cake batter. $NaHCO_3$ dissociates in water to form the bicarbonate ion $HCO_3{}^-$, which can act as a base and accept a proton from the water:

$$H_2O(l) + HCO_3{}^-(aq) \rightleftharpoons OH^-(aq) + H_2CO_3(aq)$$

Since $HCO_3{}^-$ is a fairly weak base, only some of the $HCO_3{}^-$ ions in solution actually accept protons; thus there are more reactants than products at equilibrium. However, when a cake is baked, the carbonic acid (H_2CO_3) that *is* formed decomposes:

$$H_2CO_3(aq) \rightleftharpoons CO_2(g) + H_2O(l)$$

The CO_2 gas escapes and drives the forward reactions of both equations to the right (Le Châtelier's Principle, page 311). It is the CO_2 gas which causes cake batter to expand and rise.

12.4 Equilibrium Constants for Acids

So far we have been saying that most of the molecules of strong acids transfer their protons to water, but only a few molecules of weak acids transfer their protons. In order to consider the behavior of acids and bases more quantitatively, we must consider the relationship between the strength of an acid or base and its equilibrium constant.

All Brønsted-Lowry acids react with water to a greater or lesser degree according to the following equation:

$$HX(aq) + H_2O(l) \rightleftharpoons H_3O^+(aq) + X^-(aq)$$

Again, this reaction does not necessarily go to completion but, in any case, will quickly reach an equilibrium state for which we can write an equilibrium expression:

$$K' = \frac{[H_3O^+][X^-]}{[HX][H_2O]}$$

Since the concentration of water is essentially constant (water is present as the solvent in excess), we can combine the two constants K' and $[H_2O]$ to arrive at the **equilibrium constant for an acid, K_a:**

$$K_a = K'[H_2O] = \frac{[H_3O^+][X^-]}{[HX]}$$

Sometimes, in a holdover from older terminology, K_a is called K_{dissoc}, a dissociation constant. The notation K_a, however, represents a bona fide equilibrium constant, whose value depends only on the acid HX and on the temperature.

The magnitude of K_a is determined by measuring the concentration of H_3O^+ in a solution of the acid. A small value for K_a indicates that the concentration of the products, $[H_3O^+][X^-]$, is small compared to the concentration of the acid, $[HX]$. Hence the reaction has occurred to only a limited extent, and we are talking about a weak acid. In a similar manner

Table 12–2

Equilibrium Constants for Typical Acids

ACID	K_a
$HClO_4$	$\sim 10^8$
HCl	$> 10^2$
HF	3.5×10^{-4}
$HOAc$	1.8×10^{-5}
NH_4^+	5.6×10^{-10}
HCN	4.9×10^{-10}

a large value for K_a indicates that the reaction has gone essentially to completion; hence, a strong acid has a large value for K_a. Typical values for K_a are listed in Table 12–2 (page 335). Note that HCN is a very weak acid, HOAc is a fairly weak acid, and HCl is a strong acid.

EXAMPLE 12.4a   In a 1.0 M solution of HCN, $[H_3O^+]$ was measured to be 2.22×10^{-5} M. Calculate K_a for HCN.

$$HCN(aq) + H_2O(l) \rightleftharpoons H_3O^+(aq) + CN^-(aq)$$

In order to calculate K_a, we must first determine the equilibrium concentrations of H_3O^+, CN^-, and HCN. The chemical equation shows that for each molecule of HCN which dissociates, one H_3O^+ ion and one CN^- ion are formed. Therefore the concentrations of H_3O^+ and CN^- at equilibrium must be equal: $[H_3O^+] = 2.22 \times 10^{-5}$ M and $[CN^-] = 2.22 \times 10^{-5}$ M. In order to attain these values, 2.22×10^{-5} M of HCN must have dissociated, since concentration is measured in moles of solute per liter of solution. Hence the equilibrium concentration of HCN will be the initial concentration (1.0 M) minus the concentration that dissociated:

$$[HCN] = 1.0\ M - 2.22 \times 10^{-5}\ M$$
$$= 1.0\ M - 0.0000222\ M$$
$$[HCN] = 1.0\ M$$

Thus, when HCN is put in water, the change in its concentration is insignificant because so few molecules dissociate.

The final step in calculating K_a is to substitute the concentration values into the expression for K_a:

$$K_a = \frac{[H_3O^+][CN^-]}{[HCN]} = \frac{(2.22 \times 10^{-5})(2.22 \times 10^{-5})}{1.0}$$

$$K_a = 4.9 \times 10^{-10}$$

Similarly, from the equilibrium constant it is possible to determine the concentrations of the various species in solution and the percentage of dissociation of the acid.

EXAMPLE 12.4b   Calculate the concentrations of H_3O^+, OAc^-, and HOAc and the percentage of dissociation of HOAc in a 0.1 M HOAc solution.

$$HOAc(aq) + H_2O(l) \rightleftharpoons H_3O^+(aq) + OAc^-(aq)$$

For convenience, we shall let $x = [H_3O^+]$. Using the logic in the preceding example, $[OAc^-]$ must also equal x, and at equilibrium [HOAc] must equal $0.1 - x$. From the table, we find that K_a for HOAc is 1.8×10^{-5}. Therefore, we have:

$$K_a = \frac{[H_3O^+][OAc^-]}{[HOAc]}$$

$$1.8 \times 10^{-5} = \frac{(x)(x)}{0.1 - x} = \frac{x^2}{0.1 - x}$$

This equation could be solved exactly by using the general quadratic formula, an algebraic expression. However, it is convenient to simplify the equation by making an assumption about the magnitude of x. Since we are dealing with a weak acid (K_a is small), we can assume that it dissociates only slightly; that is, we can assume that x is negligibly small compared to 0.1 and that $0.1 - x \approx 0.1$. Therefore, we have:

$$1.8 \times 10^{-5} = \frac{x^2}{0.1}$$

$$x^2 = 1.8 \times 10^{-6}$$

$$x = \sqrt{1.8 \times 10^{-6}}$$

$$x = 1.3 \times 10^{-3}$$

Since all equilibrium constants in this book are based on molarity as the unit of concentration, we can assume that all calculated concentrations are in units of M. Hence $x = 1.3 \times 10^{-3}\ M$.

Now that we have solved for x, we can check our assumption that x is negligible compared to 0.1. Since $0.1 - 0.0013 = 0.1$, our assumption is correct. The concentrations of the products and reactants are thus:

$$[H_3O^+] = 1.3 \times 10^{-3}\ M$$

$$[OAc^-] = 1.3 \times 10^{-3}\ M$$

$$[HOAc] = 0.1\ M$$

To solve the second part of the problem, we multiply the fraction of HOAc that dissociates by 100%:

$$\text{percentage of dissociation} = \frac{[\text{HOAc dissociated}]}{[\text{HOAc initial}]} \times 100\%$$

$$= \frac{1.3 \times 10^{-3}\ M}{0.1\ M} \times 100\%$$

$$= 1.3\%$$

This means that at equilibrium 1.3% of the molecules in a 0.1 M HOAc solution are dissociated at any given time.

Bases also interact with the solvent molecules, as previously discussed; they can accept a proton and thereby release OH^- ions. For example:

$$NH_3(g) + H_2O(l) \rightleftharpoons NH_4^+(aq) + OH^-(aq)$$

By analogy to acids, the **equilibrium constant for bases, K_b,** is given by the concentrations of the products divided by the concentrations of the reactants, or in this case:

$$K_b = \frac{[NH_4^+][OH^-]}{[NH_3]}$$

EXAMPLE 12.4c   Trimethylamine, $(CH_3)_3N$, is a weak base. A 1.00 M solution of $(CH_3)_3N$ is found to have $[OH^-] = 0.0080\ M$. Calculate K_b for this base.

$$(CH_3)_3N(l) + H_2O(l) \rightleftharpoons (CH_3)_3NH^+(aq) + OH^-(aq)$$

$$K_b = \frac{[(CH_3)_3NH^+][OH^-]}{[(CH_3)_3N]}$$

By the stoichiometry of the reaction we know that $[(CH_3)_3NH^+] = [OH^-] = 0.0080\ M$. Therefore:

$$K_b = \frac{(0.0080)(0.0080)}{(1.00 - 0.0080)}$$

$$K_b = 6.5 \times 10^{-5}$$

12.5 The Equilibrium Constant for Water

We have seen that water can behave as both an acid and a base:

$$H_2O(l) + H_2O(l) \rightleftharpoons H_3O^+(aq) + OH^-(aq)$$

The hydrogen ion (proton) from one water molecule is transferred to another, forming the species H_3O^+ and OH^-. The probability of such a reaction occurring between two water molecules is very small, however. In fact, at any one time the concentration of H_3O^+ ions in pure water at 25 °C is only 1.0×10^{-7} M. This is equivalent to saying that only about two in every billion water molecules are dissociated in this manner at any given instant. Since for every H_3O^+ ion formed in pure water there is one OH^- ion formed, the concentration of OH^- is the same as that of H_3O^+, that is, 1.0×10^{-7} M at 25 °C.

The equilibrium expression for pure water can be written as follows:

$$K' = \frac{[H_3O^+][OH^-]}{[H_2O]^2}$$

Again, since the concentration of H_2O is a constant, we write the equilibrium constant for water, K_w, as:

$$K_w = [H_2O]^2 K' = [H_3O^+][OH^-]$$

The numerical value for K_w is then:

$$K_w = (1.0 \times 10^{-7})(1.0 \times 10^{-7})$$

$$K_w = 1.0 \times 10^{-14}$$

This relationship, that $[H_3O^+][OH^-] = 1.0 \times 10^{-14}$, holds for any aqueous solution at 25 °C, since K_w is an equilibrium constant. As an example, let us assume we have a 5.0 M solution of NaOH. Since NaOH is a strong base and is completely dissociated in solution, the concentration of OH^- is also 5.0 M. To calculate $[H_3O^+]$, we can use the K_w expression directly:

$$K_w = [H_3O^+][OH^-]$$

$$[H_3O^+] = \frac{K_w}{[OH^-]}$$

$$= \frac{1.0 \times 10^{-14}}{5.0}$$

$$[H_3O^+] = 2.0 \times 10^{-15} \ M$$

12.6 The pH Scale

Although different concepts of acids and bases may be used in different situations, the measure of acidity in an aqueous solution is nearly always based on the concentration of H_3O^+. As we have seen, $[H_3O^+]$ for pure water is $1.0 \times 10^{-7} \ M$. Any solution having $[H_3O^+]$ greater than this is acidic. A solution in which $[H_3O^+]$ is $1.0 \times 10^{-3} \ M$ is thus 10,000 times more acidic than water, and a 0.10 M solution of HCl is 1 million times more acidic than water. A 0.10 M solution of NaOH, however, is 1 million times *less* acidic than water.

Thus it can be appreciated that the possible values for $[H_3O^+]$ in an aqueous solution cover a vast scale. To avoid working with very large or small numbers, the acidity of a solution is measured against a reduced scale, called the **pH scale**. Each unit on this scale represents a difference in acidity of a factor of 10, with the lower numbers representing higher acidities. Thus a solution with pH = 3 is 10 times more acidic than a solution with pH = 4; that is, $[H_3O^+]$ is 10 times greater.

Scales such as the pH scale, on which one unit represents a power of 10, are called logarithmic scales. A review of the use of logarithms is provided along with a table in the Appendix. We use logarithms to define the pH of a solution:

$$pH = -\log[H_3O^+]$$

To determine the range of the pH scale, let's calculate the pH of a very acidic solution, a neutral solution, and a very basic solution. An example of a very acidic solution is 0.10 M HCl. We know that HCl dissociates completely in solution (page 330) and that all of the H^+ ions combine with water molecules. Therefore the concentration (molarity) of H_3O^+ is equal to that of the original HCl, or $[H_3O^+] = 1.0 \times 10^{-1}$ M. From this we can calculate the pH of the solution:

$$pH = -\log(1.0 \times 10^{-1})$$
$$pH = -(0.00 - 1)$$
$$pH = 1.00$$

In pure water, which is neutral, $[H_3O^+] = 1.0 \times 10^{-7}$ M. The pH of water, then, is:

$$pH = -\log(1.0 \times 10^{-7})$$
$$pH = -(0.00 - 7)$$
$$pH = 7.00$$

An example of a very basic solution is 0.10 M NaOH. The NaOH dissociates completely in solution, so $[OH^-] = 1.0 \times 10^{-1}$ M. To determine the concentration of H_3O^+, we use the equilibrium expression for water:

$$[H_3O^+] = \frac{K_w}{[OH^-]}$$

$$[H_3O^+] = \frac{(1.0 \times 10^{-14})}{(1.0 \times 10^{-1})}$$

$$[H_3O^+] = 1.0 \times 10^{-13} \ M$$

The pH value of the solution is therefore:

$$pH = -\log(1.0 \times 10^{-13})$$
$$pH = -(0.00 - 13)$$
$$pH = 13.00$$

Thus most solutions have a pH between 1 and 13, with acidic solutions below 7 and basic solutions above 7. Occasionally we encounter pHs as low as -1 ($[H_3O^+] = 10$ M) or as high as 15 ($[OH^-] = 10$ M, $[H_3O^+] = 1.0 \times 10^{-15}$ M). Table 12–3 shows the pH scale and the positions of some representative solutions on the scale.

Table 12–3

The pH Scale

	pH			pOH
	14 —	extremely basic	—	0
	12 —		—	2
		— household ammonia —		
Basic	10 —		—	4
		— baking soda —		
	8 —		—	6
		— blood —		
Neutral —	7 —	pure water	—	7
	6 —	— urine —	—	8
		— coffee —		
Acidic	4 —		—	10
		— wine —		
		— orange juice —		
	2 —	— lemon juice —	—	12
		— stomach acid —		
	0 —	extremely acidic	—	14
	−1 —		—	15
		— concentrated H_2SO_4 —		

Sometimes the acidity of a solution is referred to the OH^- ion concentration instead of the H_3O^+ ion concentration. In such cases the **pOH scale** is used:

$$pOH = -\log[OH^-]$$

Since $[OH^-]$ is related to $[H_3O^+]$ by the equation $K_w = [H_3O^+][OH^-] = 1.0 \times 10^{-14}$, there must be a definite relationship between the pH scale and the pOH scale. This relationship is found by taking the logarithm of each side of the equilibrium equation:

$$\log([H_3O^+][OH^-]) = \log(1.0 \times 10^{-14})$$

The logarithm of a product is the sum of the logarithms of the factors. Therefore:

$$\log[H_3O^+] + \log[OH^-] = \log(1.0 \times 10^{-14})$$
$$= -14$$

or

$$-\log[H_3O^+] + (-\log[OH^-]) = -(-14)$$

Since the first term is the pH by definition, and the second term the pOH, we have:

$$pH + pOH = 14$$

Thus, if the pOH is known, the pH can be obtained by subtracting the pOH from 14. The fact that the sum of the pH and the pOH is equal to 14 is reflected in Table 12–3. Note that the more acidic the solution is, the lower the pH, but the higher the pOH.

EXAMPLE 12.6a Find the pH, pOH, $[H_3O^+]$, and $[OH^-]$ of a 0.076 M HCl solution. Since HCl completely dissociates in solution, we have:

$$[H_3O^+] = 0.076\ M = 7.6 \times 10^{-2}\ M$$

We use the equilibrium expression for water to determine $[OH^-]$:

$$[OH^-] = \frac{K_w}{[H_3O^+]} = \frac{1.0 \times 10^{-14}}{7.6 \times 10^{-2}} = 1.3 \times 10^{-13}\ M$$

Knowing the concentration value of H_3O^+ enables us to calculate the pH and thus the pOH of the solution:

$$pH = -\log(7.6 \times 10^{-2}) = -(0.88 - 2) = -(-1.12) = 1.12$$
$$pOH = 14 - pH = 14 - 1.12 = 12.88$$

EXAMPLE 12.6b A solution has a pH of 4.55. Is it acidic or basic? What are $[H_3O^+]$ and $[OH^-]$?

Since 4.55 is less than 7, the solution is acidic. To calculate $[H_3O^+]$ we use the pH expression:

$$pH = -\log[H_3O^+] = 4.55$$
$$\log[H_3O^+] = -4.55 = 0.45 - 5$$

$$[H_3O^+] = 2.8 \times 10^{-5}\ M$$

From this we can easily determine $[OH^-]$:

$$[OH^-] = \frac{K_w}{[H_3O^+]} = \frac{1.0 \times 10^{-14}}{2.8 \times 10^{-5}} = 3.6 \times 10^{-10} \; M$$

12.7 Neutralization Reactions

It was pointed out in the introduction to this chapter that acids and bases react with each other in neutralization reactions, producing salts and water. In writing net ionic equations for such reactions, the relative strength or weakness of the acid or base must be taken into account, as the following examples will illustrate.

1. Strong acid-strong base:

$$HCl(aq) + NaOH(aq) \longrightarrow NaCl(aq) + H_2O(l)$$

ionic equation: $H_3O^+(aq) + Cl^-(aq) + Na^+(aq) + OH^-(aq) \longrightarrow$
$$Na^+(aq) + Cl^-(aq) + 2\,H_2O(l)$$

net ionic equation: $H_3O^+(aq) + OH^-(aq) \longrightarrow 2\,H_2O(l)$

This is the net ionic equation for any reaction between a strong acid and a strong base.

2. Strong acid-weak base:

$$HCl(aq) + NH_3(aq) \longrightarrow NH_4Cl(aq)$$

ionic equation: $H_3O^+(aq) + Cl^-(aq) + NH_3(aq) \longrightarrow$
$$NH_4^+(aq) + Cl^-(aq) + H_2O(l)$$

net ionic equation: $H_3O^+(aq) + NH_3(aq) \longrightarrow NH_4^+(aq) + H_2O(l)$

3. Weak acid-strong base:

$$HOAc(aq) + NaOH(aq) \longrightarrow NaOAc(aq) + H_2O(l)$$

ionic equation: $HOAc(aq) + Na^+(aq) + OH^-(aq) \longrightarrow$
$$Na^+(aq) + OAc^-(aq) + H_2O(l)$$

(Since HOAc is a weak acid, it has been written in its undissociated form.)

net ionic equation: $HOAc(aq) + OH^-(aq) \longrightarrow OAc^-(aq) + H_2O(l)$

4. Weak acid-weak base:

$$HOAc(aq) + NH_3(aq) \longrightarrow NH_4OAc(aq)$$

ionic equation: $HOAc(aq) + NH_3(aq) \longrightarrow NH_4^+(aq) + OAc^-(aq)$

This is also the net ionic equation, since none of the species will cancel.

12.8 Acid-Base Titration

The concentration of an acidic solution of unknown strength may be determined by measuring how much base of a known concentration will completely react with a certain volume of the acid. This process, the gradual neutralization of an acid with a base, is an example of titration (page 286).

As an example, let us assume that we measure out exactly 35.00 mL of an HCl solution of unknown concentration and put it into a flask. We then add a 0.120 M NaOH solution a little at a time (Figure 12–1) until the HCl is neutralized. The neutralization is determined by adding a few drops of an indicator, such as phenolphthalein, to the HCl; this indicator will cause the solution to turn pink when it has been neutralized. Suppose the solution turns pink when 31.50 mL of NaOH have been added to the HCl. We now have enough information to calculate the concentration of the HCl:

$$V_{\text{HCl}} = 35.00 \text{ mL}$$

$$V_{\text{NaOH}} = 31.50 \text{ mL}$$

$$M_{\text{NaOH}} = 0.120 \ M$$

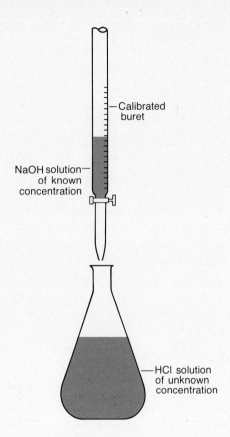

—Calibrated buret

NaOH solution— of known concentration

—HCl solution of unknown concentration

Figure 12–1
An acid-base
titration experiment

The balanced equation for the reaction is:

$$HCl(aq) + NaOH(aq) \longrightarrow NaCl(aq) + H_2O(l)$$

Our first step in solving the problem is to determine the number of moles of NaOH used. Recall (page 278) that the number of moles of a solute is equal to the molarity of the solution times the volume (in liters). Therefore:

$$\text{no. of mol NaOH} = 0.120 \text{ mol/L} \times 0.03150 \text{ L}$$
$$= 3.78 \times 10^{-3} \text{ mol NaOH}$$

According to the equation, one mole of HCl is chemically equivalent to one mole of NaOH. Thus we have:

$$3.78 \times 10^{-3} \text{ mol NaOH} \times \frac{1 \text{ mol HCl}}{1 \text{ mol NaOH}} = 3.78 \times 10^{-3} \text{ mol HCl}$$

This is the number of moles of HCl present in 35.00 mL. The concentration of HCl is therefore:

$$[\text{HCl}] = \frac{\text{no. of mol}}{\text{no. of L}} = \frac{3.78 \times 10^{-3} \text{ mol}}{0.03500 \text{ L}} = 0.108 \ M$$

EXAMPLE 12.8a If 25.00 mL of a solution of H_2SO_4 of unknown concentration is titrated with 27.50 mL of 0.0980 M NaOH, what is the concentration of the H_2SO_4 solution?

The balanced equation for the reaction is:

$$H_2SO_4(aq) + 2 \ NaOH(aq) \longrightarrow Na_2SO_4(aq) + 2 \ H_2O(l)$$

Our first step is to determine the number of moles of NaOH:

$$\text{no. of mol NaOH} = 0.0980 \text{ mol/L} \times 0.02750 \text{ L}$$
$$= 2.70 \times 10^{-3} \text{ mol NaOH}$$

We then convert moles of NaOH to moles of H_2SO_4:

$$2.70 \times 10^{-3} \text{ mol NaOH} \times \frac{1 \text{ mol } H_2SO_4}{2 \text{ mol NaOH}}$$

$$= 1.35 \times 10^{-3} \text{ mol } H_2SO_4$$

We can now calculate the concentration of H_2SO_4:

$$[H_2SO_4] = \frac{1.35 \times 10^{-3} \text{ mol}}{0.02500 \text{ L}} = 0.0540 \ M$$

A titration is usually monitored by plotting the pH versus the number of milliliters of reagent added. Figure 12–2 illustrates a titration curve for the titration of 50 mL of a 0.10 M HCl solution with a 0.10 M NaOH solution. The pH varies from 1.00 at the onset through 7.00 at the point of

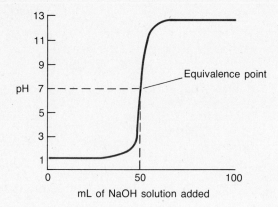

Figure 12–2
A titration curve for the addition of a 0.10 *M* NaOH solution to 50 mL
of a 0.10 *M* HCl solution

neutrality and approaches 13.00 when a large excess of NaOH has been
added. More important, there is a very sharp change in the pH near the
equivalence point for the titration of a strong acid with a strong base;
between 49.9 and 50.1 mL of base added, the pH changes from 4.00 to
10.00, making the accurate determination of the equivalence point
possible.

12.9 Buffer Solutions

Suppose we take 1.00 L of a solution of 1.8×10^{-5} *M* HCl and add to it
0.100 L of a 0.10 *M* NaOH solution. The original pH of the acidic solution
is $-\log(1.8 \times 10^{-5})$, which is equal to $-(0.26 - 5.00)$, or 4.74. To calculate the pH of the solution after adding the basic solution, we must calculate the number of moles of acid and base in order to take into account
the effect of dilution. (We are combining 1.00 L with 0.100 L to give a new
volume of 1.10 L.)

$$V \qquad \times \qquad M \qquad = \qquad \text{no. of mol}$$

1.00 L HCl $\times 1.8 \times 10^{-5}$ mol/L HCl $= 1.8 \times 10^{-5}$ mol HCl

0.100 L NaOH $\times 0.10$ mol/L NaOH $= 0.010$ mol NaOH

The neutralization reaction for a strong acid and a strong base is:

$$H_3O^+ \quad + \quad OH^- \longrightarrow 2\ H_2O$$

initial no. of mol	1.8×10^{-5}	0.010
no. of mol after neutralization	~ 0	~ 0.010

In other words, we have neutralized all of the acid and, since 1.8×10^{-5} is much less than 0.010, we can neglect the amount of OH^- used up in the neutralization reaction.

The next step in calculating the new pH is to determine the concentration of H_3O^+ in the neutralized solution, which can be done by using the equilibrium expression for water once we know the concentration of OH^-:

$$[OH^-] = \frac{0.010\ \text{mol}}{1.10\ \text{L}} = 0.0091\ M$$

$$[H_3O^+] = \frac{K_w}{[OH^-]} = \frac{1.0 \times 10^{-14}}{0.0091}$$

$$[H_3O^+] = 1.1 \times 10^{-12}\ M$$

When we substitute this value into the pH expression, we have:

$$pH = -\log(1.1 \times 10^{-12})$$

$$pH = -(0.04 - 12.00) = 11.96$$

Thus the pH has changed from 4.74 to 11.96, from a slightly acidic to a very basic solution.

Now let us see what happens when we add our base to what is known as a **buffer solution**. An *acidic* buffer solution is prepared from a weak acid and a salt whose anion is the conjugate base of the weak acid; an example is a solution containing HOAc and NaOAc. Similarly, a *basic* buffer solution is prepared from a weak base and a salt whose cation is its conjugate acid, such as a solution of NH_3 and NH_4Cl. Buffer solutions have the very useful characteristic of resisting large changes in pH. This characteristic results from the ability of a weak acid, for example, to neutralize any strong base that is added, and the ability of its conjugate base to neutralize any strong acid that is added.

Let us consider the acetic acid-sodium acetate buffer as an example. The equilibrium we are dealing with is the following:

$$HOAc(aq) + H_2O(l) \rightleftharpoons H_3O^+(aq) + OAc^-(aq)$$

In preparing the buffer solution, HOAc and OAc$^-$ are made to be present in approximately equal concentrations. Most of the OAc$^-$ present comes from the dissociation of NaOAc and not from the HOAc, which as a weak acid dissociates only slightly.

The equilibrium expression for this solution is:

$$K_a = \frac{[H_3O^+][OAc^-]}{[HOAc]}$$

Solving for $[H_3O^+]$, we have:

$$[H_3O^+] = K_a \frac{[HOAc]}{[OAc^-]}$$

This says that the $[H_3O^+]$ in a buffer solution has a value near K_a for the weak acid, since the concentrations of HOAc and OAc$^-$ are approximately equal.

If a strong acid such as HCl is added to a solution in which this equilibrium is operative, the OAc$^-$ will react with the H_3O^+ formed through dissociation of HCl; that is, the equilibrium is shifted to the left (Le Châtelier's Principle) and the $[H_3O^+]$ will return almost to its initial value. If there had been no OAc$^-$ to "absorb" the additional H_3O^+, the $[H_3O^+]$ would have gone up sharply.

Let us now quantitatively consider a solution that is 0.10 M in HOAc and 0.10 M in OAc$^-$. Since HOAc is a weak acid and only slightly dissociated, [HOAc] = 0.10 M. Therefore:

$$[H_3O^+] = K_a \frac{[HOAc]}{[OAc^-]}$$

$$= (1.8 \times 10^{-5}) \frac{(0.10)}{(0.10)}$$

$$[H_3O^+] = 1.8 \times 10^{-5} \; M$$

and

$$pH = 4.74$$

Now let us add 0.10 L of 0.10 M NaOH to 1.00 L of this solution. To take dilution into account, we convert to moles (as was done in the previous example):

initial no. of mol   1.00 L $\times$ 0.10 mol/L HOAc = 0.10 mol HOAc

1.00 L $\times$ 0.10 mol/L OAc$^-$ = 0.10 mol OAc$^-$

no. of mol added   0.10 L $\times$ 0.10 mol/L NaOH = 0.010 mol NaOH

The new volume is 1.10 L.

The net ionic equation for the neutralization reaction between a weak acid and a strong base is:

$$\text{HOAc}(aq) + \text{OH}^-(aq) \longrightarrow \text{OAc}^-(aq) + \text{H}_2\text{O}(l)$$

initial no. of mol	0.10	0.010	0.10
no. of mol after neutralization	0.09	~0	0.11
concentration after neutralization	$\dfrac{0.09}{1.10} = 0.082$ mol/L		$\dfrac{0.11}{1.10} = 0.10$ mol/L

In the neutralized solution, all of the OH$^-$ ion has been used up by the neutralization reaction and the HOAc and OAc$^-$ are in equilibrium. Therefore, the equilibrium expression for HOAc must be obeyed:

$$\text{HOAc}(aq) + \text{H}_2\text{O}(l) \rightleftharpoons \text{H}_3\text{O}^+(aq) + \text{OAc}^-(aq)$$

and

$$[\text{H}_3\text{O}^+] = K_a \frac{[\text{HOAc}]}{[\text{OAc}^-]}$$

$$= 1.8 \times 10^{-5}\left(\frac{0.082}{0.10}\right)$$

$$[\text{H}_3\text{O}^+] = 1.5 \times 10^{-5} \ M$$

$$\text{pH} = -\log(1.5 \times 10^{-5})$$

$$= -(.18 - 5)$$

$$\text{pH} = 4.82$$

The Buffer System of Blood

Because most chemical reactions that take place in living systems are dependent on pH, it is important that the pH of a cell or tissue does not vary too greatly. In higher organisms, the necessary ranges of pH are maintained by various conjugate acid-base pairs that act as buffers.

The pH of blood is kept at a constant level by the carbonic acid-bicarbonate ion (H_2CO_3 — HCO_3^-) conjugate acid-base system:

$$H_2O + H_2CO_3 \rightleftharpoons H_3O^+ + HCO_3^-$$

The system is made more complex by the fact that carbonic acid is also in equilibrium with dissolved carbon dioxide, $CO_2(aq)$, which in turn is in equilibrium with gaseous CO_2 in the lungs. The entire system may be represented as follows:

$$CO_2(g) \overset{H_2O}{\rightleftharpoons} H_2O(l) + CO_2(aq) \rightleftharpoons$$

$$H_2CO_3(aq) \overset{H_2O}{\rightleftharpoons} H_3O^+(aq) + HCO_3^-(aq)$$

Thus any excess base in the blood is neutralized by H_3O^+, which is replenished by a shift to the right by all of the above equilibria, ultimately drawing upon the reservoir of CO_2 in the lungs. Excess acid reacts with the HCO_3^- present and thus causes the equilibria to shift to the left, leaving the pH at very nearly the same value it was before the equilibrium was disturbed.

If the pH of blood falls below 7.0, coma occurs, and if it rises above 7.8, tetany (contractive muscle spasms) results. In either case death will occur if the situation is not corrected. Even small deviations from the normal pH of 7.40 are indicative of serious disorders. A condition resulting in a pH that is higher than normal is known as *alkalosis*; it is caused by excessive loss of H_3O^+ from the system. Any condition causing an excessive formation of H_3O^+, resulting in a pH lower than normal, is known as *acidosis*. Mild acidosis is a temporary result of exercise and is due to the formation of lactic acid ($HC_3H_5O_3$). The blood pH is prevented from falling too low during exercise by the expulsion of CO_2 from the lungs by rapid breathing.

For this buffer solution, then, the pH has changed from 4.74 to only 4.82. Recall that when the same amount of NaOH (base) was added to a non-buffered solution (page 349), the pH was raised from 4.74 to 11.96.

Buffers are extremely useful in stabilizing the pH of chemical systems when the efficiency of the reaction being carried out depends critically on the H_3O^+ concentration. This is the case in practically all reactions involving biochemical systems.

12.10   The Lewis Concept of Acids and Bases

A still broader concept of acids and bases than that of Brønsted and Lowry was proposed by G. N. Lewis in 1923. Lewis defined a base as a species that donates a pair of electrons to another species with the resultant formation of a covalent bond, and an acid as a species that accepts the pair of electrons. This definition of a base is not practically different from the Brønsted-Lowry definition, since every Brønsted-Lowry base (proton acceptor) has a free electron pair to which the proton binds and forms a covalent bond. The proton donor is also an acid in the Lewis sense, since the proton "accepts" the electron pair from the base. Thus the reaction below can be regarded as an acid-base reaction in terms of either the Brønsted-Lowry or the Lewis definition.

$$H_3O^+(aq) \quad + \quad :NH_3(aq) \longrightarrow NH_4^+(aq) + H_2O(l)$$

proton donor,   proton acceptor,
electron pair acceptor   electron pair donor

However, the Lewis definition broadens the concept of acids beyond requiring the presence of the H^+ ion, since there are many other species capable of accepting an electron pair to form a covalent bond. Nearly any metal ion in aqueous solution, for example, will form a bond with one of the free electron pairs on a water molecule in a hydration reaction:

$$H_2O: + M^{n+} \longrightarrow M(H_2O)^{n+}$$

Thus the metal ion acts as a Lewis acid and the water molecule acts as a Lewis base.

Certain compounds of the Group IIIA elements in the periodic table also act as Lewis acids, since such compounds have fewer than the stable octet of electrons in their valence shells (page 164). These compounds tend to react with Lewis bases in order to attain the stable configuration of eight valence electrons (four electron pairs). Two examples are BF_3 and $AlCl_3$, which have only six electrons in the valence shells of the boron and aluminum:

$$BF_3 + :NH_3 \longrightarrow F_3BNH_3$$

$$AlCl_3(aq) + :Cl:^-(aq) \longrightarrow AlCl_4^-(aq)$$

The compounds BF_3 and $AlCl_3$ act as Lewis acids in these reactions since they accept a pair of electrons from another species (the Lewis base) to form a covalent bond. The compound formed in a Lewis acid-base reaction is sometimes called an **acid-base adduct** (F_3BNH_3 in the above example).

TERMS AND CONCEPTS	

- Neutralization
- Acids, bases, and salts
- Arrhenius acids and bases
- Strong and weak acids
- Hydronium ion, H_3O^+
- Acid and basic anhydrides
- Brønsted-Lowry acids and bases
- Conjugate acid-base pairs
- Amphoteric substances

- Equilibrium constant for an acid, K_a
- Equilibrium constant for a base, K_b
- Equilibrium constant for water, K_w
- pH and pOH scales
- Acid-base titration
- Buffer solution
- Lewis acids and bases
- Acid-base adduct

QUESTIONS

1. Name the acid and base that could be combined to give the following salts. Write the equation for each reaction.
   - a. $Ca(NO_3)_2$
   - b. Na_2S
   - c. Na_2SO_4
   - d. NaCl
   - e. NH_4Cl
   - f. $Sr(C_2H_3O_2)_2$

2. What was Arrhenius' explanation for the observation that compounds that had strong acid properties were also strong electrolytes and that weak acids were weak electrolytes?

3. What is the basic anhydride of LiOH?

4. Name the predominant species in solution if solutions containing equimolar amounts of the following reactants are mixed:
   - a. $NH_4Cl + Na_2CO_3$
   - b. $HClO_4 + NaF$
   - c. $HOAc + KOAc$
   - d. $HCN + NH_3$
   - e. $HNO_3 + Na_2SO_4$
   - f. $H_2SO_4 + H_2O$

5. The two strongest bases listed in Table 12–1 are O^{2-} and S^{2-}. Can these two ions exist in aqueous solution? Explain. (Hint: Which is the stronger acid, H_2O or HS^-?)

6. The compounds HS^- and HSO_4^- are amphoteric. Explain.

7. A 0.010 M solution of benzoic acid, $C_6H_5CO_2H$, is found to have a hydronium ion concentration of 7.63×10^{-4} M. What is K_a for benzoic acid?

8. A 0.150 M solution of chloroacetic acid, $C_2H_2ClO_2H$, is found to have $[H_3O^+] = 0.136$ M. Calculate K_a for this acid.

9. If 1.96 g of trichloroacetic acid, $C_2Cl_3O_2H$, is dissolved in enough water to make 100 mL of solution and $[H_3O^+]$ is found to be 0.0871 M, what is K_a?

10. A 0.304 M solution of formic acid, HCO_2H, has $[H_3O^+] = 7.24 \times 10^{-3}$ M. What is K_a for formic acid?

11. Calculate the percentage of dissociation of a 1.50 M benzoic acid solution (C_6H_5COOH; $K_a = 5.82 \times 10^{-5}$).

12. Methylamine is a weak base which reacts according to the equilibrium expression:

$$CH_3NH_2 + H_2O \rightleftharpoons CH_3NH_3^+ + OH^-$$

If $[OH^-]$ is found to be 9.16×10^{-3} M in a 0.20 M solution of methylamine, what is K_b?

13. A 1.00 M solution of trimethylamine has $[H_3O^+] = 1.29 \times 10^{-12}$ M. Calculate K_b.

$$(CH_3)_3N + H_2O \rightleftharpoons (CH_3)_3NH^+ + OH^-$$

14. If 7.062 g of benzylamine are dissolved in enough water to make 150. mL of solution, with $[H_3O^+]$ measured as 3.16×10^{-12} M, what is K_b?

$$C_6H_5CH_2NH_2 + H_2O \rightleftharpoons C_6H_5CH_2NH_3^+ + OH^-$$

15. The equilibrium constant for water, K_w, depends upon the temperature. At 100 °C, $K_w = 5.13 \times 10^{-13}$. Calculate the pH of a neutral solution at 100 °C.

16. Calculate the hydronium ion concentration and the pH for solutions of the following acids, each of which dissociates to give one proton:
    a. 0.25 M acetic acid; $K_a = 1.8 \times 10^{-5}$
    b. 0.12 M butyric acid; $K_a = 1.5 \times 10^{-5}$
    c. 0.05 M phenylacetic acid; $K_a = 4.9 \times 10^{-5}$
    d. 0.50 M proprionic acid; $K_a = 1.34 \times 10^{-5}$

17. Calculate the pH of solutions that have hydronium ion concentrations of:
    a. 3.6×10^{-3} M e. 0.065 M
    b. 4.8×10^{-9} M f. 2.00 M
    c. 1.0×10^{-7} M g. 1.00 M
    d. 6.0×10^{-11} M h. 0.0025 M

18. Identify which solutions in Question 17 are acidic and which are basic.

19. Calculate the hydronium ion concentration from the following pHs:
    a. 4.00   d.   0.69
    b. 5.85   e.   −0.69
    c. 11.41   f.   9.77

20. Suppose that 25.0 mL of a potassium hydrogen oxalate (KHC_2O_4) solution were titrated with 0.113 M NaOH solution. If 33.5 mL were required for complete reaction, what was the concentration of KHC_2O_4?

$$KHC_2O_4 + NaOH \longrightarrow KNaC_2O_4 + H_2O$$

21. A solution of KOH was standardized using solid potassium hydrogen phthalate, $KHC_8H_4O_4$. Exactly 37.21 mL of KOH solution were required to neutralize 0.7686 g of $KHC_8H_4O_4$ which was dissolved in water. What was the concentration of KOH?

$$KHC_8H_4O_4 + KOH \longrightarrow K_2C_8H_4O_4 + H_2O$$

22. The concentration of a H_2SO_4 solution was determined by titration with a 0.245 M NaOH solution. If 43.3 mL of NaOH solution were needed to neutralize 50.0 mL of the acid, what was the concentration of the acid?

23. It required 41.8 mL of 0.255 M HNO_3 solution to neutralize 50.0 mL of a methylamine solution. What was the concentration of methylamine?

$$CH_3NH_2 + HNO_3 \longrightarrow CH_3NH_3^+ + NO_3^-$$

24. A solution of HCl was standardized using sodium carbonate. Then 0.291 g of Na_2CO_3 was dissolved in water and titrated with 35.4 mL of the HCl solution. What was the concentration of HCl?

$$Na_2CO_3 + 2\ HCl \longrightarrow H_2O + CO_2 + 2\ NaCl$$

25. Calculate the concentration of H_3O^+ and the pH of a solution made by adding 0.100 mol of formic acid, HCOOH, and 0.0750 mol of sodium formate, NaHCOO, to enough water to make 1.00 L of solution. The equilibrium constant, K_a, for formic acid is 1.8×10^{-4}.

26. Why is it that a buffer solution will change pH only a little if either a strong acid or a strong base is added?

27. Calculate the change in pH when 150 mL of a 0.100 M NaOH solution are added to 1.00 L of the buffer solution described in Question 25.

13

Oxidation-Reduction Reactions and Electrochemistry

Guidelines

After completing this chapter the student should be able to:

- identify the oxidizing and reducing agents in a redox reaction
- balance redox equations
- discuss the principles operating in electrochemical cells
- use electrode potentials to calculate the potential and predict the direction of redox reactions
- describe the operation of the alkaline dry cell, the zinc-mercuric oxide cell, and the automobile battery
- describe the process of electrolysis
- use Faraday's Laws

13.1 Introduction

In this chapter the large class of chemical reactions called oxidation-reduction reactions (abbreviated *redox* reactions) is considered. Redox reactions are important for several reasons. One is that the energy released in spontaneous redox reactions can be converted directly to usable electrical energy. For example, all types of batteries, as well as fuel cells, which have been used in spacecraft, derive their energy from redox reactions. Redox reactions are also utilized in electroplating and in the industrial production of certain materials, some of which, such as fluorine and metallic sodium, cannot be produced by other methods. Furthermore, the use of reduction potentials allows one to predict the feasibility of a proposed reaction or to choose a reagent for carrying out a desired chemical change. Thus oxidation-reduction reactions are the foundation of some of the most practical applications of chemistry.

13.2 Oxidation-Reduction Reactions

An **oxidation-reduction reaction** (or redox reaction) is a chemical reaction in which there is a transfer of electrons from one chemical species (atom, molecule, or ion) to another. When electrons are transferred, there is an accompanying change in oxidation state (page 185), since electrons are negatively charged. The species that loses electrons increases in charge and therefore goes to a higher oxidation state, whereas the species that receives the electrons decreases in charge and thus goes to a lower oxidation state.

The following equation represents a simple redox reaction:

$$Zn(s) + Cu^{2+}(aq) \longrightarrow Zn^{2+}(aq) + Cu(s)$$

In this reaction zinc metal is placed in a solution containing Cu^{2+} ions. The zinc reacts to give Zn^{2+} ions in solution, and copper metal appears on the surface of the zinc. The oxidation state of the zinc changes from 0 to $+2$ and that of the copper changes from $+2$ to 0, since two electrons are transferred from Zn to Cu^{2+}.

The process of losing electrons is called **oxidation**. In our example Zn is *oxidized* because it loses two electrons to become Zn^{2+}. When a species is oxidized, its oxidation state increases. The process of receiving electrons is defined as **reduction**. In the example Cu^{2+} is *reduced* because it receives two electrons to become Cu. When a species is reduced, its oxidation state decreases.

In a redox reaction the species that is being oxidized (Zn in this case) is said to be the **reducing agent**, or **reductant**, because it is reducing the other species. Similarly, the **oxidizing agent**, or **oxidant**, is the species which oxidizes the other one, but which itself is reduced (Cu^{2+} in this example). Although these terms tend to be confusing at first, they will become familiar with usage.

EXAMPLE 13.2a For equations (1) and (2), identify which species is oxidized and which is reduced and name the oxidizing and reducing agents.

(1) $$4\ NH_3(g) + 5\ O_2(g) \longrightarrow 4\ NO(g) + 6\ H_2O(g)$$

For a review of how to determine the oxidation state of an element in a compound, refer to pages 185–86. In this example, we know that hydrogen has the oxidation state of $+1$ on both sides of the equation (Rule 4, page 185); thus it is neither oxidized nor reduced. Nitrogen, however, is -3 on the left side and $+2$ on the right. Since it increases in oxidation number (loses electrons), it is oxidized. (Alternatively, one may say that the species of which N is a part, NH_3, ammonia, is oxidized.) The only other element in the equation, oxygen, is 0 on the left and -2 on the right. Since it decreases in oxidation number (gains electrons), it is reduced. Therefore nitrogen (or ammonia) is the reducing agent and oxygen is the oxidizing agent.

(2) $$16\ H^+(aq) + 10\ Cl^-(aq) + 2\ MnO_4^-(aq) \longrightarrow$$
$$2\ Mn^{2+}(aq) + 5\ Cl_2(g) + 8\ H_2O(l)$$

In this reaction chlorine increases in oxidation state from -1 to 0 (it loses electrons). Therefore it is oxidized and is the reducing agent. Manganese decreases in oxidation state from $+7$ to $+2$. Thus manganese (or permanganate ion, MnO_4^-) is reduced and is the oxidizing agent.

13.3 Balancing Redox Equations

Equations describing oxidation-reduction reactions are often too complicated to balance in a simple way (by inspection). Hence, it is best to learn a methodical approach to balancing such equations. One method, which always works if carried out correctly, is the method of **half-reactions**. By this method the reaction is broken into two separate reactions, one involving the oxidizing agent and the other involving the reducing agent. These half-reactions are balanced separately and then added together to give the overall equation.

The first step, then, is to separate the redox equation to be balanced into two unbalanced half-reactions. This is done by identifying the element that is oxidized and writing an unbalanced equation involving only the species in which this element appears. The same is done for the element that is reduced. For example:

(1) $$NH_3(g) + O_2(g) \longrightarrow NO(g) + H_2O(g)$$

Nitrogen is oxidized   Oxygen is reduced

$$NH_3 \longrightarrow NO \qquad\qquad O_2 \longrightarrow H_2O$$

(2) $$Cl^-(aq) + MnO_4^-(aq) \longrightarrow Mn^{2+}(aq) + Cl_2(g)$$

Chlorine is oxidized   Manganese is reduced

$$Cl^- \longrightarrow Cl_2 \qquad\qquad MnO_4^- \longrightarrow Mn^{2+}$$

(3) $$Mn^{2+}(aq) + HBiO_3(aq) \longrightarrow MnO_4^-(aq) + Bi^{3+}(aq)$$

Manganese is oxidized   Bismuth is reduced

$$Mn^{2+} \longrightarrow MnO_4^- \qquad\qquad HBiO_3 \longrightarrow Bi^{3+}$$

The second step is to balance each of the two half-reactions as follows. (The first half-reaction of example (3) will be carried through as an illustration.)

a. First, the number of atoms of the element oxidized or reduced is balanced, as well as additional elements that might accompany it, other than hydrogen or oxygen.

$$Mn^{2+} \longrightarrow MnO_4^-$$

This step is complete in this case, since one Mn atom appears on each side, and there is no additional element other than oxygen to be balanced.

b. The number of oxygen atoms is now balanced by adding H_2O to the appropriate side of the equation. This procedure is allowed since the water in an aqueous solution may participate in a reaction taking place in the solution.

$$4\ H_2O + Mn^{2+} \longrightarrow MnO_4^-$$

The oxygens are now balanced, since there are 4 on each side.

c. The procedure for balancing the number of hydrogen atoms depends on whether the reaction is being carried out in an acidic or basic solution. If this is not specified, we may assume that the solution is acidic, unless a base appears in the original unbalanced equation. To balance the hydrogen atoms in an acidic solution, H^+ ions are added to the appropriate side of the equation:

$$4\ H_2O + Mn^{2+} \longrightarrow MnO_4^- + 8\ H^+$$

The hydrogens are now balanced, since there are 8 on each side. If the solution is basic, we count up the number of hydrogen *atoms* that are lacking and add that number of H_2O *molecules* to the side deficient in hydrogen. We must then add the same number of OH^- ions to the other side. The net result of this operation is to add hydrogen to the side deficient in it, but to maintain the oxygen balance at the same time. An example of balancing a redox reaction taking place in a basic solution is given on page 364.

d. Finally, the charges in the half-reaction must be balanced by adding electrons to the appropriate side:

$$4\ H_2O + Mn^{2+} \longrightarrow MnO_4^- + 8\ H^+ + 5\ e^-$$

There is now a net $+2$ charge on each side of the equation.

The first half-reaction from example (3) is now balanced. The second half-reaction can be balanced in a similar manner as follows:

a. $HBiO_3 \longrightarrow Bi^{3+}$ (Bi is already balanced)

b. $HBiO_3 \longrightarrow Bi^{3+} + 3\ H_2O$ (O is now balanced)

c. $5\ H^+ + HBiO_3 \longrightarrow Bi^{3+} + 3\ H_2O$ (H is now also balanced)

d. $2\ e^- + 5\ H^+ + HBiO_3 \longrightarrow Bi^{3+} + 3\ H_2O$ (charges are now balanced)

Since the number of electrons lost in the oxidation process must be the same as the number of electrons gained in the reducing process, the third step in balancing a redox equation is to equalize the number of electrons in the two balanced half-reactions. This is accomplished by multiplying through each half-reaction by an appropriate factor. In our example, the first half-reaction is multiplied by 2, and the second half-reaction is multiplied by 5. This gives 10 electrons used in each of the half-reactions. In other words, 10 electrons are produced in oxidation and 10 electrons are consumed in reduction.

$$8\ H_2O + 2\ Mn^{2+} \longrightarrow 2\ MnO_4^- + 16\ H^+ + 10\ e^-$$

$$10\ e^- + 25\ H^+ + 5\ HBiO_3 \longrightarrow 5\ Bi^{3+} + 15\ H_2O$$

The fourth step is to add the two half-reactions:

$$8\ H_2O + 2\ Mn^{2+} + 10\ e^- + 25\ H^+ + 5\ HBiO_3 \longrightarrow$$
$$2\ MnO_4^- + 16\ H^+ + 10\ e^- + 5\ Bi^{3+} + 15\ H_2O$$

This result may be simplified by "canceling" the 10 electrons that appear on each side of the equation and by recognizing that eight H_2O molecules may be subtracted from each side to give a net number of seven on the right side. The number of H^+ ions may be reduced in a similar manner. The final result is:

$$2\ Mn^{2+}(aq) + 9\ H^+(aq) + 5\ HBiO_3(aq) \longrightarrow$$
$$2\ MnO_4^-(aq) + 5\ Bi^{3+}(aq) + 7\ H_2O(l)$$

The fifth and last step in the balancing process is to check the final result to ascertain whether all of the elements and the net charges are balanced. In the example there are two Mn atoms, five Bi atoms, fourteen H atoms, fifteen O atoms, and a net charge of $+13$ on each side of the equation. Therefore it is balanced.

In summary, the five steps in balancing a redox reaction are these:

STEP 1. Separate the given equation into two half-reactions.
STEP 2. Balance each of the two half-reactions.
    a. Balance the number of atoms of the element oxidized or reduced.
    b. Balance the oxygen by adding H_2O.
    c. Balance the hydrogen by adding H^+ (in an acidic solution) or H_2O and OH^- (in a basic solution).
    d. Balance the charges by adding electrons.
STEP 3. Equalize the number of electrons in the two half-reactions by multiplying through each by an appropriate factor.
STEP 4. Add the two half-reactions and simplify.
STEP 5. Check the final results.

EXAMPLE 13.3a Balance the following reaction which takes place in a basic solution:

$$OBr^-(aq) + HPO_3^{2-}(aq) \longrightarrow Br^-(aq) + PO_4^{3-}(aq)$$

Step 1. $OBr^- \longrightarrow Br^-$ and $HPO_3^{2-} \longrightarrow PO_4^{3-}$

Step 2. (first half-reaction)
    a. $OBr^- \longrightarrow Br^-$
    b. $OBr^- \longrightarrow Br^- + H_2O$
    c. $2\,H_2O + OBr^- \longrightarrow Br^- + H_2O + 2\,OH^-$ or
       $H_2O + OBr^- \longrightarrow Br^- + 2\,OH^-$
    d. $2\,e^- + H_2O + OBr^- \longrightarrow Br^- + 2\,OH^-$

Step 2. (second half-reaction)
    a. $HPO_3^{2-} \longrightarrow PO_4^{3-}$
    b. $H_2O + HPO_3^{2-} \longrightarrow PO_4^{3-}$
    c. $3\,OH^- + H_2O + HPO_3^{2-} \longrightarrow PO_4^{3-} + 3\,H_2O$ or
       $3\,OH^- + HPO_3^{2-} \longrightarrow PO_4^{3-} + 2\,H_2O$
    d. $3\,OH^- + HPO_3^{2-} \longrightarrow PO_4^{3-} + 2\,H_2O + 2\,e^-$

Step 3. $2\,e^- + H_2O + OBr^- \longrightarrow Br^- + 2\,OH^-$
$3\,OH^- + HPO_3{}^{2-} \longrightarrow PO_4{}^{3-} + 2\,H_2O + 2\,e^-$

Step 4. $2\,e^- + H_2O + OBr^- + 3\,OH^- + HPO_3{}^{2-} \longrightarrow$
$Br^- + 2\,OH^- + PO_4{}^{3-} + 2\,H_2O + 2\,e^-$

or

$$OBr^-(aq) + OH^-(aq) + HPO_3{}^{2-}(aq) \longrightarrow$$
$$Br^-(aq) + PO_4{}^{3-}(aq) + H_2O(l)$$

Step 5. There are 5 oxygens, 1 bromine, 2 hydrogens, 1 phosphorus atom, and 4 negative charges on each side of the equation.

13.4 Electrochemical Cells

Let us consider the following simple redox reaction:

$$Pb(s) + Cu^{2+}(aq) \longrightarrow Pb^{2+}(aq) + Cu(s)$$

This reaction may be carried out by placing a strip of metallic lead into a solution of $Cu(NO_3)_2$, which contains Cu^{2+} ions (see Figure 13–1). The lead will react to give Pb^{2+} ions in solution, and metallic copper will form on the surface of the lead strip. In this reaction the lead loses electrons ($Pb \rightarrow Pb^{2+} + 2\,e^-$) and the copper ions gain electrons ($Cu^{2+} + 2\,e^- \rightarrow Cu$). Electrons flow spontaneously, therefore, from the lead strip to the copper ions in the solution.

The presence of a spontaneous flow of electrons, which is an electric

Figure 13–1
A simple redox
reaction

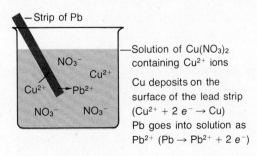

— Strip of Pb

$NO_3{}^-$

Cu^{2+}

Cu^{2+} → Pb^{2+}

$NO_3{}^-$ $NO_3{}^-$

—Solution of $Cu(NO_3)_2$
containing Cu^{2+} ions

Cu deposits on the
surface of the lead strip
($Cu^{2+} + 2\,e^- \rightarrow Cu$)
Pb goes into solution as
Pb^{2+} ($Pb \rightarrow Pb^{2+} + 2\,e^-$)

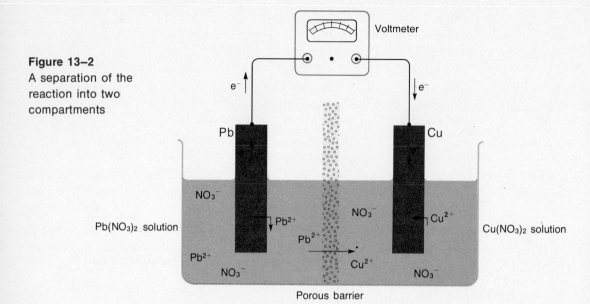

Figure 13–2

A separation of the reaction into two compartments

current, indicates that useful energy is being produced in a redox reaction. This energy can be captured if the electrons are made to flow through a wire on their way from the reducing agent to the oxidizing agent. To accomplish this for the reaction of Pb with Cu^{2+} ions, the experimental situation has to be altered, as shown in Figure 13–2. Here the strip of lead is in contact with a solution containing lead ions, not copper ions. There is also a strip of copper in contact with a solution containing copper ions. The two solutions are kept from mixing by a porous barrier such as a ceramic. If the lead and copper strips are then connected to a voltmeter, the presence of a voltage indicates electric potential. In other words, a voltage indicates that if the lead and copper strips were joined by a wire, electrons would spontaneously flow from the lead through the wire and on through the copper to the Cu^{2+} ions. Since an electric current can be used to power useful devices, the energy of the chemical reaction can be harnessed in this manner.

However, the current could not flow very long if there were no way to compensate for the charge separation brought about by the continuous transfer of negative electrons from left to right in the example. The right side would become more and more negative, while the left side would become increasingly positive, until it would become impossible for more electrons to be transferred. This situation is prevented, and the electrical circuit completed, by the diffusion of ions through the electrolyte solutions (page 274) and through the porous barrier separating the two solutions. To prevent a build-up of negative charge on the right, anions will move across the barrier from right to left, and/or cations will move across the barrier from left to right. Since cations will not move from the right side of the barrier to the left, Cu^{2+} ions are prevented from entering the solution on the left and reacting directly with the Pb as in Figure 13–1, which would cause them to short out the circuit.

Many times the porous barrier is replaced by a **salt bridge**, shown in Figure 13–3. A salt bridge can be a gel saturated with an electrolyte such as KCl. It serves the same function as the porous barrier.

The type of device illustrated in Figures 13–2 and 13–3 is called an **electrochemical cell**. An electrochemical cell is defined as any device in which a redox reaction occurs such that the electrons are transferred through an external circuit. Often it is necessary to separate an electrochemical cell into **half-cells** (as in the figures) to prevent a direct reaction between the oxidizing and reducing agents.

Electrodes

Electrochemical cells always have **electrodes**, which are the conductors that make contact with the solution. In Figures 13–2 and 13–3 the metal strips are the electrodes. One of the two electrodes is called the anode and the other the cathode, depending on the type of reaction that takes place at their surfaces. The **anode** is the electrode at which oxidation takes place. Thus, in the figures the lead strip is the anode, since Pb is being oxidized. The **cathode** is the electrode at which reduction takes

Figure 13–3
The use of a salt bridge to separate two half-reactions

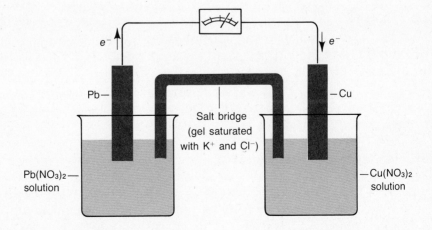

place. Since Cu^{2+} is being reduced at the surface of the copper strip, the copper strip is the cathode.

The half-reactions that occur in the cell are as follows:

$$\text{anode (oxidation)} \quad Pb(s) \longrightarrow Pb^{2+}(aq) + 2\ e^-$$

$$\text{cathode (reduction)} \quad Cu^{2+}(aq) + 2\ e^- \longrightarrow Cu(s)$$

Of course, if the two half-reactions occurring at the two electrodes are added, the overall redox reaction is the result:

$$Pb(s) + Cu^{2+}(aq) \longrightarrow Pb^{2+}(aq) + Cu(s)$$

Types of Electrochemical Cells

There are two types of electrochemical cells: the **galvanic** or **voltaic cell** and the **electrolytic cell**. The first type is used to produce energy and is therefore driven by the spontaneous redox reaction. The two cells discussed in the preceding paragraphs are of this type. The second type of electrochemical cell, the electrolytic cell, uses energy from the outside to drive a redox reaction in the opposite direction from which it would go spontaneously. If we were to put a power source in the external circuit in Figures 13–2 and 13–3 in such a way as to drive electrons from right to left, the redox reaction would be reversed, and the cell would become an electrolytic one.

$$Pb^{2+}(aq) + Cu(s) \longrightarrow Pb(s) + Cu^{2+}(aq)$$

Since the two half-reactions would also be reversed, the naming of the anode and the cathode would be reversed.

Electrochemical cells may also be classified into primary or secondary cells. A **primary cell** may act only as a galvanic cell; that is, it cannot be recharged. A **secondary cell**, on the other hand, can be recharged by an electrolytic process. One of the most common primary cells is the alkaline manganese cell, a type of "dry" cell; the most common secondary cell is the lead-acid automobile battery. Both will be described in Section 13.6.

13.5 Electrode Potentials

The voltage, or **potential**, of a particular galvanic cell, symbolized by E, is dependent on solution concentrations, temperature, and pressure. In order to compare the potentials of different reactions, it is convenient to define **standard conditions** for a galvanic cell:

$$\text{concentration of any solute} = 1.00 \, M$$

$$\text{partial pressure of any gas} = 1.00 \text{ atm}$$

$$\text{temperature} = 25 \, °C$$

A **standard potential** (one measured under standard conditions) is given the symbol E^0. For the reaction of the sample cell in Figure 13–2, $E^0 = 0.47$ V, since this is the potential measured when $[Pb^{2+}] = 1.00 \, M$, $[Cu^{2+}] = 1.00 \, M$, and T = 25 °C.

This potential of electrons to flow from Pb to Cu^{2+} is actually the combined potentials of Pb to be oxidized and Cu^{2+} to be reduced. Since the oxidation and reduction half-reactions may be added to give the overall reaction, it seems reasonable to hypothesize that the standard potentials of the half-reactions, if they were known, could be added to give the standard potential of the overall reaction. Therefore, the half-reaction for the oxidation of Pb and the half-reaction for the reduction of Cu^{2+} should have standard potentials that add to give 0.47 V.

Half-Reaction Potentials

However, the potential for any given half-reaction cannot be measured absolutely, since any half-reaction must always be coupled with a second one in order to proceed at all. Only the potential of two coupled half-reactions, that is, of an overall process, can be measured directly. This problem can be circumvented, and a table of *relative* half-reaction potentials established, if one particular standard half-reaction is arbitrarily defined to have a potential of zero. If a second half-reaction is then coupled to it and the potential of the overall reaction is measured, this overall potential is the potential of the second half-reaction relative to the reference half-reaction.

The **standard hydrogen half-cell** is used as the reference:

$$H_2(g) \longrightarrow 2 \, H^+(aq) + 2 \, e^-$$

Standard conditions in this case mean that the pressure of the hydrogen gas is 1.00 atm, the concentration of H^+ ions is 1.00 M, and the temperature is 25 °C. The standard potential for this reference reaction is defined

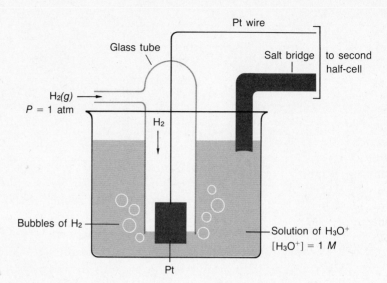

Figure 13–4
The standard
hydrogen half-cell

as $E^0 = 0.0000$ V. A hypothetical half-cell for this half-reaction is shown in Figure 13–4.

To determine the potential for any other half-reaction, we couple a half-cell employing that half-reaction with the standard hydrogen half-cell and measure the voltage. For example, let us take one of the half-reactions from our example in the previous section and couple it to the standard hydrogen electrode. The half-reaction is:

$$Cu^{2+}(aq) + 2\ e^- \longrightarrow Cu(s)$$

where $[Cu^{2+}] = 1\ M$. The overall reaction is:

$$Cu^{2+}(aq) + H_2(g) \longrightarrow Cu(s) + 2\ H^+(aq)$$

This hypothetical experiment is diagramed in Figure 13–5. We find that the reaction proceeds as we have written it; that is, electrons flow from left to right in the figure. The measured voltage, or potential, for the overall reaction is 0.34 V. Since the hydrogen half-reaction is the reference ($E^0 = 0.00$ V), the standard reduction potential for $Cu^{2+}(aq) + 2\ e^- \rightarrow Cu(s)$ is $E^0 = +0.34$ V. The positive sign indicates that the half-reaction proceeds spontaneously as written (to the right) when coupled with the standard hydrogen electrode.

Let us carry out a similar hypothetical experiment for the other half-reaction in the example from the previous section. In order to have the

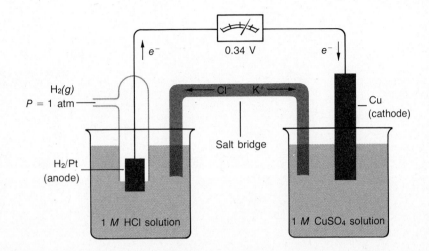

Figure 13–5
An experiment to determine the electrode potential of a standard half-cell relative to the standard hydrogen half-cell

same situation as in Figure 13–5 (except for the exchange of Pb^{2+} for Cu^{2+} and Pb for Cu), the lead half-reaction will also be written as a reduction: $Pb^{2+}(aq) + 2\ e^- \rightarrow Pb(s)$. The overall reaction is therefore:

$$Pb^{2+}(aq) + H_2(g) \longrightarrow Pb(s) + 2\ H^+(aq)$$

If we were to couple the lead half-cell with the standard hydrogen electrode, we would observe that the overall reaction proceeds spontaneously in the direction opposite to that written, and that the potential measured is 0.13 V. Thus, the standard reduction potential for $Pb^{2+}(aq) + 2\ e^- \rightarrow Pb(s)$ is $E^0 = -0.13$ V. The negative sign indicates that the reaction actually occurs opposite to the way it is written (that is, the actual reaction goes from right to left) when coupled with the standard hydrogen electrode.

Predicting Reaction Potentials

We have now determined the following standard reduction potentials relative to the standard hydrogen electrode:

$$Cu^{2+}(aq) + 2\ e^- \longrightarrow Cu(s) \qquad E^0 = +0.34 \text{ V}$$
$$Pb^{2+}(aq) + 2\ e^- \longrightarrow Pb(s) \qquad E^0 = -0.13 \text{ V}$$

To express the standard oxidation potentials, we would reverse each of the equations and change the sign of each E^0.

Given this information, we could have predicted the potential of the cell in the previous section by reversing the second half-reaction just discussed and adding the two half-reactions and their potentials.

$$
\begin{array}{lr}
\text{Cu}^{2+}(aq) + 2\ e^- \longrightarrow \text{Cu}(s) & +0.34 \text{ V} \\
\text{Pb}(s) \longrightarrow \text{Pb}^{2+}(aq) + 2\ e^- & +0.13 \text{ V} \\
\hline
\text{Pb}(s) + \text{Cu}^{2+}(aq) \longrightarrow \text{Pb}^{2+}(aq) + \text{Cu}(s) & +0.47 \text{ V}
\end{array}
$$

The positive sign on the sum of the potentials indicates that the reaction proceeds spontaneously to the right, as written. This is consistent with the observations.

If the first half-reaction had been reversed instead of the second, the resulting overall reaction would have been opposite to the one above, and the potential would have been -0.47 V, indicating spontaneity from right to left.

Table 13–1 is a list of **standard reduction potentials** for various half-reactions relative to the standard hydrogen electrode. The **standard oxidation potentials** are, of course, of opposite sign and refer to the half-reactions written in the opposite direction. The table can be used to predict whether or not a given redox reaction will take place under standard conditions. The best oxidizing agents are at the bottom and to the left of the arrow; the best reducing agents are at the top and to the right of the arrow. In general, any species to the left of the arrow will react spontaneously to oxidize any species above it and to the right of the arrow.

EXAMPLE 13.5a   Find the potential for each of the following reactions under standard conditions and predict whether or not the reaction will occur spontaneously as written.

(1) $$\text{Br}_2(l) + \text{Ni}(s) \longrightarrow 2\ \text{Br}^-(aq) + \text{Ni}^{2+}(aq)$$

From the table the two pertinent half-reactions are:

$$\text{Br}_2(l) + 2\ e^- \longrightarrow 2\ \text{Br}^-(aq) \qquad E^0 = +1.07 \text{ V}$$

$$\text{Ni}^{2+}(aq) + 2\ e^- \longrightarrow \text{Ni}(s) \qquad E^0 = -0.25 \text{ V}$$

The overall reaction can be obtained by reversing the second reaction and adding:

Table 13–1

Standard Reduction Potentials in Water

		E^0(V)
$Li^+(aq) + e^-$	$\longrightarrow Li(s)$	-3.05
$K^+(aq) + e^-$	$\longrightarrow K(s)$	-2.93
$Ca^{2+}(aq) + 2\,e^-$	$\longrightarrow Ca(s)$	-2.87
$Na^+(aq) + e^-$	$\longrightarrow Na(s)$	-2.71
$Mg^{2+}(aq) + 2\,e^-$	$\longrightarrow Mg(s)$	-2.37
$Al^{3+}(aq) + 3\,e^-$	$\longrightarrow Al(s)$	-1.66
$Mn^{2+}(aq) + 2\,e^-$	$\longrightarrow Mn(s)$	-1.18
$2\,H_2O(l) + 2\,e^-$	$\longrightarrow H_2(g) + 2\,OH^-(aq)$	-0.83
$Zn^{2+}(aq) + 2\,e^-$	$\longrightarrow Zn(s)$	-0.76
$Cr^{3+}(aq) + 3\,e^-$	$\longrightarrow Cr(s)$	-0.74
$Fe^{2+}(aq) + 2\,e^-$	$\longrightarrow Fe(s)$	-0.44
$Co^{2+}(aq) + 2\,e^-$	$\longrightarrow Co(s)$	-0.28
$Ni^{2+}(aq) + 2\,e^-$	$\longrightarrow Ni(s)$	-0.25
$Pb^{2+}(aq) + 2\,e^-$	$\longrightarrow Pb(s)$	-0.13
$Fe^{3+}(aq) + 3\,e^-$	$\longrightarrow Fe(s)$	-0.04
$2\,H^+(aq) + 2\,e^-$	$\longrightarrow H_2(g)$	0.00
$Sn^{4+}(aq) + 2\,e^-$	$\longrightarrow Sn^{2+}(aq)$	0.15
$Cu^+(aq) + e^-$	$\longrightarrow Cu(s)$	0.15
$Cu^{2+}(aq) + 2\,e^-$	$\longrightarrow Cu(s)$	0.34
$I_2(s) + 2\,e^-$	$\longrightarrow 2\,I^-(aq)$	0.54
$Fe^{3+}(aq) + e^-$	$\longrightarrow Fe^{2+}(aq)$	0.77
$Ag^+(aq) + e^-$	$\longrightarrow Ag(s)$	0.80
$Br_2(l) + 2\,e^-$	$\longrightarrow 2\,Br^-(aq)$	1.07
$O_2(g) + 4\,H^+(aq) + 4\,e^-$	$\longrightarrow 2\,H_2O$	1.23
$Cr_2O_7{}^{2-}(aq) + 14\,H^+(aq) + 6\,e^-$	$\longrightarrow 2\,Cr^{3+}(aq) + 7\,H_2O$	1.33
$Cl_2(g) + 2\,e^-$	$\longrightarrow 2\,Cl^-(aq)$	1.36
$MnO_4{}^-(aq) + 8\,H^+(aq) + 5\,e^-$	$\longrightarrow Mn^{2+}(aq) + 4\,H_2O$	1.51
$Au^+(aq) + e^-$	$\longrightarrow Au(s)$	1.68
$F_2(g) + 2\,e^-$	$\longrightarrow 2\,F^-(aq)$	2.87

$$
\begin{array}{ll}
Br_2(l) + 2\,e^- \longrightarrow 2\,Br^-(aq) & +1.07\ V \\
\underline{Ni(s) \longrightarrow Ni^{2+}(aq) + 2\,e^-} & \underline{+0.25\ V} \\
Br_2(l) + Ni(s) \longrightarrow 2\,Br^-(aq) + Ni^{2+}(aq) & +1.32\ V
\end{array}
$$

Since the sign of E^0 is positive, the reaction will proceed as written. This could also have been concluded from the fact that $Br_2(l)$ is to the left of the arrow and below $Ni(s)$, which is to the right of the arrow in the table.

(2) $\qquad\qquad 2\,Au(s) + Co^{2+}(aq) \longrightarrow 2\,Au^+(aq) + Co(s)$

The two pertinent half-reactions from the table are:

$$Au^+(aq) + e^- \longrightarrow Au(s) \qquad E^0 = +1.68 \text{ V}$$

$$Co^{2+}(aq) + 2\ e^- \longrightarrow Co(s) \qquad E^0 = -0.28 \text{ V}$$

The overall reaction is obtained by multiplying the first half-reaction by 2, reversing it, and adding:

$$
\begin{array}{ll}
2\ Au(s) \longrightarrow 2\ Au^+(aq) + 2\ e^- & -1.68 \text{ V} \\
\underline{Co^{2+}(aq) + 2\ e^- \longrightarrow Co(s)} & \underline{-0.28 \text{ V}} \\
2\ Au(s) + Co^{2+}(aq) \longrightarrow 2\ Au^+(aq) + Co(s) & -1.96 \text{ V}
\end{array}
$$

Since the sign of E^0 is negative, the reaction will proceed spontaneously in the direction *opposite* to that written. Note that although the first half-reaction had to be multiplied by 2 in order to equalize the number of electrons with the second, the potential was not multiplied. As long as the *concentration* of Au^+ remains 1 M (standard concentration), the number of moles of Au^+ expressed in the equation is irrelevant to the value of the potential E^0.

EXAMPLE 13.5b Will dichromate oxidize Fe^{2+} to Fe^{3+}?
Dichromate ($Cr_2O_7^{2-}$) is to the left of the arrow in the table, and the reaction involving Fe^{3+} and Fe^{2+} is above it, with Fe^{2+} to the right of the arrow. Therefore, $Cr_2O_7^{2-}$ will react with Fe^{2+} to give Fe^{3+}. It can easily be verified that E^0 for this reaction is $+0.56$ V.

EXAMPLE 13.5c Will aluminum metal reduce Mg^{2+} to Mg?
Mg^{2+} is to the left of the arrow, and Al is below it to the right. Therefore, Al will not react with Mg^{2+} ions. Demonstrate for yourself that Mg will react with Al^{3+} ions, with $E^0 = +0.71$ V.

It should be emphasized that predictions based directly on the table are valid only for standard conditions. Changing any of the conditions of concentration, temperature, or pressure will change the value of E in magnitude, and may even change its sign. In addition, it should be noted that the standard potential is related to the equilibrium constant K for the particular redox reaction and, as such, tells how far a reaction will go. However, as with all equilibrium constants, it does not tell anything about the reaction rate.

13.6 Common Electrochemical Cells

Galvanic Cells

The alkaline manganese dry cell and the zinc-mercuric oxide cell are two of the most widely used galvanic cells for powering small devices such as flashlights, portable radios, and toys. The alkaline manganese dry cell (Figure 13–6), which normally operates only as a primary cell, consists of zinc and manganese dioxide as the active materials. Since each is mixed

Figure 13–6
A cross-sectional diagram of an alkaline manganese dry cell

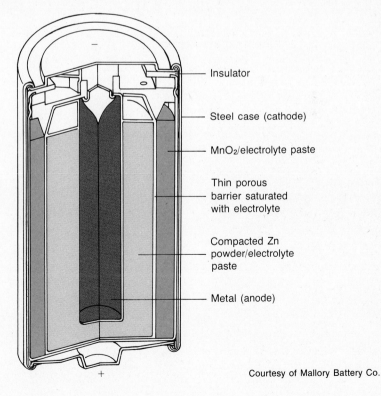

Insulator

Steel case (cathode)

MnO_2/electrolyte paste

Thin porous barrier saturated with electrolyte

Compacted Zn powder/electrolyte paste

Metal (anode)

Courtesy of Mallory Battery Co.

with only enough liquid electrolyte to make a thick paste, the alkaline manganese cell is known as a "dry" cell. As implied by the word "alkaline," the electrolyte is a strongly basic solution, unlike other types of dry cells. The zinc is the reductant in the cell and is oxidized to Zn^{2+} at the anode, while the MnO_2 is reduced to MnOOH at the cathode. The cell has a potential of 1.5 V.

An alkaline zinc-mercuric oxide cell is diagramed in Figure 13–7. The top cover, which is connected to the anode, is insulated from the steel can, which is connected to the cathode. Inside, there are three layers. The top layer is the anode, a porous zinc pellet, which is oxidized in a basic environment:

$$Zn(s) + 2\,OH^-(aq) \longrightarrow ZnO(s) + H_2O(l) + 2\,e^-$$

The middle layer is a porous material containing a solution of KOH. The bottom layer, the cathode, is a pellet of mercuric oxide (with some graphite for conduction), which is reduced:

$$HgO(s) + H_2O(l) + 2\,e^- \longrightarrow Hg(l) + 2\,OH^-(aq)$$

The overall net reaction is:

$$Zn(s) + HgO(s) \longrightarrow ZnO(s) + Hg(l) \qquad \sim 1.35\ V$$

Since in the net reaction there are only pure substances and no solutions whose concentrations may change and thus alter the potential, this cell has the advantage of operating at constant voltage.

Figure 13–7
A cross-sectional diagram of an alkaline zinc-mercuric oxide cell

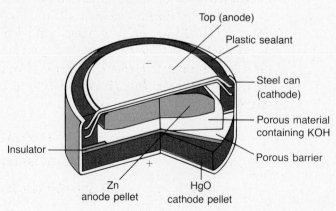

Top (anode)

Plastic sealant

Steel can (cathode)

Porous material containing KOH

Porous barrier

Insulator

Zn anode pellet

HgO cathode pellet

The Automobile Battery

The most common example of a secondary cell is the lead storage battery used in automobiles (Figure 13–8). The two electrodes in an automobile battery are made of Pb and PbO_2, respectively, and are immersed in sulfuric acid, or "battery acid." The half-reactions and the net reaction are:

(anode) $\qquad Pb(s) + HSO_4^-(aq) \longrightarrow PbSO_4(s) + H^+(aq) + 2\,e^-$

(cathode) $\qquad PbO_2(s) + HSO_4^-(aq) + 3\,H^+(aq) + 2\,e^- \longrightarrow PbSO_4(s) + 2\,H_2O(l)$

$$Pb(s) + PbO_2(s) + 2\,HSO_4^-(aq) + 2\,H^+(aq) \longrightarrow 2\,PbSO_4(s) + 2\,H_2O(l)$$

Since both the oxidant and the reductant are solids, there is no need for a porous barrier to prevent mixing.

The above reactions are those which occur when the battery is being used as a galvanic cell, that is, when it is being used to start a car. Here the Pb is the anode and PbO_2 the cathode; the only products of the reaction are the white precipitate $PbSO_4$ and water. The net reaction has a potential of about 2 V under standard conditions for a single pair of electrodes. If several cells are connected in series, a higher voltage is produced. As with any electrochemical reaction involving solutions, this one delivers a decreased voltage at low temperatures, and thus a battery may seem to be "dead" on a very cold morning, although it is merely at too low a temperature to produce the desired voltage.

Since sulfuric acid participates in both of the half-reactions in an

Figure 13–8
The lead storage battery

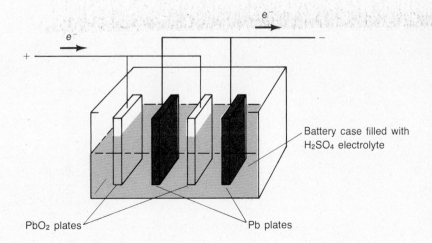

PbO₂ plates

Pb plates

Battery case filled with H₂SO₄ electrolyte

automobile battery, the acid concentration affects the voltage, and the battery actually will become "dead" if this concentration becomes too low. This would occur after only a few starts if the battery were not reversible. As it is, after the battery is used to start the engine, the engine begins driving an electrical generator, which in turn drives electric current back through the battery, reversing its reactions and thus turning it into an electrolytic cell. This recharging process replenishes the acid and regenerates the Pb and PbO_2 which were consumed in the starting process. However, the regenerated Pb and PbO_2 sometimes do not stick well to the original electrodes and may fall off. Hence the electrodes eventually deteriorate, and the battery has to be replaced.

The Fuel Cell

An electrochemical cell which may someday replace the internal combustion engine is the fuel cell (diagramed schematically in Figure 13–9). In a fuel cell the normally explosive reaction between oxygen and a gaseous fuel such as hydrogen is controlled to give an electric current. The oxygen is reduced and the hydrogen is oxidized in separate half-reactions, with the net formation of water.

$$O_2(g) + 2\,H_2O(l) + 4\,e^- \longrightarrow 4\,OH^-(aq) \quad \text{(cathode)}$$
$$\underline{2\,H_2(g) + 4\,OH^-(aq) \longrightarrow 4\,H_2O(l) + 4\,e^- \quad \text{(anode)}}$$
$$O_2(g) + 2\,H_2(g) \longrightarrow 2\,H_2O(l)$$

Since the only product is water, the fuel cell has the advantage of being

Figure 13–9
The fuel cell

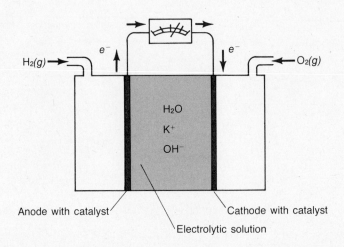

$H_2(g)$ e^- e^- $O_2(g)$

H_2O

K^+

OH^-

Anode with catalyst   Cathode with catalyst

Electrolytic solution

pollution-free. Although the fuel cell has been used in spacecraft, several problems remain to be solved before it can become economically viable for powering automobiles.

13.7 Electrolysis

The passage of an electric current through a solution is called **electrolysis** and is carried out in an electrolytic cell. An electrolytic cell is usually built with one of two purposes in mind. One purpose is to reverse the direction of a galvanic cell so that energy may be stored in the form of oxidizing and reducing agents and released at a later time. The car battery, which we have discussed, is the best example of this type of cell. The other purpose for which electrolysis is used is to prepare materials which are not easily produced (if at all) by other methods.

Electroplated materials, for example, are prepared by electrolysis. In the process of **electroplating**, the cathode is the object to be plated and the anode is the plating metal (see Figure 13–10). Both are immersed in a solution containing the metal ion. The power source in the external circuit removes electrons from the silver, which goes into solution as Ag^+ ions, and transfers these electrons to the object, which becomes negatively charged. The Ag^+ ions in the solution therefore move toward the object and are reduced to metallic silver on its surface: $Ag^+(aq) + e^- \rightarrow Ag(s)$. Only a very thin coating is necessary to give a bright luster after polishing.

Although most metals can be obtained by electrolytic reduction of the ions in aqueous solution, the most "active" metals (that is, the best reducing agents) cannot. If we pass a current through an aqueous solution

Figure 13–10
An electrolytic cell for electroplating silver

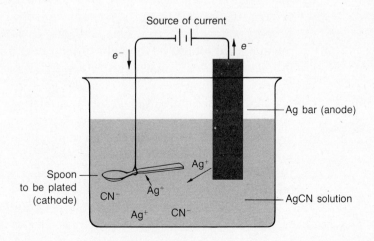

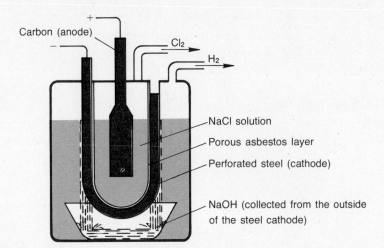

Figure 13–11
The Nelson cell

containing Na^+ ions, for example, we find that water is reduced instead of Na^+: $2 H_2O(l) + 2 e^- \rightarrow H_2(g) + 2 OH^-(aq)$. This is because the reduction potential for H_2O is very much greater than that for Na^+. Therefore, if we pass a current through a solution of sodium chloride in water, the product at the anode is gaseous chlorine, but the product at the cathode is gaseous hydrogen and not metallic sodium.

$$
\begin{array}{ll}
2 H_2O(l) + 2 e^- \longrightarrow H_2(g) + 2 OH^-(aq) & \text{(cathode)} \\
\underline{2 Cl^-(aq) \longrightarrow Cl_2(g) + 2 e^-} & \text{(anode)} \\
2 H_2O(l) + 2 Cl^-(aq) \longrightarrow H_2(g) + Cl_2(g) + 2 OH^-(aq) &
\end{array}
$$

The cell in which this operation is carried out commercially is called the Nelson cell, shown in Figure 13–11. The purpose of the porous asbestos layer is to prevent the products from mixing. The Nelson cell is the primary source of chlorine and of sodium hydroxide ("caustic soda") for the chemical industry. About 10 million tons each are produced yearly by this electrolytic process in the United States alone. The chlorine is used as a water purifier, as a bleaching agent, and as a raw material in the manufacture of hundreds of chemical products, such as herbicides, pesticides, plastics, cleaning agents, pharmaceuticals, floor and wall coverings, and refrigerants, to name a few. Sodium hydroxide is used extensively in many chemical and other industrial processes, such as in the production of paper, rayon, soap and detergents, pharmaceuticals, dyes, cosmetics, and bleaching agents.

Although very active metals cannot be produced by the electrolysis of aqueous solutions, they may be obtained by the electrolysis of fused

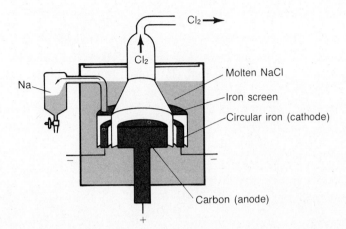

Figure 13–12
The Downs cell

(molten) salts. For example, metallic sodium is the product at the cathode when a current is passed through molten NaCl in a Downs cell (see Figure 13–12). Metallic sodium is used as a reducing agent and in its liquid form as a coolant in certain nuclear reactors.

As we have seen, it is possible to oxidize Cl^- ions to chlorine gas in aqueous solution by electrolysis in the Nelson cell. It is not possible to carry out the similar process of oxidizing F^- ions to fluorine, because H_2O is more readily oxidized than F^-: $2 H_2O(l) \rightarrow O_2(g) + 4 H^+(aq) + 4 e^-$. Thus, if a solution of KF is electrolyzed, H_2O, not K^+, is reduced at the cathode to give H_2, and H_2O, not F^-, is oxidized at the anode to give O_2. We have merely carried out the electrolysis of water to form its elemental constituents, hydrogen and oxygen. The K^+ and F^- ions carry most of the current in the solution and thus make the process faster than if we had used pure water. As with the very active metals, the only way to prepare elemental fluorine is by electrolysis of a molten salt such as KF.

13.8 Faraday's Laws

Thus far we have considered only the identities of the products to be expected from an electrolytic cell, but not the amounts. It is possible to predict the quantities of products obtained by a given current over a given time by using the relationships derived by the English chemist Michael Faraday (1791–1867).

When we measure electric current in a wire, we are measuring the amount of charge flowing past a certain point in a given time. The unit of charge is the coulomb (C), and the unit of current is the ampere (A). One

ampere is one coulomb of charge flowing past a point in one second, or $1 A = 1 C/\text{sec}$. Knowing the current (measured by an ammeter) and the time, we can therefore calculate the charge transferred through the system during that time (charge $=$ current $\times$ time). Since the charge of a mole of electrons is known (96,500 C), we can also calculate the number of moles of electrons transferred, and from the half-reaction, we can determine the number of moles of product.

For example, suppose we pass a current of 2.50 A through a solution containing $CuSO_4$ for 5.00 min. How much copper and how much oxygen are produced? The reactions are:

$$2\,H_2O(l) \longrightarrow O_2(g) + 4\,H^+(aq) + 4\,e^- \qquad \text{(anode)}$$
$$\underline{2 \times [Cu^{2+}(aq) + 2\,e^- \longrightarrow Cu(s)]} \qquad\qquad \text{(cathode)}$$
$$2\,Cu^{2+}(aq) + 2\,H_2O(l) \longrightarrow 2\,Cu(s) + O_2(g) + 4\,H^+(aq)$$

First the total charge transferred is calculated:

$$\text{charge} = 2.50\ A \times 5.00\ \text{min} \times 60\frac{\text{sec}}{\text{min}}$$

$$= 750.\ \text{A-sec} = 750.\ C$$

The next step is to determine the number of moles of electrons transferred:

$$\text{no. of mol of } e^- = 750.\ C \times \frac{1\ \text{mol } e^-}{96,500\ C}$$

$$= 7.77 \times 10^{-3}\ \text{mol } e^-$$

Since the second half-reaction shows that 1 mol Cu $\equiv$ 2 mol e^-:

$$\text{no. of mol of Cu} = 7.77 \times 10^{-3}\ \text{mol } e^- \times \frac{1\ \text{mol Cu}}{2\ \text{mol } e^-}$$

$$= 3.89 \times 10^{-3}\ \text{mol Cu}$$

Therefore, the weight of copper obtained is:

$$\text{wt. of Cu} = 3.89 \times 10^{-3}\ \text{mol Cu} \times \frac{63.55\ \text{g Cu}}{1\ \text{mol Cu}}$$

$$= 0.247\ \text{g Cu}$$

After the charge was determined, the calculation was carried out in steps for the sake of clarity. However, it could have been carried out in one operation, as seen in the following calculation for the weight of oxygen:

$$\text{wt. of } O_2 = 750. \text{ C} \times \frac{1 \text{ mol } e^-}{96,500 \text{ C}} \times \frac{1 \text{ mol } O_2}{4 \text{ mol } e^-} \times \frac{32.00 \text{ g } O_2}{1 \text{ mol } O_2}$$

$$= 0.0622 \text{ g } O_2$$

EXAMPLE 13.8a   Suppose we wanted to produce 1.50 g of fluorine by the electrolysis of fused KF in one hour. What current would be needed?
The half-reaction is:

$$2 \text{ F}^- \longrightarrow \text{F}_2(g) + 2 \ e^-$$

Our first step is to calculate the total charge transferred:

$$\text{charge} = 1.50 \text{ g } F_2 \times \frac{1 \text{ mol } F_2}{38.00 \text{ g } F_2} \times \frac{2 \text{ mol } e^-}{1 \text{ mol } F_2} \times \frac{96,500 \text{ C}}{1 \text{ mol } e^-}$$

$$= 7,620 \text{ C}$$

We can now calculate the current:

$$\text{current} = \frac{\text{charge}}{\text{time}} = \frac{7,620 \text{ C}}{1 \text{ h}} \times \frac{1 \text{ h}}{3,600 \text{ sec}}$$

$$= 2.12 \text{ C/sec} = 2.12 \text{ A}$$

TERMS
AND
CONCEPTS

- Oxidation-reduction (redox) reactions
- Oxidation
- Reduction
- Oxidizing agent (oxidant)
- Reducing agent (reductant)
- Half-reactions
- Electrochemical cells
  salt bridge
  half-cells

- Electrodes
  anode
  cathode
- Galvanic (voltaic) cell
- Electrolytic cell
- Primary cell
- Secondary cell
- Potential, E
- Standard potential, E^0

- Half-reaction potentials
  standard hydrogen half-cell
- Standard reduction and oxidation
  potentials

- Electrolysis
- Electroplating
- Faraday's Laws
  ampere

QUESTIONS

1. Name several general applications of oxidation-reduction reactions.
2. For each of the following unbalanced equations, identify the reagent that is oxidized, the reagent that is reduced, the oxidizing agent, and the reducing agent.
   In acid solution:
   a. $Cu(s) + NO_3^-(aq) \longrightarrow Cu^{2+}(aq) + NO(g)$
   b. $Cr_2O_7^{2-}(aq) + U^{4+}(aq) \longrightarrow Cr^{3+}(aq) + UO_2^{2+}(aq)$
   c. $Cl_2(aq) + I_2(aq) \longrightarrow IO_3^-(aq) + Cl^-(aq)$
   d. $MnO_4^-(aq) + W^{3+}(aq) \longrightarrow WO_4^{2-}(aq) + Mn^{2+}(aq)$
   e. $CrO_4^{2-}(aq) + Fe^{2+}(aq) \longrightarrow Cr^{3+}(aq) + Fe^{3+}(aq)$
   f. $VO_3^-(aq) + Fe^{2+}(aq) \longrightarrow VO^{2+}(aq) + Fe^{3+}(aq)$
   g. $Cr_2O_7^{2-}(aq) + H_2S(g) \longrightarrow Cr^{3+}(aq) + S(s)$
   h. $S_2O_3^{2-}(aq) + I^-(aq) \longrightarrow S^{2-}(aq) + I_2(g)$
   i. $As_2O_3(s) + NO_3^-(aq) \longrightarrow AsO_4^{3-}(aq) + NO(g)$
   j. $NO_3^-(aq) + I^-(aq) \longrightarrow NO(g) + I_2(s)$

   In basic solution:
   k. $CrO_4^{2-}(aq) + Fe(OH)_2(s) \longrightarrow Cr(OH)_3(s) + Fe(OH)_3(s)$
   l. $S_3O_6^{2-}(aq) + Cl_2(aq) \longrightarrow H_2SO_3(aq) + Cl^-(aq)$
   m. $Sn(OH)_4^{2-}(aq) + ClO_3^-(aq) \longrightarrow Sn(OH)_6^{2-}(aq) + Cl^-(aq)$
   n. $Cu_2SnS_2(s) + S_2O_8^{2-}(aq) \longrightarrow Cu(OH)_2(s) + Sn(OH)_6^{2-}(aq) + SO_4^{2-}(aq)$
   o. $H_3COH(l) + MnO_4^-(aq) \longrightarrow MnO_2(s) + CO_2(g)$
   p. $C_2O_4^{2-}(aq) + MnO_4^-(aq) \longrightarrow MnO_2(s) + CO_2(g)$
   q. $Al(s) + NO_3^-(aq) \longrightarrow AlO_2^-(aq) + NH_3(g)$
   r. $Al(s) + OH^-(aq) \longrightarrow AlO_2^-(aq) + H_2(g)$
   s. $ClO_2(g) \longrightarrow ClO_2^-(aq) + ClO_3^-(aq)$
   t. $NH_3(g) + OCl^-(aq) \longrightarrow N_2H_4(l) + Cl^-(aq)$
3. Balance each of the reactions in Question 2.
4. a. In principle the energy of any spontaneous redox reaction could be used to do useful work. Explain.
   b. Why can the energy of a redox reaction *not* be used if the two reactants are in direct contact?
5. Why is the presence of an electrolyte necessary in an electrochemical cell? What would happen if an electrolyte were not present?

6. Why is a porous barrier or a salt bridge necessary in some electrochemical cells?

7. Differentiate between galvanic and electrolytic cells and between primary and secondary cells. Give examples of each.

8. What are standard conditions for an electrochemical reaction?

9. Find the potential for each of the following reactions and indicate whether the reaction proceeds spontaneously to the right or to the left. Assume standard conditions for all reactants.

a. $3 Ag^+(aq) + Cr(s) = Cr^{3+}(aq) + 3 Ag(s)$

b. $Zn(s) + Mg^{2+}(aq) = Mg(s) + Zn^{2+}(aq)$

c. $Cu(s) + Br_2(l) = Cu^{2+}(aq) + 2 Br^-(aq)$

d. $Sn^{4+}(aq) + 2 Cr^{3+}(aq) + 7 H_2O(l) = Cr_2O_7^{2-}(aq) + Sn^{2+}(aq) + 14 H^+(aq)$

e. $Ca(OH)_2(s) + H_2(g) = Ca(s) + 2 H_2O(l)$

f. $Fe(s) + 2 H^+(aq) = Fe^{2+}(aq) + H_2(g)$

g. $2 Fe(s) + 6 H^+(aq) = 2 Fe^{3+}(aq) + 3 H_2(g)$

h. $2 Fe^{2+}(aq) + 2 H^+(aq) = 2 Fe^{3+}(aq) + H_2(g)$

i. $4 Fe^{2+}(aq) + O_2(g) + 4 H^+(aq) = 4 Fe^{3+}(aq) + 2 H_2O(l)$

10. Use the results of parts f through i of Question 9 to answer the following questions:

a. If metallic iron is reacted with 1 M HCl, what is the charge on the iron ions produced: +2 or +3? Explain.

b. If this solution is allowed to stand exposed to air, or if oxygen is bubbled through it, what will happen?

11. Show that the following statements are consistent with Table 13–1 (page 373):

a. A solution containing Fe^{3+} ions will oxidize iodide (I^-) ions to iodine (I_2), but will not oxidize bromide ions to bromine.

b. A 1 M HCl solution will react with all of the metals listed except copper, silver, and gold. (The general nonreactivity of these metals has earned them, along with tin and mercury, the designation of "noble metals.")

12. For each of the following devices, draw a diagram and label the component parts. Identify the cathode and anode and the chemical reactions that occur at each.

a. the common dry cell

b. the zinc-mercuric oxide cell

c. the automobile battery

13. Why is a salt bridge not necessary in the lead-acid (automobile) battery?

14. Explain the process of electroplating.

15. What are the products of the Nelson cell? Why is metallic sodium not a product?

16. A current of 0.100 A is passed through a solution containing I^- ions for 2.00 h.

a. What is the charge which has been passed through the solution?

    b. How many Faradays (moles of electrons) is this?

    c. How many moles and how many grams of iodine have been liberated?

17. If a current of 1.56 A is passed through a solution of $AgNO_3$ for 45 min, how many grams of silver are electroplated onto the cathode?

18. Molten $CaCl_2$ is electrolyzed with a current of 2.11 A for 2.00 h.

    a. How many grams of calcium are produced?

    b. How many grams and how many moles of Cl_2 are produced?

    c. What volume will the Cl_2 gas occupy at 32 °C and 1.00 atm pressure?

19. What volume of O_2 at 25 °C and 0.95 atm would be liberated by the electrolysis of an aqueous solution of NaOH with 1.95 A flowing for 2.00 h?

20. How long would it take to plate an object with 0.500 g of chromium metal from a solution containing Cr^{3+} ions using a current of 0.750 A?

21. How long would it take to produce 35.0 mL of H_2 gas at 24 °C and 0.93 atm by the electrolysis of an acidic solution using a current of 0.375 A?

22. Assume you want to remove the copper from 250 mL of a 0.050 M $CuSO_4$ solution by plating it out electrolytically. If this is to be accomplished in 2.00 h, what current is needed?

14

Organic Chemistry

Guidelines

After completing this chapter the student should be able to:

- explain why the field of organic chemistry is so broad
- explain why projection formulas often give a distorted view of the actual structure of a molecule
- differentiate among alkanes, alkenes, alkynes, and cyclic aliphatics
- draw the structures of all of the isomers for a given empirical formula
- tell how the boiling point, melting point, and density of normal alkanes vary as the number of carbons in the molecule increases
- identify the various functional groups which can appear on organic molecules
- differentiate among primary, secondary, and tertiary functional groups
- apply Markovnikov's rule
- write reactions showing the preparation of alcohols, aldehydes, ketones, and acids
- discuss the mechanism of the cleansing action of soap
- write a reaction showing the preparation of a given ester
- discuss the resonance structure of benzene
- tell what a polymer is and list the three broad categories of commercial polymers

14.1 Introduction

In the early nineteenth century compounds of carbon were said to be "organic" because the most common ones, such as alcohol and acetic acid, could be produced only by living matter. It was believed that a "vital force" present in living matter was necessary for their synthesis. By 1850 the "vital force" idea was in disrepute, as several compounds of carbon had been produced from nonliving sources. However, the name "organic" is still given to the branch of chemistry concerned with carbon, despite the fact that most organic chemicals are not associated with life processes. Today, **organic chemistry** is defined simply to be the chemistry of carbon compounds. Biochemistry, sometimes considered to be a branch of organic chemistry, is the study of the chemistry of living matter (Chapter 15).

Traditionally, organic chemistry was concerned almost exclusively with compounds in which carbon is combined with other nonmetallic elements. However, in recent years the study of compounds in which carbon is combined with a metal has become very important, and a large field called **organometallic chemistry** has emerged. **Inorganic chemistry**, of course, is the chemistry of all of the elements other than carbon.

The field of organic chemistry is extremely broad; in fact, more compounds involving carbon have been prepared than compounds involving all of the other elements combined (except hydrogen, which also appears in most organic compounds). The primary reason for the existence of so many carbon compounds is the carbon atom's unique capacity to form strong, relatively nonreactive bonds with up to four other carbon atoms. Thus carbon atoms may be joined sequentially to form an infinite variety

$$H-C-H$$

a. Methane, CH_4

b. Ethylene, C_2H_4

Figure 14–1
Bonding to a
carbon atom

$$H-C\equiv C-H$$

c. Acetylene, C_2H_2

d. Allene, C_3H_4

of molecules made up of chains and/or rings, as the various figures in this chapter will indicate.

The carbon atom has four electrons in its outer shell, each of which may be paired with an electron from another atom (carbon or otherwise) to form a covalent bond. The four covalent bonds always exhibited by carbon in its compounds do not all have to be single bonds, as in methane (Figure 14–1a). Each carbon in ethylene (Figure 14–1b), for example, has a double bond and two single bonds, while each carbon in acetylene (Figure 14–1c) has a triple bond and one single bond. A carbon atom may even have two double bonds, as the central carbon atom in allene illustrates (Figure 14–1d).

When a carbon atom forms four identical single bonds, the bonds are directed so that they are equally spaced around the carbon atom. For example, the hydrogen atoms in methane (CH_4) are located at the four corners of a regular tetrahedron, and each H—C—H angle is 109.5° (page 171). This molecule, shown in perspective in Figure 14–2a, is

Figure 14–2
Methane, CH_4
(tetrahedral
arrangement of
hydrogen atoms
about the central
carbon atom)

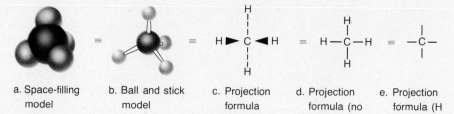

a. Space-filling
model

b. Ball and stick
model

c. Projection
formula
showing
perspective

d. Projection
formula (no
perspective)

e. Projection
formula (H
is assumed
to lie at the
end of each
bond)

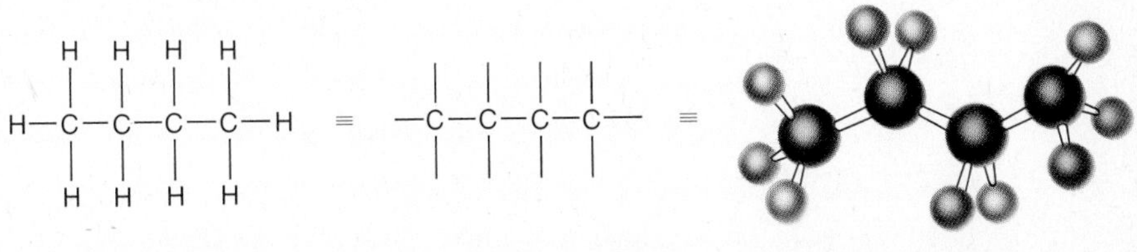

Figure 14–3
Butane, C_4H_{10}

a. Projection formula

b. Projection formula

c. Ball and stick model

difficult to represent realistically in two dimensions. It is normally represented in projection as in Figure 14–2d or 14–2e. In any case it should be remembered that carbon *never* is surrounded by four bonds in a square array as suggested by these projection formulas.

By the same token, with any projection formula containing a chain of singly-bonded carbon atoms, it should be realized that the chain cannot be linear, though it may appear to be so in the formula. For example, butane is normally represented as in Figure 14–3a or 14–3b. However, the carbon atoms cannot in reality lie in a straight line; each C—C—C angle must be about 109°, with each bond being free to rotate, thus making possible a variety of molecular shapes, one of which is shown in Figure 14–3c. The use of "ball and stick" models is a useful aid for understanding the geometry of organic molecules, since without these models it is often difficult to see, for example, that Figures 14–4a and 14–4b represent the same molecule, as do Figures 14–4c and 14–4d.

14.2 Aliphatic Compounds

The simplest and least reactive organic compounds are composed only of carbon and hydrogen. These **hydrocarbons** fall into two major classes: aliphatic compounds and aromatic compounds. We will deal with the aliphatics in this section and with the aromatics in Section 14.7. The

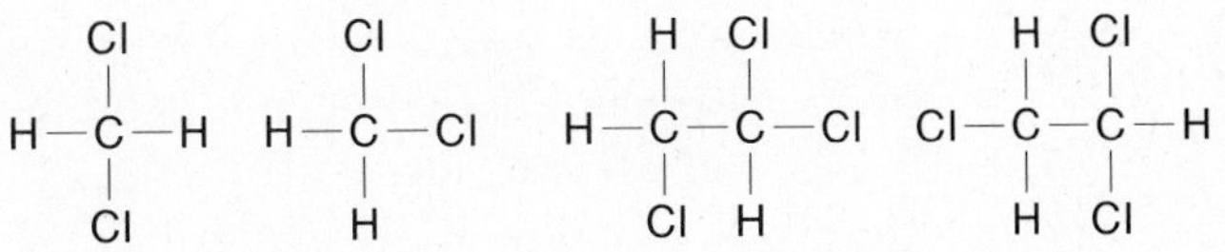

Figure 14–4
Two different projection formulas for CH_2Cl_2 and $C_2H_3Cl_3$

a.

b.

c.

d.

Dichloromethane, CH_2Cl_2

1,1,2-trichloroethane, $C_2H_3Cl_3$

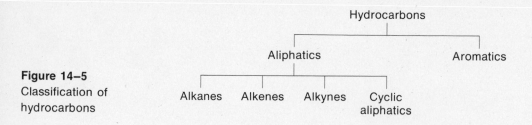

Figure 14–5
Classification of
hydrocarbons

aliphatic compounds may be classified into four groups (Figure 14–5):
the **alkanes**, which have only single bonds between carbon atoms; the
alkenes, which have at least one double bond; the **alkynes**, which have at
least one triple bond; and the **cyclic aliphatics**, characterized by rings
of carbon atoms.

Alkanes

The first few members of the alkane family are listed in Table 14–1
along with their common names, each of which ends in *-ane*. Notice that
there are two different compounds having the molecular formula C_4H_{10}:
n-butane and isobutane. Compounds that have the same molecular
formula but different molecular structures are called **isomers**. The number of possible isomers for alkanes increases very rapidly as the number of
carbon atoms increases. There are only three C_5H_{12} isomers, but 75
isomers are possible for $C_{10}H_{22}$, and over 350,000 for $C_{20}H_{42}$. The isomer
for each formula that has all of the carbon atoms in one chain (no branches
or "side" chains of carbon atoms) is called the *normal* alkane. For example,
normal hexane (abbreviated *n*-hexane) has six carbon atoms in one
sequence (Table 14–1).

The physical properties of the normal alkanes vary in a regular
fashion, as shown in Table 14–2. The first four are gases at room temperature, while those having five to sixteen carbon atoms are liquids. The
higher members are solids. All of the alkanes are nonpolar and therefore
do not dissolve in water, but they will dissolve in organic solvents such as
ether and benzene.

The alkanes are described as **saturated** hydrocarbons because a
maximum amount of hydrogen is combined with the carbon chains. The
alkenes and alkynes, on the other hand, are referred to as being **unsaturated** hydrocarbons, because they contain double or triple bonds so
that more hydrogen atoms could be added to the carbon atoms.

Table 14-1

Simple Alkanes

FORMULA	NAME	STRUCTURE
CH_4	methane	$-\overset{\mid}{\underset{\mid}{C}}-$
C_2H_6	ethane	$-\overset{\mid}{\underset{\mid}{C}}-\overset{\mid}{\underset{\mid}{C}}-$
C_3H_8	propane	$-\overset{\mid}{\underset{\mid}{C}}-\overset{\mid}{\underset{\mid}{C}}-\overset{\mid}{\underset{\mid}{C}}-$
C_4H_{10} (2 compounds)	n-butane	$-\overset{\mid}{\underset{\mid}{C}}-\overset{\mid}{\underset{\mid}{C}}-\overset{\mid}{\underset{\mid}{C}}-\overset{\mid}{\underset{\mid}{C}}-$
	isobutane	$-\overset{\mid}{\underset{\mid}{C}}-\overset{\mid}{\underset{\mid}{C}}-\overset{\mid}{\underset{\mid}{C}}-$ $-\overset{\mid}{\underset{\mid}{C}}-$
C_5H_{12} (3 compounds)	n-pentane	$-\overset{\mid}{\underset{\mid}{C}}-\overset{\mid}{\underset{\mid}{C}}-\overset{\mid}{\underset{\mid}{C}}-\overset{\mid}{\underset{\mid}{C}}-\overset{\mid}{\underset{\mid}{C}}-$
	isopentane	$-\overset{\mid}{\underset{\mid}{C}}-\overset{\mid}{\underset{\mid}{C}}-\overset{\mid}{\underset{\mid}{C}}-\overset{\mid}{\underset{\mid}{C}}-$ $-\overset{\mid}{\underset{\mid}{C}}-$
	neopentane	$-\overset{\mid}{\underset{\mid}{C}}-$ $-\overset{\mid}{\underset{\mid}{C}}-\overset{\mid}{\underset{\mid}{C}}-\overset{\mid}{\underset{\mid}{C}}-$ $-\overset{\mid}{\underset{\mid}{C}}-$
C_6H_{14} (5 compounds, only 1 shown)	n-hexane	$-\overset{\mid}{\underset{\mid}{C}}-\overset{\mid}{\underset{\mid}{C}}-\overset{\mid}{\underset{\mid}{C}}-\overset{\mid}{\underset{\mid}{C}}-\overset{\mid}{\underset{\mid}{C}}-\overset{\mid}{\underset{\mid}{C}}-$

Alkenes

Some of the simple alkenes (also called olefins) are listed in Table 14-3. The prefixes in their names correspond to the prefixes for the alkanes

Table 14–2

Physical Properties of *n*-Alkanes

FORMULA	MELTING POINT (°C)	BOILING POINT (°C)	LIQUID DENSITY
CH_4	−184	−161.4	0.415
C_2H_6	−172	−88.3	0.546
C_3H_8	−189.9	−44.5	0.585
C_4H_{10}	−135	−0.55	0.578
C_5H_{12}	−131.5	36.2	0.626
C_6H_{14}	−94.3	69	0.660
C_7H_{16}	−90	98.4	0.684
C_8H_{18}	−56.5	124.6	0.703
C_9H_{20}	−51	150.6	0.718
$C_{10}H_{22}$	−32	174	0.730

having the same number of carbon atoms, and all have the suffix *-ene*. A numeral in the name of an alkene indicates the position of a double bond. For example, in 1-pentene the first carbon-carbon bond is a double bond.

Unlike carbon atoms joined by a single bond, those joined by a double bond are unable to rotate, or twist, about the bond axis. As a result, the two carbon atoms at the ends of a double bond and the atoms attached directly to them are fixed in the same plane. The planar parts of the alkene molecules shown in Table 14–3 are indicated by the shaded area. Also, since a double bond is not free to rotate about its axis, the alkenes exhibit a type of structural isomerism not encountered in the alkanes. This **geometric isomerism** is illustrated in the table by *cis*- and *trans*-2-butene. The *cis* compound has the two CH_3 groups on the same side of the double bond, but the *trans* compound (*trans* means across) has the two CH_3 groups on opposite sides of the double bond.

Alkynes

The alkynes, some of which are listed in Table 14–4, are named similarly to the alkenes, except that the suffix used is *-yne*. Because of the presence of a triple bond, four of the atoms in an alkyne always lie on a straight line. The shaded areas in the table indicate the linear part of each molecule.

Table 14–3

Simple Alkenes

	NAME	STRUCTURE
C_2H_4	ethylene or ethene	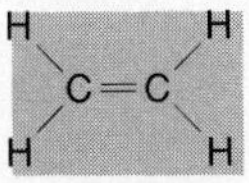
C_3H_6	propylene or propene	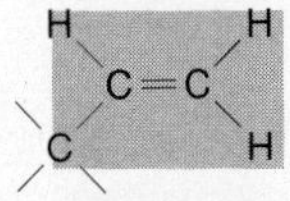
C_4H_8	1-butene	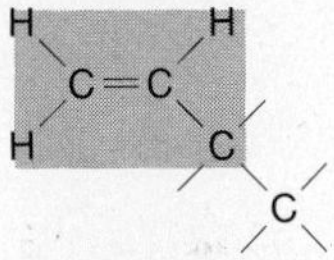
	cis-2-butene	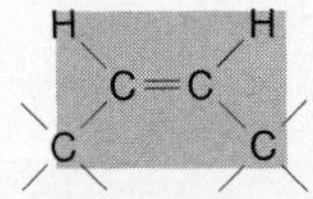
	trans-2-butene	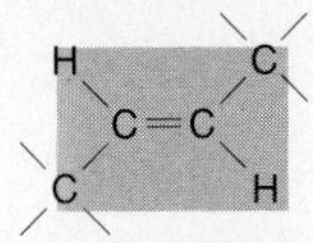
	isobutene	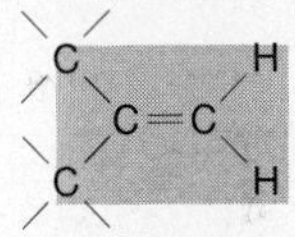
C_5H_{10} (6 alkenes)	1-pentene	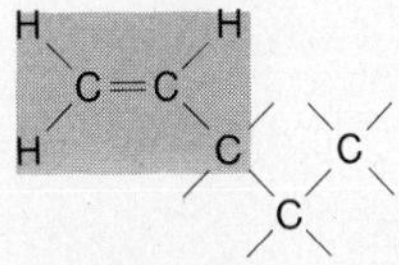

Cyclic Aliphatics

The fourth class of aliphatic hydrocarbons are the cyclic aliphatics, which have at least one ring of three or more carbon atoms. The cyclic aliphatics are named similarly to the first three classes, except that each has the prefix *cyclo-*. The presence of a double bond is indicated by the suffix *-ene*, and the presence of a triple bond is indicated by *-yne*. For

Table 14–4

Simple Alkynes

FORMULA	NAME	STRUCTURE
C_2H_2	acetylene or ethyne	 H—C≡C—H
C_3H_4	propyne	 H—C≡C—C—
C_4H_6	1-butyne	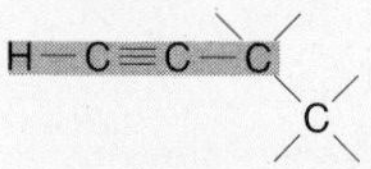 H—C≡C—C
	2-butyne	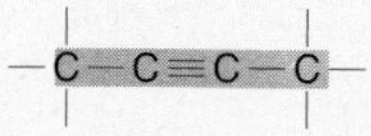 —C—C≡C—C—
C_5H_8	1-pentyne	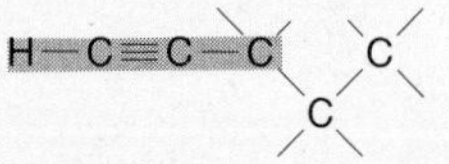 H—C≡C—C

example, cyclopropane has a ring of three carbon atoms; cyclopentene has five carbons in a ring which includes a double bond (Table 14–5). Each of the cyclic aliphatics has at least one alkene or alkyne isomer. Cyclopropane and propene are isomers, and cyclopentene is an isomer of the pentynes.

Combustion of Aliphatic Compounds

Perhaps the most useful of the properties of the aliphatic hydrocarbons is that they have high heats of combustion, as do the aromatic hydrocarbons (Section 14.7). The **heat of combustion** is defined as the heat (enthalpy) evolved in the reaction of a compound with oxygen. The heats

Table 14–5
Simple Cyclic Aliphatics

FORMULA	NAME	STRUCTURE
C_3H_6	cyclopropane	
C_4H_8	cyclobutane	
C_5H_{10}	cyclopentane	
C_5H_8	cyclopentene	

of combustion for three aliphatic hydrocarbon gases per mole of gas are as follows:

$$C_2H_6 + \tfrac{7}{2} O_2 \longrightarrow 2\ CO_2 + 3\ H_2O \qquad \Delta H = -370\ kcal$$
ethane

$$C_2H_4 + 3\ O_2 \longrightarrow 2\ CO_2 + 2\ H_2O \qquad \Delta H = -333\ kcal$$
ethylene

$$C_2H_2 + \tfrac{5}{2} O_2 \longrightarrow 2\ CO_2 + H_2O \qquad \Delta H = -312\ kcal$$
acetylene

Thus natural gas (composed mostly of methane and lesser amounts of ethane, propane, and other alkanes) is useful for heating and cooking.

Petroleum

Probably the mineral resource most important to modern society is petroleum, since petroleum and the natural gas found with it currently account for most of the energy consumed in the United States. It is also the raw material for the huge petro-chemical industries, whose products include plastics and synthetic fibers (Section 14.8).

Petroleum is a mixture of hydro-carbons having various chain lengths and thus various boiling points (see Table 14–2, for example). In order to produce useful products from raw petroleum, or crude oil, it must be refined. The process of refinement always includes the separation of petroleum into component mixtures having characteristic properties, and it may include later chemical modification to obtain a desired end product.

The first and most important step in oil refinement is fractional distillation, a process in which the components of petroleum are separated according to their boiling ranges. The petroleum is heated to about 400 °C, and the vapors rise in a fractionating column, cooling and condensing as they rise. The fraction having the highest boiling point con-denses first and is drawn off from the lower part of the column. Fractions having successively lower boiling points then condense and are drawn off from higher sections of the column, with the lowest-boiling fraction, which reaches the top of the column, remaining in the vapor state.

The lowest-boiling fraction of petroleum (boiling point = 20–60 °C) is called "petroleum ether," although it consists not of ethers, but of low-boiling hydrocarbons. The next fraction, which consists of molecules having five to ten carbon atoms and which has a boiling range of 40–205 °C, is natural gasoline. The higher-boiling fractions are kerosene and gas oil, the familiar furnace oil. The substances left in the pot at the bottom of the column after fractional distillation are lubricating oil and the solids asphalt and coke.

Each fraction drawn off the column may be further separated or chemically modified to give a desired product. For example, the gasoline fraction is further refined to remove sulfur impurities, which cause air pollution when burned (page 228), and to produce branched chains, which make better fuels.

Higher alkanes, which are liquids, make up gasoline and other fuels. Acetylene is used in welding and cutting torches because it burns with an intensely hot flame.

14.3 Alkyl Halides

Compared to other organic compounds the alkanes are not very reactive. The alkenes and alkynes, as we shall see, are more reactive because of the

Table 14–6

Common Functional Groups

NAME	FORMULA OR STRUCTURE
halide	$-X$ ($-F$, $-Cl$, $-Br$, or $-I$)
alcohol	$R-OH$
nitro	$-NO_2$
amine	$-NH_2$
ene	$-C=C-$
yne	$-C\equiv C-$
aldehyde	$R-\overset{\displaystyle O}{\overset{\displaystyle \|}{C}}-H$
ketone	$R-\overset{\displaystyle O}{\overset{\displaystyle \|}{C}}-R'$
ether	$R-O-R'$
acid	$R-\overset{\displaystyle O}{\overset{\displaystyle \|}{C}}-OH$
ester	$R-\overset{\displaystyle O}{\overset{\displaystyle \|}{C}}-O-R'$
amide	$R-\overset{\displaystyle O}{\overset{\displaystyle \|}{C}}-NH_2$

high concentration of electrons in double and triple bonds. Also more reactive are hydrocarbon molecules in which one or more hydrogen atoms have been replaced by another chemical species such as a halogen atom or a hydroxyl ($-OH$) group. Such species attached to the carbon chain are called **functional groups**, since they determine the reactivity of the compound. A list of some of the common functional groups is given in Table 14–6. Note that since double and triple bonds are sites of reactivity, they also are considered to be functional groups.

The simplest functional group is a halogen atom. Some of the halogen derivatives of alkanes are shown in Table 14–7. As indicated in the table, they are often named by naming the alkyl group first and then the halide. An **alkyl group** is the alkane minus one hydrogen atom. In the symbolism of organic chemistry, an alkyl group is generally designated by the symbol R, with any different alkyl groups on a molecule indicated by R'. Since X usually indicates a halogen atom, an alkyl halide is symbolized by $R-X$. It is possible, however, for a given carbon atom to have more than one halogen atom bonded to it, such as in $CHCl_3$, which is known by its common name chloroform, or CCl_4, carbon tetrachloride, formerly a widely used cleaning agent.

Table 14–7

Some Halogen Derivatives of Alkanes

ALKANE	ALKYL GROUP (R)	ALKYL HALIDE (RX)
CH_4 methane	CH_3— methyl	CH_3Cl methyl chloride
C_2H_6 ethane	C_2H_5— ethyl	C_2H_5Cl ethyl chloride
C_3H_8 propane	$CH_3CH_2CH_2$— n-propyl	$CH_3CH_2CH_2Cl$ n-propyl chloride
	CH₃CHCH₃ Isopropyl	$\overset{\displaystyle Cl}{\overset{\displaystyle \vert}{CH_3CHCH_3}}$ Isopropyl chloride
C_4H_{10} butane	$CH_3CH_2CH_2CH_2$— n-butyl	$CH_3CH_2CH_2CH_2Cl$ n-butyl chloride
	$\overset{\displaystyle CH_3}{\overset{\displaystyle \vert}{CH_3CHCH_2}}$— isobutyl	$\overset{\displaystyle CH_3}{\overset{\displaystyle \vert}{CH_3CHCH_2Cl}}$ isobutyl chloride
	$\overset{\displaystyle \vert}{CH_3CH_2CHCH_3}$ sec-butyl	$\overset{\displaystyle Cl}{\overset{\displaystyle \vert}{CH_3CH_2CHCH_3}}$ sec-butyl chloride
	$\underset{\displaystyle CH_3}{\overset{\displaystyle \vert}{\underset{\displaystyle \vert}{CH_3CCH_3}}}$ tert-butyl	$\overset{\displaystyle Cl}{\underset{\displaystyle CH_3}{\overset{\displaystyle \vert}{\underset{\displaystyle \vert}{CH_3CCH_3}}}}$ tert-butyl chloride

The chlorides of butane (Table 14–7) illustrate the different types of structural isomers that are possible for the alkyl halides. The first two listed, n-butyl chloride and isobutyl chloride, are called **primary** alkyl halides because the carbon atom to which the halogen is attached is joined to only one other carbon atom. The third compound, sec-butyl chloride, is called a **secondary** alkyl halide because the carbon atom to which the halogen is attached is bonded to two other carbon atoms. The fourth butyl chloride listed is an example of a **tertiary** alkyl halide. The halogen here is attached to a carbon atom that is joined to three other carbon atoms.

Preparation of Alkyl Halides

One method for preparing alkyl halides is by direct reaction of the alkane with a halogen molecule. This reaction is usually initiated or made more rapid by strong light, and the identity of the products depends on the nature of the alkane and the quantity of halogen present. A mixture of products is usually the result.

$$CH_4(g) + Cl_2(g) \longrightarrow HCl(g) + CH_3Cl(g)$$

$$CH_3Cl(g) + Cl_2(g) \longrightarrow HCl(g) + CH_2Cl_2(l)$$

$$CH_2Cl_2(l) + Cl_2(g) \longrightarrow HCl(g) + CHCl_3(l)$$

$$CHCl_3(l) + Cl_2(g) \longrightarrow HCl(g) + CCl_4(l)$$

Alkyl halides may also be prepared by addition of X_2 or $H-X$ to an alkene or alkyne:

$$H_2C{=}CH_2 + Cl_2 \longrightarrow \underset{\underset{Cl}{|}}{\overset{\overset{H}{|}}{H-C}}-\underset{\underset{Cl}{|}}{\overset{\overset{H}{|}}{C}}-H$$

$$H_2C{=}CH_2 + H-Cl \longrightarrow \underset{\underset{H}{|}}{\overset{\overset{H}{|}}{H-C}}-\underset{\underset{Cl}{|}}{\overset{\overset{H}{|}}{C}}-H$$

$$HC{\equiv}CH + Cl_2 \longrightarrow \overset{Cl}{\underset{H}{\diagdown}}C{=}C\overset{Cl}{\underset{H}{\diagup}}$$

$$\underset{HC{=}CH}{\overset{Cl\ \ Cl}{|\ \ |}} + Cl_2 \longrightarrow \underset{\underset{Cl}{|}\ \underset{Cl}{|}}{\overset{\overset{Cl}{|}\ \overset{Cl}{|}}{H-C-C}}-H$$

$$HC{\equiv}CH + H-Cl \longrightarrow \overset{H}{\underset{H}{\diagdown}}C{=}C\overset{H}{\underset{Cl}{\diagup}}$$

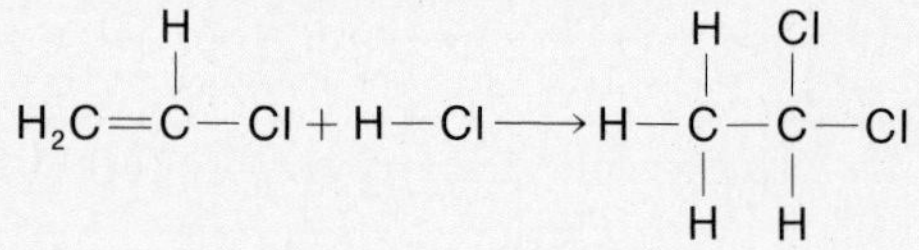

$$H_2C{=}\overset{\displaystyle H}{\underset{}{C}}{-}Cl + H{-}Cl \longrightarrow H{-}\overset{\displaystyle H}{\underset{\displaystyle H}{C}}{-}\overset{\displaystyle Cl}{\underset{\displaystyle H}{C}}{-}Cl$$

In the last reaction above, you may also have expected to see the following molecule as a product:

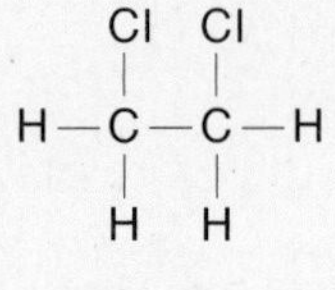

$$H{-}\overset{\displaystyle Cl}{\underset{\displaystyle H}{C}}{-}\overset{\displaystyle Cl}{\underset{\displaystyle H}{C}}{-}H$$

This is not the case, however. Such a situation is governed by **Markovnikov's Rule**: in the ionic addition of an acid (HCl in this example) to the carbon-carbon double bond of an alkene, the hydrogen of the acid attaches itself to the carbon atom that already holds the greater number of hydrogens. Another example of the use of this rule is in the following reaction:

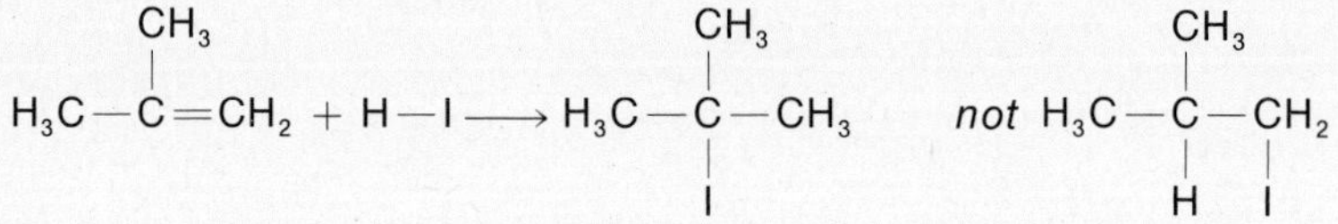

$$H_3C{-}\overset{\displaystyle CH_3}{\underset{}{C}}{=}CH_2 + H{-}I \longrightarrow H_3C{-}\overset{\displaystyle CH_3}{\underset{\displaystyle I}{C}}{-}CH_3 \quad \textit{not} \; H_3C{-}\overset{\displaystyle CH_3}{\underset{\displaystyle H}{C}}{-}\overset{}{\underset{\displaystyle I}{C}H_2}$$

14.4 Alcohols

An alkane in which a hydrogen atom is replaced by an —OH functional group is called an alkyl **alcohol**. The alcohols are named in a similar manner to the alkyl halides; for example, CH_3OH is methyl alcohol or methanol, and C_2H_5OH is ethyl alcohol or ethanol. As with the halides, there may be primary, secondary, or tertiary alcohols.

A general method for the preparation of alcohols is by the displacement of the halogen in an alkyl halide by a base:

$$\underset{\substack{\text{alkyl} \\ \text{halide}}}{R{-}X} + \underset{\text{base}}{OH^-} \longrightarrow \underset{\text{alcohol}}{R{-}OH} + X^-$$

The simple alcohols, which are used in large quantities, have specific preparations. For example, methanol, CH_3OH, is prepared by the reaction of carbon monoxide and hydrogen, using a catalyst:

$$CO + 2 H_2 \xrightarrow[\text{Cr}_2\text{O}_3,\ \text{ZnO}]{350\text{--}400\ °\text{C}} CH_3OH$$

Methanol is also known as wood alcohol, because it is a byproduct of the manufacture of charcoal by the distillation of wood. Methanol is a major chemical commodity, used primarily in the manufacture of intermediates for many products, such as polyester fibers and film.

Isopropyl alcohol, or rubbing alcohol, is usually made from propylene:

$$CH_3CH{=}CH_2 + H_2O \longrightarrow CH_3-\overset{\displaystyle OH}{\underset{\displaystyle H}{C}}-CH_3$$

This alcohol's most important use is in the manufacture of acetone (page 404).

Perhaps the most familiar alcohol is ethyl alcohol, or grain alcohol, which is produced for consumption by fermentation. The starting material may be nearly any foodstuff containing a large amount of starch (such as potatoes, rice, corn, or other grains) or sugar (grapes or other fruits). Starches are first broken down into sugar by adding malt (sprouted barley), which contains the proper enzyme to catalyze the reaction. This step is not necessary when using fruits. Yeast is added to the sugar, and the mixture is allowed to ferment. During this process, the sugar is converted to ethyl alcohol:

$$\underset{\text{sugar}}{C_6H_{12}O_6} \longrightarrow \underset{\text{ethyl alcohol}}{2\ C_2H_5OH} + \underset{\text{carbon dioxide}}{2\ CO_2(g)}$$

Beverages that contain up to 15% alcohol (beer and wines) are produced in this way. Higher concentrations are obtained only by distillation.

It should be noted that ethyl alcohol sold for laboratory or industrial use contains small amounts of poisonous material and is thus said to be "denatured." It is unfit to drink.

14.5 Aldehydes, Ketones, and Acids

Primary alcohols may be oxidized under mild conditions to form **alde-hydes**, characterized by the functional group $-\overset{\displaystyle O}{\overset{\|}{C}}-H$. One common oxidizing agent used is a solution of sodium dichromate in sulfuric acid, as in the following reaction:

$$3\ CH_3CH_2CH_2OH + Cr_2O_7{}^{2-} + 8\ H^+ \longrightarrow 3\ CH_3CH_2-\overset{\displaystyle O}{\overset{\|}{C}}-H + 2\ Cr^{3+} + 7\ H_2O$$

n-propyl alcohol   propionaldehyde

Another method is to pass the alcohol vapors over a heated copper or silver catalyst:

$$CH_3OH \xrightarrow[250\ °C]{Cu} H-\overset{\displaystyle O}{\overset{\|}{C}}-H + H_2$$

methanol   methanal
(formaldehyde)

$$CH_3CH_2OH \xrightarrow[250\ °C]{Cu} CH_3-\overset{\displaystyle O}{\overset{\|}{C}}-H + H_2$$

ethanol   ethanal
(acetaldehyde)

The same procedure can be used to oxidize a secondary alcohol to a **ketone** $(R-\overset{\displaystyle O}{\overset{\|}{C}}-R')$. The oxidation of isopropyl alcohol to acetone is an example:

$$CH_3\overset{\displaystyle OH}{\overset{|}{C}H}CH_3 \xrightarrow[250\ °C]{Cu} CH_3-\overset{\displaystyle O}{\overset{\|}{C}}-CH_3 + H_2$$

isopropyl   propanone
alcohol   (acetone)

Acetone is an important laboratory and industrial solvent.

Carboxylic Acids

Aldehydes and ketones may be further oxidized to **acids** $(R-\overset{\overset{\displaystyle O}{\|}}{C}-OH)$ if excess or more concentrated oxidizing agent is used.

$$3\ C_2H_5-\overset{\overset{\displaystyle O}{\|}}{C}-H + Cr_2O_7^{2-} + 8\ H^+ \longrightarrow 3\ C_2H_5-\overset{\overset{\displaystyle O}{\|}}{C}-OH + 2\ Cr^{3+} + 4\ H_2O$$

propionaldehyde · propionic acid

Although such preparations of acids from aldehydes are often useful, the oxidation of ketones always involves breaking a carbon-carbon bond, usually resulting in a mixture of products. Hence, this reaction has little use.

Organic acids are known as **carboxylic acids**, and their characteristic functional group $(-\overset{\overset{\displaystyle O}{\|}}{C}-OH)$ is called the **carboxyl group**. Acids in the family $R-\overset{\overset{\displaystyle O}{\|}}{C}-OH$, where R is an alkyl group, are called **fatty acids** (Table 14–8), since many of them are derived from fats. The common names of the fatty acids are often related to the Latin words for where they are found in significant amounts. For example, formic acid (*formica* means ant) is the agent that causes an ant bite to sting or itch. Acetic acid (*acetum*, vinegar) is the agent that gives vinegar its characteristic sour taste and smell. Vinegar is about three percent acetic acid. Butyric acid (*butyrum*, butter) is found in rancid butter.

All of the fatty acids in Table 14–8 are saturated, since they have no carbon-carbon double or triple bonds. The unsaturated fatty acids do have double or triple bonds, and the *polyunsaturated* fatty acids have several. Table 14–9 shows three of the most common unsaturated fatty acids. These acids, in contrast to the saturated acids having the same number of carbon atoms, are liquid at room temperature. Both types are used as cooking oil; the solid, saturated ones (contained in Crisco, for example) melt upon heating.

Carboxylic acids that have one to four carbon atoms are polar molecules and are therefore soluble in water. The five-carbon acid is partially soluble, and those with more than five carbons are virtually

Table 14–8

Representative Fatty Acids

SYSTEMATIC NAME	COMMON NAME	FORMULA	K_a (0.1 M/25 °C)
methanoic acid	formic acid	$H-\overset{\overset{O}{\|\|}}{C}-OH$	2.1×10^{-4}
ethanoic acid	acetic acid	$CH_3-\overset{\overset{O}{\|\|}}{C}-OH$	1.8×10^{-5}
propanoic acid	propionic acid	$CH_3CH_2-\overset{\overset{O}{\|\|}}{C}-OH$	1.3×10^{-5}
butanoic acid	n-butyric acid	$CH_3(CH_2)_2-\overset{\overset{O}{\|\|}}{C}-OH$	1.5×10^{-5}
pentanoic acid	n-valeric acid	$CH_3(CH_2)_3-\overset{\overset{O}{\|\|}}{C}-OH$	1.5×10^{-5}
hexanoic acid	caproic acid	$CH_3(CH_2)_4-\overset{\overset{O}{\|\|}}{C}-OH$	
dodecanoic acid	lauric acid	$CH_3(CH_2)_{10}-\overset{\overset{O}{\|\|}}{C}-OH$	
tetradecanoic acid	myristic acid	$CH_3(CH_2)_{12}-\overset{\overset{O}{\|\|}}{C}-OH$	
hexadecanoic acid	palmitic acid	$CH_3(CH_2)_{14}-\overset{\overset{O}{\|\|}}{C}-OH$	
octadecanoic acid	stearic acid	$CH_3(CH_2)_{16}-\overset{\overset{O}{\|\|}}{C}-OH$	

insoluble, because of their longer, nonpolar alkyl chains. All of the soluble acids are weak acids, ionizing to some extent in aqueous solution according to the following equilibrium. Their equilibrium constants are listed in Table 14–8.

Table 14–9

Three Common Unsaturated Fatty Acids

NAME	FORMULA
oleic acid	$CH_3(CH_2)_7CH=CH(CH_2)_7COOH$
linoleic acid	$CH_3(CH_2)_4CH=CHCH_2CH=CH(CH_2)_7COOH$
linolenic acid	$CH_3CH_2CH=CHCH_2CH=CHCH_2CH=CH(CH_2)_7COOH$

$$R-\overset{\overset{\displaystyle O}{\|}}{C}-OH + H_2O \rightleftharpoons R-\overset{\overset{\displaystyle O}{\|}}{C}-O^- + H_3O^+$$

Recall that acetic acid was used in Chapter 12 (page 330) to illustrate the behavior of a weak acid in aqueous solution. In that chapter its formula was written as $HC_2H_3O_2$, but we may now write it as CH_3COOH to emphasize its structure as a carboxylic acid.

14.6 Ethers and Esters

Two types of compounds that have oxygen atoms as part of the molecular chain are the **ethers** ($R-O-R'$) and the **esters** ($R-\overset{\overset{\displaystyle O}{\|}}{C}-O-R'$). Some of the common ethers are shown in Table 14–10. Perhaps the most familiar is ethyl ether, used as an anesthetic and as a general purpose solvent. A common cyclic ether is tetrahydrofuran, abbreviated THF, which is also a solvent:

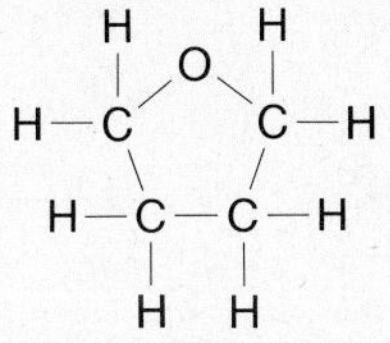

Ethers are usually prepared industrially by heating an alcohol with sulfuric acid. In the reaction, called a **dehydration** reaction, water is removed from the alcohol. For example:

Soap

The carboxylic acids can be neutralized by bases to form salts according to the following reaction:

$$R-\overset{\overset{\displaystyle O}{\|}}{C}-OH + NaOH \longrightarrow$$

acid   base

$$R-\overset{\overset{\displaystyle O}{\|}}{C}-O^{-}Na^{+} + H_2O$$

salt

The sodium and potassium salts of the fatty acids are soluble in water. The ones with long alkyl chains are also soluble in oils, and it is this property which gives them their cleaning power as **soaps**. The "dirt" upon which soap acts is made up of various nonpolar fats, oils, and grease, which water alone, being a polar solvent, will not wash away. The nonpolar alkyl ends of soap molecules, however, will mix with the dirt and surround small particles of it (Figure 14I–1). The resulting small globules have charged surfaces due to the —COO⁻ ends of the soap molecule;

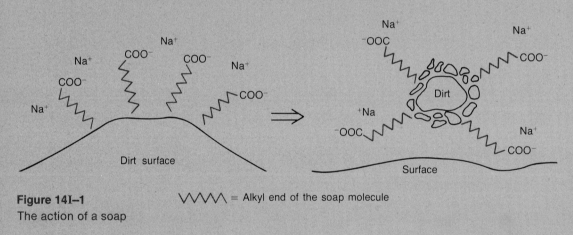

Figure 14I–1
The action of a soap

$\vee\!\!\vee\!\!\vee\!\!\vee\!\!\wedge$ = Alkyl end of the soap molecule

$$CH_3CH_2-OH + HO-CH_2CH_3 \xrightarrow[\text{H}_2\text{SO}_4]{\text{heat}} CH_3CH_2-O-CH_2CH_3 + H_2O$$

ethanol   ethyl ether

The ether linkage is quite stable toward most reagents and can be broken only by concentrated acids at high temperatures.

It should be remembered that ethers, including ethyl ether, a common laboratory chemical, are highly flammable and form explosive mix-

they can therefore be absorbed into the aqueous soap solution and be rinsed away.

Commercial soaps are not pure compounds, but are mixtures of sodium salts of long-chain fatty acids having from 12 to 18 carbon atoms. These soaps are usually produced from natural fats, which are largely esters of glycerol and fatty acids. The fats are hydrolyzed by NaOH (see below) or, in the case of "soft" soaps, by KOH.

Calcium ions contained in "hard" water will precipitate a soap from solution:

$$2 \; R-\overset{\overset{\displaystyle O}{\|}}{C}-O^-Na^+(aq) + Ca^{2+}(aq) \longrightarrow$$
$$(RCOO^-)_2Ca^{2+}(s) + 2 \; Na^+(aq)$$

The precipitate is observed in a sink or bathtub as a deposit which builds up over a period of time.

a glyceride (a fat) + 3 NaOH → glycerol + mixture of fatty acid salts (soap)

tures with air. They should never be used near a flame or a possible source of a spark.

Esters, like ethers, may be prepared by dehydration reactions using an H_2SO_4 catalyst, but in this case an alcohol is reacted with an acid:

formic acid + n-propyl alcohol $\xrightarrow{H_2SO_4}$ n-propyl formate + H_2O

Table 14–10

Some Common Ethers

NAME	FORMULA OR STRUCTURE
methyl ether	CH_3-O-CH_3
methylethyl ether	$CH_3-O-CH_2CH_3$
ethyl ether	$CH_3CH_2-O-CH_2CH_3$
isopropyl ether	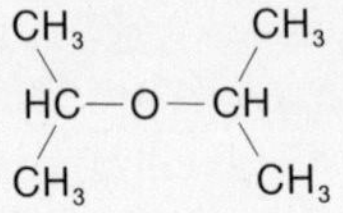 $\begin{array}{cc} CH_3 & CH_3 \\ HC-O-CH \\ CH_3 & CH_3 \end{array}$

$$\underset{\text{propionic acid}}{CH_3CH_2\overset{\overset{\textstyle O}{\|}}{C}-OH} + \underset{\text{methanol}}{HO-CH_3} \xrightarrow{H_2SO_4} \underset{\text{methyl propionate}}{CH_3CH_2-\overset{\overset{\textstyle O}{\|}}{C}-O-CH_3} + H_2O$$

Esters may also be produced by the reaction of a salt with an alkyl halide:

$$R-\overset{\overset{\textstyle O}{\|}}{C}-O^-\,Ag^+ + R'-X \longrightarrow R-\overset{\overset{\textstyle O}{\|}}{C}-O-R' + AgX$$

The **waxes** are esters in which both the alcohol and the acid parts of the molecule contain a large number of carbon atoms, usually between sixteen and thirty. Myricyl alcohol, $C_{31}H_{63}OH$, and palmitic acid, $C_{15}H_{31}COOH$, for example, are the constituents of the ester which largely makes up beeswax:

$$\underset{\text{myricyl palmitate (beeswax)}}{C_{15}H_{31}-\overset{\overset{\textstyle O}{\|}}{C}-O-C_{31}H_{63}}$$

It is possible to make inorganic esters as well as organic esters, if the acid used is an inorganic acid, such as nitric acid, sulfuric acid, or phosphoric acid. The reaction of sulfuric acid and ethyl alcohol, for example, yields ethyl sulfate, $(C_2H_5)_2SO_4$:

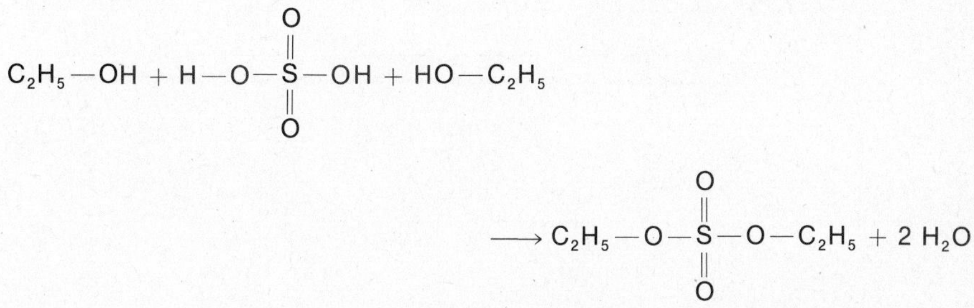

$$C_2H_5-OH + H-O-\overset{\displaystyle O}{\underset{\displaystyle O}{\overset{\|}{\underset{\|}{S}}}}-OH + HO-C_2H_5$$

$$\longrightarrow C_2H_5-O-\overset{\displaystyle O}{\underset{\displaystyle O}{\overset{\|}{\underset{\|}{S}}}}-O-C_2H_5 + 2\,H_2O$$

A similar reaction using phosphoric acid gives triethyl phosphate, $(C_2H_5)_3PO_4$, which is used as a flame-retarding coating for materials. As we shall see in Chapter 15, ester linkages of phosphoric acid make up the backbone of the double helix of DNA.

14.7 Aromatic Compounds

All **aromatic compounds** have at least one ring of carbon atoms. They differ from the cyclic aliphatics in that the rings in aromatic compounds can always be represented by resonant structures (page 168). For example, benzene, the most common aromatic compound, has the formula C_6H_6 and is composed of one ring of carbon atoms, each of which has a hydrogen atom bonded to it. Since each carbon must have four bonds, there are two ways to write a structural formula for benzene. I and II show these formulas, along with their simplified symbols:

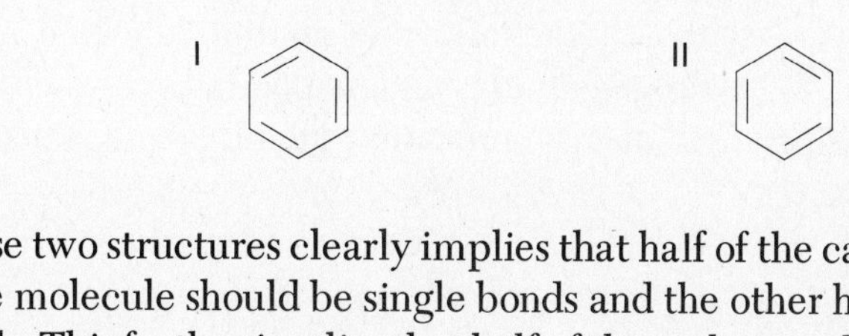

Each of these two structures clearly implies that half of the carbon-carbon bonds in the molecule should be single bonds and the other half should be double bonds. This further implies that half of the carbon-carbon distances should be shorter than the other half, since double bonds, being stronger, are shorter than single bonds (page 167). However, experimental evidence

Table 14–11

Aromatic Derivatives of Benzene

NAME	STRUCTURE	NAME	STRUCTURE
bromobenzene	Br	benzoic acid	$\overset{O}{\overset{\|}{C}}-OH$
nitrobenzene	NO_2		
toluene	CH_3	trinitrotoluene (TNT)	CH_3, O_2N, NO_2, NO_2
aniline	NH_2	sulfanilamide	$O=S=O$, NH_2, NH_2
phenol (carbolic acid)	OH		

shows that all six of the carbon-carbon bonds in benzene are of the same length, and that this length is between the characteristic double and single bond lengths. Thus, according to the evidence, neither of the two structures I and II represents the true structure, which seems to be "intermediate" between the two. We therefore have an example of resonant structures. The true structural formula for benzene is most often represented by the following symbol, in which a carbon atom with an attached hydrogen atom is understood to lie at each corner of the hexagon. Experiment also confirms that the molecule is planar.

Some of the more familiar aromatic derivatives of benzene are shown in Table 14–11. Benzene and toluene are produced directly as byproducts of the distillation of coal or indirectly from petroleum. The others must be produced synthetically.

Aromatic compounds have a great variety of uses. Benzene is widely used as a solvent and as a starting material for the synthesis of many other compounds. Phenol is used as a disinfectant, and TNT is the well-known explosive. Sulfanilamide was the first sulfa drug known; its antibacterial properties were discovered in 1933.

Many aromatic compounds have more than one aromatic ring or include atoms other than carbon in the ring, as the following examples illustrate.

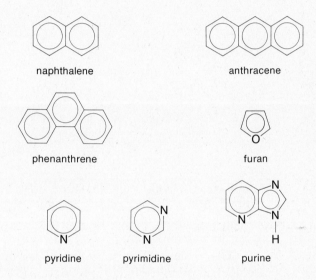

naphthalene   anthracene

phenanthrene   furan

pyridine   pyrimidine   purine

According to the symbolism used here, there is a carbon atom at each vertex unless otherwise indicated, and one hydrogen is assumed to be attached to each carbon except for carbon atoms that are shared by two rings. These carbons have no hydrogen atoms.

14.8 Polymers

Certain molecules can be covalently bonded to one another to form "giant" molecules known as **polymers**. The molecules that make up a polymer are called **monomers**, and the reaction, which requires a particular catalyst, is called a **polymerization reaction.** The giant molecule polyethylene, for example, is a polymer in which the monomer units are covalently bonded molecules of ethylene:

ethylene molecules

polyethylene

A shorthand notation for this reaction is

$$n\ CH_2 = CH_2 \longrightarrow \; \left(CH_2 - CH_2 \right)_n$$

where the segment inside the parentheses is the repeat unit, or **monomer residue,** and n is the number of times this unit is repeated. The horizontal line through each parenthesis indicates a covalent bond to the adjacent monomer unit.

The manufacture of synthetic polymer products accounts for a significant portion of the gross national product of the United States. These products, derived primarily from petroleum, include plastics, synthetic fibers, and elastomers (synthetic rubbers). For the most part, the synthetic polymer industry has developed since the late 1930s, although polystyrene was known as early as 1839, and celluloid was used to make billiard balls in the late nineteenth century. Commercial progress was impeded prior to the 1930s by the false impression that polymers were colloidal aggregates of smaller molecules. This view was corrected largely by the work of Hermann Staudinger, who received the Nobel Prize for his investigations into the structure of polymers.

The synthetic polymers are usually classified into three types—plastics, fibers, and elastomers—although there is no clear dividing line between them. Polyethylene is a well-known plastic, as are polystyrene, polyvinylchloride, and polytetrafluoroethylene (Teflon):

$$n \; H_2C = \underset{\underset{H}{|}}{\overset{\overset{C_6H_5}{|}}{C}} - H \longrightarrow \left(\underset{\underset{H}{|}}{\overset{\overset{H}{|}}{C}} - \underset{\underset{H}{|}}{\overset{\overset{C_6H_5}{|}}{C}} \right)_n$$

styrene   polystyrene

$$\left[C_6H_5 \text{ is } \bigcirc \right]$$

$$n \; H_2C = \underset{\underset{Cl}{|}}{\overset{\overset{H}{|}}{C}} \longrightarrow \left(\underset{\underset{H}{|}}{\overset{\overset{H}{|}}{C}} - \underset{\underset{Cl}{|}}{\overset{\overset{H}{|}}{C}} \right)_n$$

vinylchloride   polyvinylchloride

$$n \; \underset{\underset{F}{|}}{\overset{\overset{F}{|}}{C}} = \underset{\underset{F}{|}}{\overset{\overset{F}{|}}{C}} \longrightarrow \left(\underset{\underset{F}{|}}{\overset{\overset{F}{|}}{C}} - \underset{\underset{F}{|}}{\overset{\overset{F}{|}}{C}} \right)_n$$

tetrafluoroethylene   polytetrafluoroethylene
(Teflon)

There are seventeen basic types of synthetic fibers and thousands of variations. The first synthetic fiber was nylon, which was first prepared in 1935. Nylon is made of alternating units of adipic acid and hexamethylenediamine:

$$n \; HO - \overset{\overset{O}{\|}}{C} - (CH_2)_4 - \overset{\overset{O}{\|}}{C} - OH + n \; H - \underset{\underset{}{}}{\overset{\overset{H}{|}}{N}} - (CH_2)_6 - \underset{}{\overset{\overset{H}{|}}{N}} - H \xrightarrow{-2n \; H_2O}$$

adipic acid   hexamethylenediamine

$$\left(\overset{\overset{O}{\|}}{C}(CH_2)_4\overset{\overset{O}{\|}}{C} - \overset{\overset{H}{|}}{N}(CH_2)_6\overset{\overset{H}{|}}{N} \right)_n$$

nylon

Fibers that contain ester linkages are called **polyesters**. An example is Dacron:

$$n \; HO - CH_2 - CH_2 - OH + n \; HO - \overset{\overset{O}{\|}}{C} - \bigcirc - \overset{\overset{O}{\|}}{C} - OH \xrightarrow{-2n \; H_2O}$$

ethylene glycol   terephthalic acid

$$\left(\!\!\begin{array}{c} O & & & O \\ \| & & & \| \\ O\!-\!CH_2\!-\!CH_2\!-\!O\!-\!C\!-\!\bigcirc\!-\!C \end{array}\!\!\right)_n$$

Dacron

Elastomers constitute the third class of synthetic polymers. The only elastomer commercially available prior to 1930 was natural rubber itself, a polymer of isoprene and a product of the Oriental rubber plant.

$$n\ CH_2\!=\!\underset{\underset{CH_3}{|}}{C}\!-\!CH\!=\!CH_2 \longrightarrow \left(\!CH_2\!-\!\underset{\underset{CH_3}{|}}{C}\!=\!CH\!-\!CH_2\!\right)_n$$

isoprene   natural rubber

One of the first synthetic elastomers was the closely related polymer of chloroprene:

$$n\ CH_2\!=\!\underset{\underset{Cl}{|}}{C}\!-\!CH\!=\!CH_2 \longrightarrow \left(\!CH_2\!-\!\underset{\underset{Cl}{|}}{C}\!=\!CH\!-\!CH_2\!\right)_n$$

chloroprene   polychloroprene

There are now many different types of elastomers in production.

As we shall see in the next chapter, all living things contain natural polymeric material. The most important of these are the polysaccharides (sugars and starches for energy storage), polypeptides (proteins for catalysis), and polynucleotides (nucleic acids for the storage and transfer of genetic information).

TERMS
AND
CONCEPTS

- Organic chemistry
- Organometallic chemistry
- Inorganic chemistry
- Hydrocarbon
- Aliphatic compound
- Alkane
- Alkene (olefin)
- Alkyne
- Cyclic aliphatic
- Isomer
- Saturated and unsaturated compounds
- Geometric isomerism
- Heat of combustion

- Alkyl halide
- Functional group
- Alkyl group
- Primary, secondary, and tertiary groups
- Markovnikov's Rule
- Alcohol
- Aldehyde
- Ketone
- Carboxylic acid
  carboxyl group
  fatty acid
- Soap
- Ether

- Ester
- Dehydration reaction
- Wax
- Aromatic compound
- Polymer

- Monomer
- Polymerization reaction
- Monomer residue
- Polyester
- Elastomer

QUESTIONS

1. What is organic chemistry? Why are there so many organic compounds?
2. How many bonds does a carbon atom form with other atoms? Why?
3. What is the shape of the methane molecule?
4. Why do several carbon atoms joined in a chain by single bonds not lie in a straight line?
5. What are hydrocarbons? What are the two major classes of hydrocarbons?
6. Define alkane, alkene, and alkyne.
7. Write the structures for all of the isomers of C_5H_{10}. (Hint: There are ten structural isomers, two of which have geometrical isomers.) Construct a model of each of the isomers using ball-and-stick models, if available.
8. Write the structures for all of the isomers of C_3H_6O and, if possible, construct models of them.
9. What is natural gas? What is petroleum? What is gasoline?
10. Classify the following compounds according to functional group(s) (Table 14–6):

   a. CH_3NH_2

   b. $CH_3\overset{\overset{\displaystyle O}{\|}}{C}-O-CH_3$

   c. $CH_3\overset{\overset{\displaystyle O}{\|}}{C}-H$

   d. $CH_3\overset{\overset{\displaystyle O}{\|}}{C}-OH$

   e. $CH_2=CH\overset{\overset{\displaystyle O}{\|}}{C}-OH$

   f. $CH_3\overset{\overset{\displaystyle O}{\|}}{C}CH_3$

   g. $CH_3CH_2-OCH_3$

   h. $CH_3CH_2NO_2$

   i. CH_3OH

   j. CH_3I

   k. $CH_3C\equiv CCH_2CH_3$

   l. $CH_3\underset{\underset{\displaystyle NH_2}{|}}{CH}-\overset{\overset{\displaystyle O}{\|}}{C}-OH$

   m. (cyclic ether: CH_2, CH_2, CH_2, CH_2, CH_2 with O)

   n. (benzene ring)$-\overset{\overset{\displaystyle O}{\|}}{C}-OH$

   o. (benzene ring)$-NH_2$

   p. (benzene ring)$-\overset{\overset{\displaystyle O}{\|}}{C}-O-CH_2CH_3$

   q. (benzene ring with NO_2 and Br)

r. $CH_3CH_2CH_2CH_2CH_3$

s. 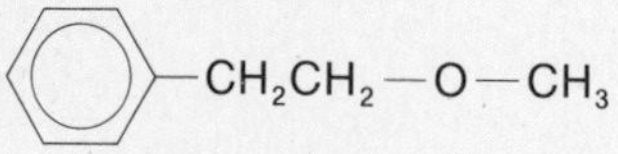 $-CH_2CH_2-O-CH_3$

t. 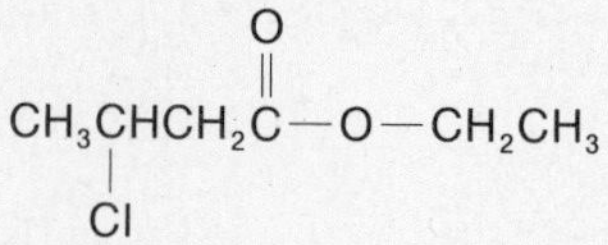 $CH_3CHCH_2\overset{\displaystyle O}{\overset{\displaystyle \|}{C}}-O-CH_2CH_3$
　　　$\underset{\displaystyle Cl}{|}$

11. How do the melting point, boiling point, and density of organic compounds having the same functional group vary as the number of carbon atoms in the compound increases?
12. What is the difference between isobutyl chloride and *sec*-butyl chloride?
13. Write a reaction for the preparation of *n*-propyl alcohol, $CH_3CH_2CH_2OH$, from an alkyl halide.
14. Write the formula for wood alcohol, for rubbing alcohol, and for ethyl alcohol.
15. How are commercial alcoholic beverages prepared?
16. Apply Markovnikov's Rule to predict the product of the following reactions:

a. 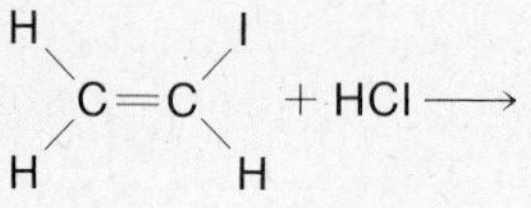 + HCl ⟶

b. 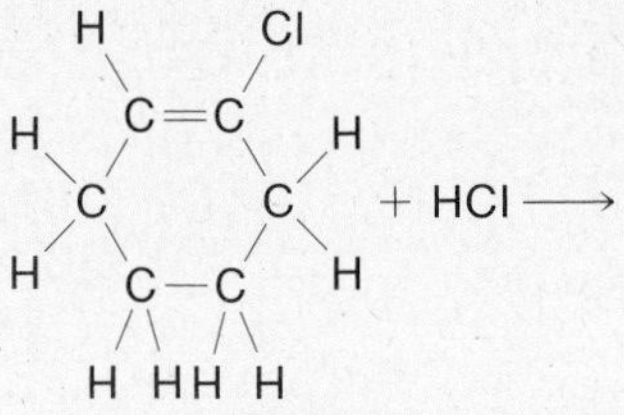 + HCl ⟶

17. What are the products when *n*-butyl alcohol and *sec*-butyl alcohol are oxidized by dichromate? If the products are further oxidized, what are the results?
18. What are polyunsaturated fatty acids?
19. The low molecular weight carboxylic acids are soluble in water, but the high molecular weight ones are not. Why?
20. Explain the cleansing action of soap.
21. What three ethers are likely to be formed if a mixture of methyl alcohol and ethyl alcohol is heated with sulfuric acid?
22. Write a reaction showing the preparation of

$$CH_3CH\overset{\displaystyle O}{\overset{\displaystyle \|}{C}}-O-CH_2CH_3$$
$$\underset{\displaystyle CH_3}{|}$$

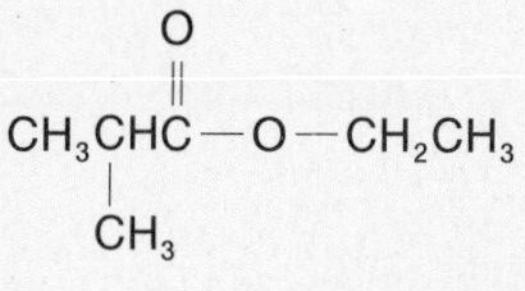

from an acid and an alcohol. Write a reaction showing the preparation of the same compound from a salt and an alkyl halide.
23. What is the distinguishing characteristic of aromatic compounds?
24. What is a polymer? Why are polymers important?
25. What are the three classes of commercial polymers?
26. Write the reaction showing the preparation of polystyrene.
27. Write the formula for natural rubber.

15

Biochemistry

Guidelines

After completing this chapter the student should be able to:

- list the most important differences between living and nonliving chemical systems

- list the chemical elements most important in living systems

- discuss the chemical features of carbohydrates, including monosaccharides, disaccharides, and polysaccharides

- identify the primary types of lipids

- discuss the nature and importance of enzymes in living systems

- write a structural formula showing several amino acids joined by peptide bonds to form a polypeptide or protein

- cite the differences between fibrous and globular proteins

- explain the importance of an enzyme's conformation

- discuss the role of vitamins in the human system, giving specific examples of deficiency symptoms

- list the three constituents of a nucleotide and show how they are bonded together

- show how nucleotides are bonded to give RNA and DNA

- describe the structure and function of DNA

- explain the driving force for GC and AT base pairing

- list and describe the three processes of the "central dogma" of molecular genetics

- describe the relationship between the sequence of bases in DNA and the sequence of amino acids in an enzyme

- discuss the various biological effects of different kinds of radiation

15.1 Introduction

Biochemistry is the study of the chemistry of living systems—the study of the structure, organization, and interaction of the substances within living matter. Since living matter *is matter*, the question, "How do living systems work?" is essentially a question of chemistry, whether one is referring to seeing, hearing, eating, breathing, aging, or even thinking and remembering. The matter that makes up living systems is no different on the molecular level than the matter in inanimate systems. The same types of atoms are present and the same physical and chemical laws are obeyed in both instances.

This is not to minimize the great differences that do exist between living and inanimate systems. Compared to nonliving systems, living systems are very complex and highly organized. Also, living matter extracts energy from its surroundings and uses this energy to carry out the functions necessary to maintain its own organization, something that nonliving systems do not do. Furthermore, living systems reproduce themselves generation after generation.

Yet 99.9% of the atoms found in the human body represent only eleven different elements (see Table 15–1). The four most abundant are hydrogen, oxygen, carbon, and nitrogen. These, along with sulfur and phosphorus, form the bulk of the large biological molecules and determine their characteristic structural features. The other atoms listed in the table exist in biological tissue as ions. They serve to maintain the charge balance in tissues and the proper osmotic pressure (page 295) across cell membranes. Sulfur and phosphorus can also exist as ions in the form of SO_4^{2-} and PO_4^{3-}.

There are several other elements necessary for life, which are all present in trace amounts. Some of these are manganese, iron, cobalt, copper, zinc, and iodine. Although the concentrations of these **trace elements** are measured on the scale of parts per million (page 284), they play a vital role in the functioning of enzyme catalysts and other proteins.

Table 15–1

Composition of the Human Body in Percent of the Total Number of Atoms

ELEMENT	%	ELEMENT	%
H	63	K	0.06
O	25.5	S	0.05
C	9.5	Na	0.03
N	1.4	Cl	0.03
Ca	0.31	Mg	0.01
P	0.22	all others <	0.01

NOTE: The total is not exactly 100% because of rounding off.
Earl Frieden, "The Chemical Elements of Life," *Scientific American,* July 1972.

The basic unit of life in most organisms is the cell. The living cell, although microscopic in size, is a great chemical machine, composed of hundreds of different compounds which interact with one another smoothly and efficiently. These compounds range from the very simple ones, such as water, to very complex enzymes, which may have molecular weights of a million or more. From a practical point of view, the number of compounds present in living systems seems almost limitless. However, in the words of a well-known biochemist, "The immense diversity of organic molecules in living organisms is reducible to an almost absurd simplicity." In this chapter we shall examine some of the basic features of the large molecules found in living systems, called **biomolecules** for convenience. They are divided into four main classes: carbohydrates, lipids, proteins, and nucleic acids.

15.2 Carbohydrates

Carbohydrates, in general terms, are sugars and sugar polymers. They are relatively high energy molecules which organisms oxidize for the release of the energy stored in them. For animals, carbohydrates therefore constitute one of the three types of food, the other two types being fats (which are lipids) and proteins. Plants, on the other hand, are able to manufacture their own carbohydrates using the energy that they absorb from sunlight. The process by which they do this is called **photosynthesis**. In both plants and animals, carbohydrates are also found as structural components. For example, the fibrous parts of plants are primarily cellulose, a carbohydrate.

Chemically, **carbohydrates** are organic compounds, many of which

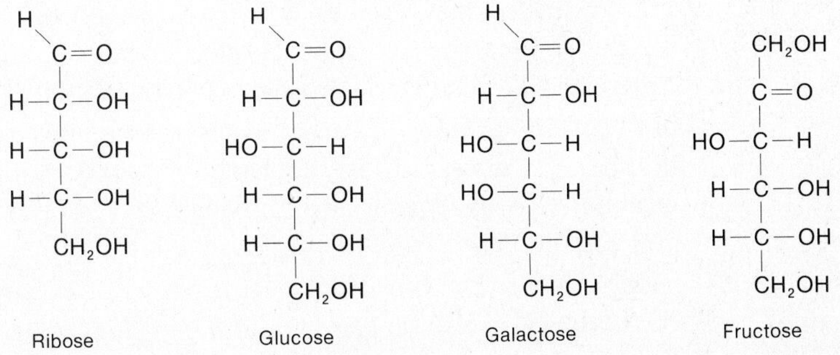

Figure 15–1
Examples of
simple sugars

Ribose   Glucose   Galactose   Fructose

have the empirical formula CH_2O—hence the name "hydrates of carbon," or carbohydrates. Actually, carbohydrates do not contain molecules of water as such; rather, they are aldehydes or ketones (or compounds that can be hydrolyzed to give aldehydes or ketones), which also have several hydroxyl groups. In short, carbohydrates are polyhydroxyaldehydes or ketones. All have the suffix *-ose*.

Some of the simplest carbohydrates, also called simple sugars, or **monosaccharides**, are shown in Figure 15–1. The simple sugars may have from three to seven carbon atoms and may be either ketoses or aldoses. Many different isomers are possible. Ribose is an example of an aldopentose, because it is an aldehyde having five carbon atoms (*penta* means five). Similarly, glucose and galactose are aldohexoses, and fructose is a ketohexose (*hexa* means six). Note that glucose, galactose, and fructose are isomers.

In aqueous solution pentoses and hexoses do not exist in the linear forms shown in Figure 15–1. Instead, the aldehyde or ketone group "condenses" with a hydroxyl group at the other end of the molecule to form a ring. Using glucose as an example, we have:

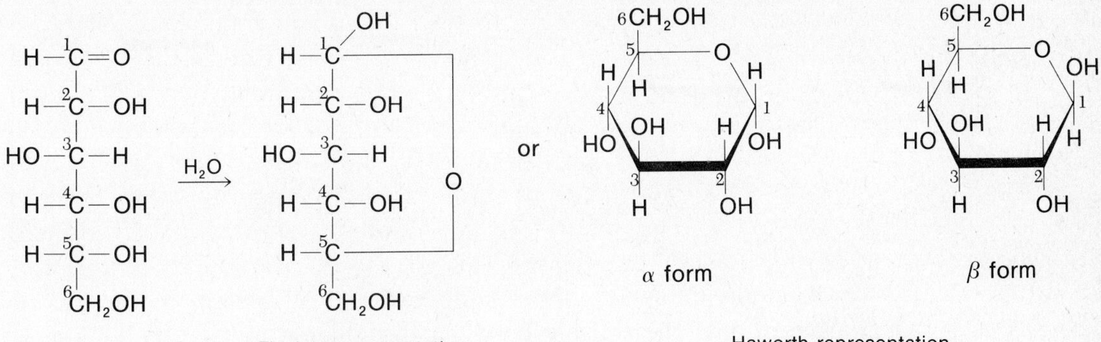

Fischer representation
of glucose

α form β form

Haworth representation
of glucose

Note that the Fischer and Haworth representations of glucose are for the same structure. The Haworth representation is preferred, since it gives a less distorted impression of the molecule. The only difference between the α and β forms of glucose is the environment around carbon number 1. Since this is the carbon involved in closing the ring, the attached hydroxyl group is found on one side of the ring in some molecules and on the other side in other molecules. None of the other hydroxyl groups may switch positions in this way. For example, arbitrarily placing the hydroxyl group on carbon number 4 above the plane instead of below it gives the structure for galactose, not glucose.

In some instances certain oxygen atoms may be missing from sugar molecules. In this case the sugar is called a **deoxy sugar.**

β-ribose β-deoxyribose

Disaccharides

A **disaccharide** is a sugar consisting of two monosaccharide units. It is formed by a dehydration reaction (page 407) involving the two monosaccharides:

α-glucose α-glucose

linkage through α-hydroxy group

maltose (a disaccharide)

The only difference between maltose and cellobiose, another disaccharide, is that the linkage between the glucose units in cellobiose is through a β-hydroxy group:

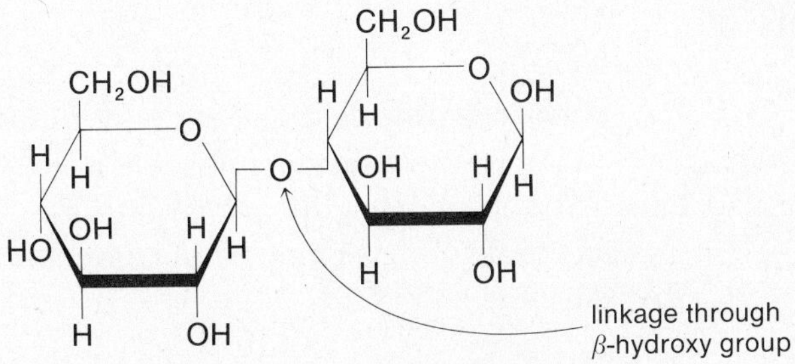

(β-glucose unit)　　　(β-glucose unit)

linkage through
β-hydroxy group

cellobiose

Two other common disaccharides are lactose, the sugar found in milk, and sucrose, the common table sugar derived from sugar cane and other plants:

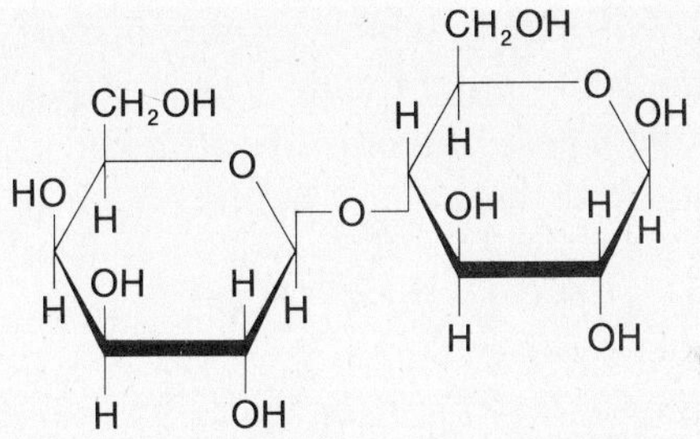

(β-galactose unit)　　　(β-glucose unit)

lactose

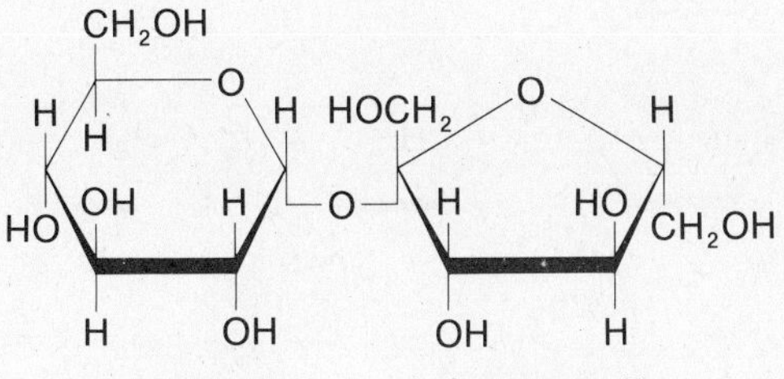

(α-glucose unit)　　　(α-fructose unit)

sucrose

Sucrose is hydrolyzed by acid or the enzyme catalyst invertase to give equal amounts of glucose and fructose. Such a mixture is called **invert sugar.**

Polysaccharides

Polysaccharides are polymers consisting of many monosaccharide units. The most common polysaccharides are starch, glycogen, and cellulose. Starch, which is the primary storage form of carbohydrates found in plants, consists of α-glucose monosaccharide units (or maltose disaccharide units).

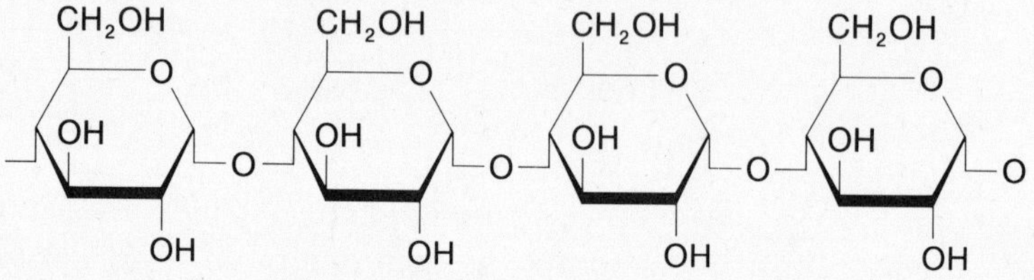

starch

The starch polymers may have molecular weights of up to 500,000.

Glycogen, which is the primary storage carbohydrate found in animals, is similar to starch except that the polymers have highly branched chains. These branches are attached at an average of every eleven glucose units, and the branch points occur at carbon atom number 6 as shown.

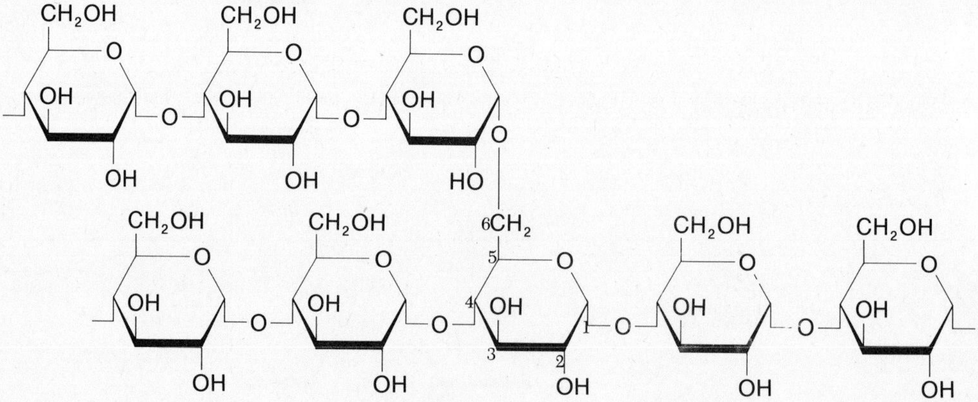

glycogen

The glycogen polymers have molecular weights of 4,000,000 or more.

Cellulose is the most abundant structural carbohydrate found in nature. Wood, for example, is 50% cellulose, and cotton is almost 100% cellulose. This polymer is similar to starch except that the linkages between glucose units are through β-hydroxy groups; that is, it consists of cellobiose rather than maltose disaccharide units.

cellulose

The molecular weight of cellulose polymers varies between 200,000 and 2,000,000.

Although starch, glycogen, and cellulose are all composed of glucose monomers, cellulose cannot be digested by human beings and thus has no nutritive value. However, a diet high in plant "fiber" (cellulose) is thought to be good for the functioning of the lower digestive tract and therefore has been increasingly emphasized by dietitians.

15.3 Lipids

Unlike carbohydrates, **lipids** are not all members of one large family of compounds. Rather, they represent several very different kinds of comparatively smaller molecules. The properties that all lipids have in common are that they are organic molecules, and they are insoluble in water but soluble in nonpolar solvents.

As indicated in Figure 15–2, lipids may be divided into two classes: (1) esters of long chain fatty acids and alcohols (page 409) and (2) nonesters. Simple lipids of the ester class include waxes (page 410), but the most common simple lipids are the neutral fats known as **triglycerides**, which are esters of glycerol and fatty acids.

glycerol   fatty acids   triglyceride

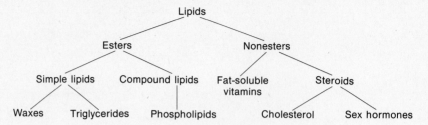

Figure 15–2
The classification
of lipids

The triglyceride fats are high energy molecules and serve as a form of stored energy.

Compound lipids of the ester class include **phospholipids**, which have a phosphate group in their molecules. Phospholipids are found as structural components in cell membranes.

$$
\begin{array}{c}
\quad\quad\quad\quad O \\
\quad\quad\quad\quad \| \\
H_2C-O-C-R' \\
\\
\quad\quad\quad\quad O \\
\quad\quad\quad\quad \| \\
HC-O-C-R' \\
\\
\quad\quad\quad\quad O \\
\quad\quad\quad\quad \| \\
H_2C-O-P-O-R'' \\
\quad\quad\quad\quad | \\
\quad\quad\quad\quad O^-
\end{array}
$$

The most prominent of the nonester lipids include the fat-soluble vitamins (Section 15.5) and the **steroids**. All of the steroids are derivatives of the four-ring "nucleus" shown below:

The most abundant steroid in the human body is cholesterol, from which the other steroids are made. It is believed that a high cholesterol level in the blood contributes to hardening of the arteries, which prompts many nutritionists to emphasize diets that are low in cholesterol. Other steroids include hormones such as estrone, a female sex hormone, and testosterone, a male sex hormone. (**Hormones** are substances that control or regulate specific chemical reactions or processes.)

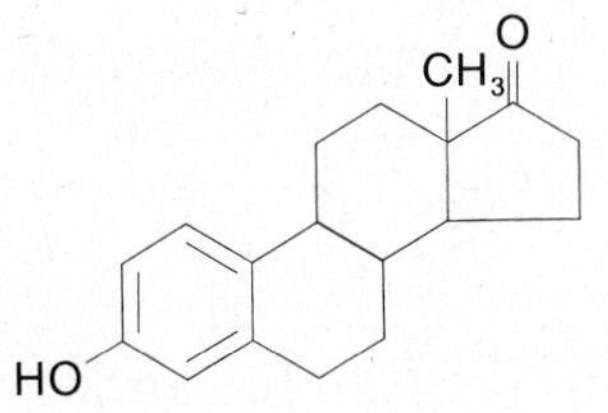

estrone

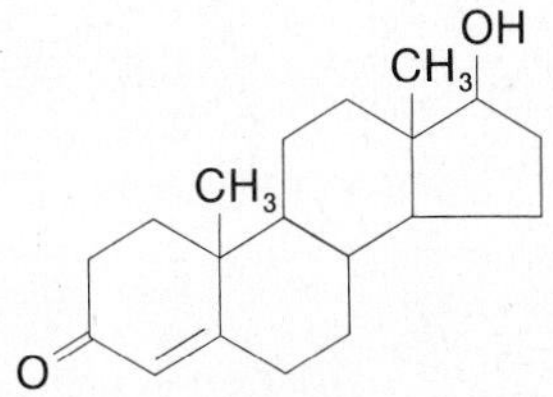

testosterone

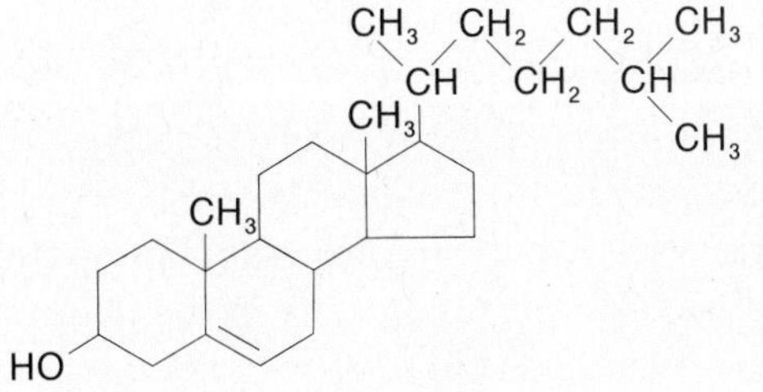

cholesterol

15.4 Proteins

The **proteins** comprise a very large class of biomolecules having many different functions. For example, the proteins found in seeds and eggs serve as nutrient stores, while those found in skin (keratin) and tendons (collagen) are structural components. Others, such as hemoglobin, which carries oxygen in blood, are involved in transport. Some proteins, such as snake venom, are poisonous, but others play a major role in the body's immune system.

The most important proteins in a living system are the **enzymes,** which function as catalysts in biochemical reactions (page 320) and which are usually named with the suffix *-ase*. There are over 1,500 different known enzymes, each of which makes possible a particular reaction or type of reaction. The enzyme *amylase,* for example, catalyzes the hydrolysis of starch to its individual glucose units in the process of digestion. However, amylase cannot catalyze the hydrolysis of cellulose to its glucose units. Since the only difference between starch and cellulose is that the glucose units are joined by α-linkages in starch and by β-linkages in cellulose, amylase is said to be "specific" for the hydrolysis of the α-linkage. The enzyme *cellulase* is necessary to hydrolyze the β-linkages in cellulose. The absence of cellulase in the human system is what makes cellulose indigestible for us (page 427).

All proteins are made up of covalently linked amino acid units. An **amino acid** is simply an organic acid (page 405) that has an amine ($-NH_2$) group. In the amino acids of proteins, the amine group is always

attached to the carbon next to the carboxyl ($-\overset{\overset{\displaystyle O}{\|}}{C}-O-$) group.

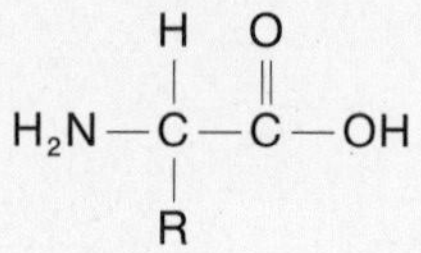

$$H_2N-\underset{\underset{\displaystyle R}{|}}{\overset{\overset{\displaystyle H}{|}}{C}}-\overset{\overset{\displaystyle O}{\|}}{C}-OH$$

There are twenty amino acids commonly found in proteins, each of which differs from the others only in the nature of the R-group (see Table 15–2).

An amino acid may be bonded to two other amino acids in a dehydration reaction:

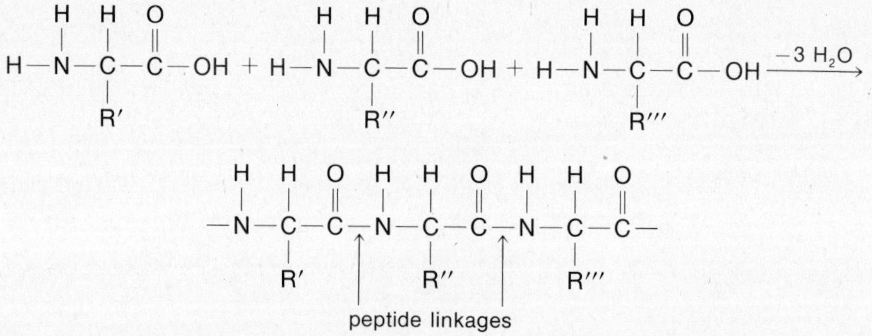

$$H-\underset{R'}{N}-\underset{}{C}-\underset{}{C}-OH + H-\underset{R''}{N}-\underset{}{C}-\underset{}{C}-OH + H-\underset{R'''}{N}-\underset{}{C}-\underset{}{C}-OH \xrightarrow{-3\ H_2O}$$

$$-N-\underset{R'}{C}-C-N-\underset{R''}{C}-C-N-\underset{R'''}{C}-C-$$

peptide linkages

The covalent bond formed between the carbon of a carboxyl group and the nitrogen of an amino group is called a **peptide bond**, and a long molecule containing monomer units linked by such bonds is called a **polypeptide**. Proteins are polypeptides that have from 50 to 1,000 amino acid units, with molecular weights ranging from several thousand up to a million or more.

Each different protein has a specific sequence in which the amino acid units appear. For example, the sequence for the simple protein insulin is shown in Figure 15–3. This was the first complete sequence determined for any protein and was finished in 1953 by F. Sanger, who was awarded a Nobel Prize for this accomplishment. As shown in the figure, insulin is actually composed of two polypeptide chains which are covalently linked by sulfur-sulfur bonds between cysteine units. Insulin is a hormone that regulates carbohydrate metabolism. Its deficiency causes diabetes.

Table 15–2

The Twenty Amino Acids Commonly Found in Proteins

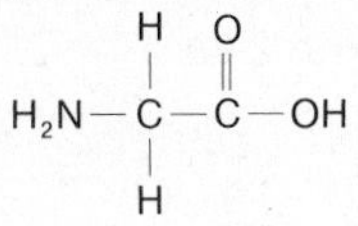

glycine (Gly)

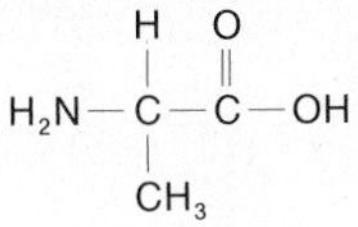

alanine (Ala)

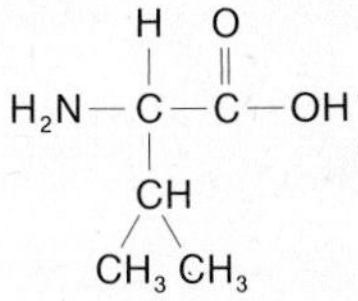

valine (Val)

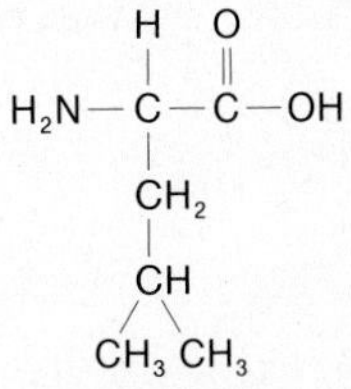

leucine (Leu)

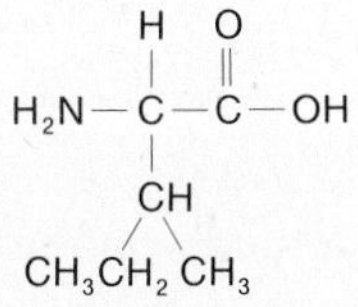

isoleucine (Ile)

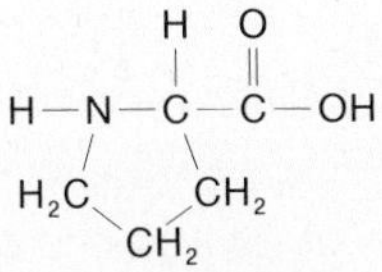

proline (Pro)

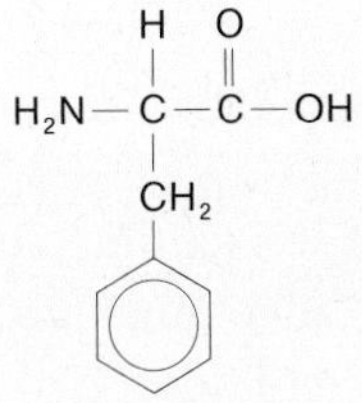

phenylalanine (Phe)

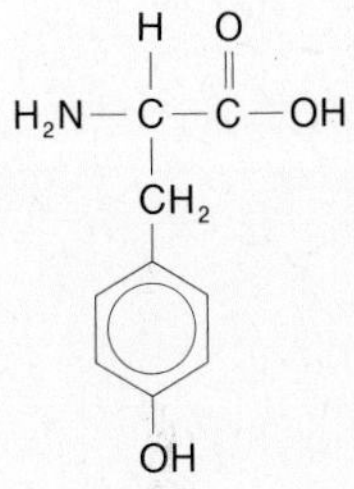

tyrosine (Tyr)

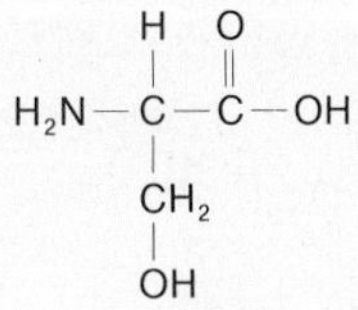

serine (Ser)

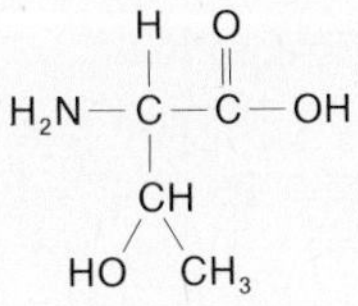

threonine (Thr)

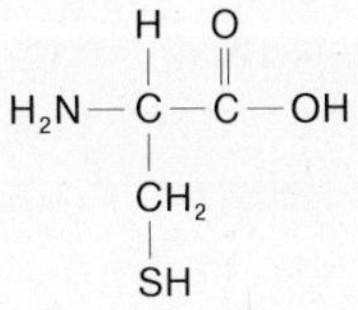

cysteine (Cys)

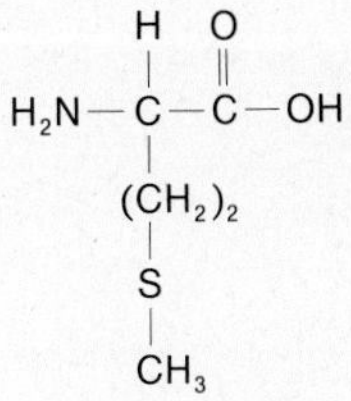

methionine (Met)

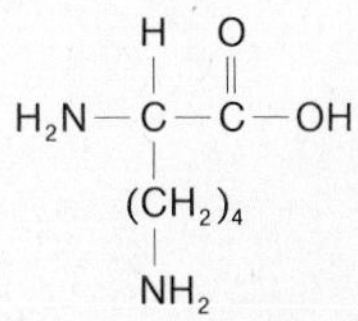

lysine (Lys)

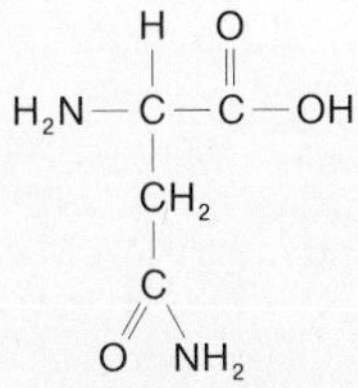

asparagine (Asn)

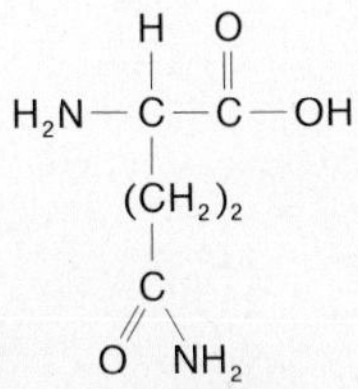

glutamine (Gln)

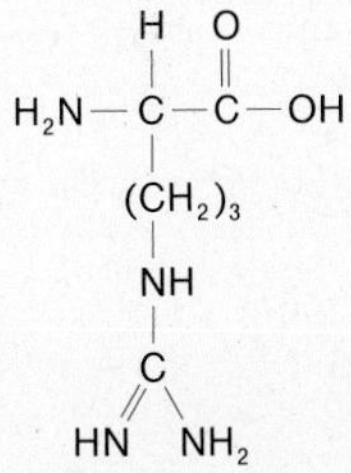

arginine (Arg)

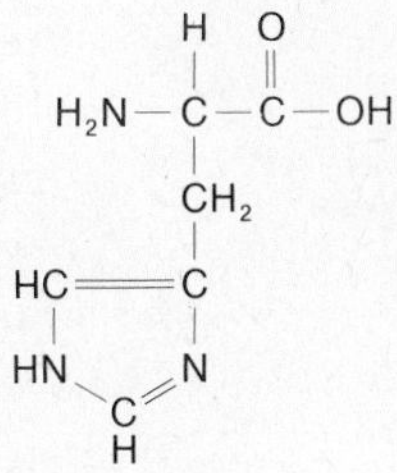

histidine (His)

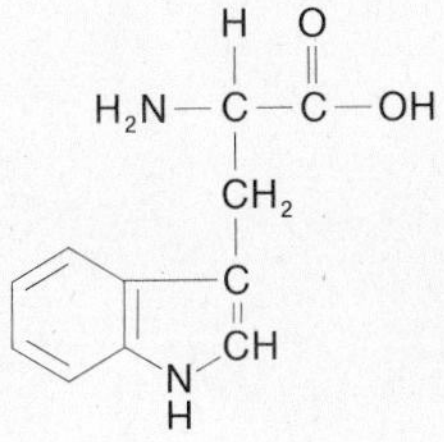

tryptophan (Trp)

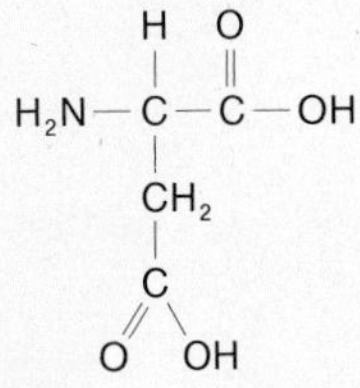

aspartic acid (Asp)

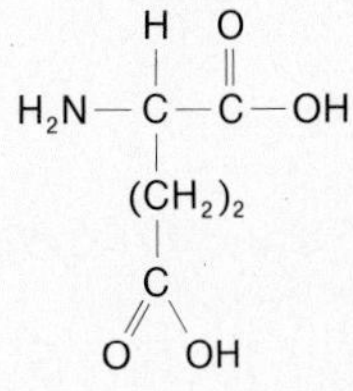

glutamic acid (Glu)

Gly-Ile-Val-Glu-Gln-Cys-Cys-Ala-Ser-Val-Cys-Ser-Leu-Tyr-Gln-Leu-Glu-Asn-Tyr-Cys-Asn

Phe-Val-Asn-Gln-His-Leu-Cys-Gly-Ser-His-Leu-Val-Glu-Ala-Leu-Tyr-Leu-Val-Cys-Gly-Glu-Arg-Gly-Phe-Phe-Tyr-Thr-Pro-Lys-Ala

Figure 15–3
The amino acid sequence in beef insulin

Protein Structure

The long amino acid chains of proteins are always folded or coiled in space in a manner characteristic of the particular protein. In general, proteins fall into two structural classes: fibrous proteins and globular proteins. The molecules of **fibrous proteins** are water insoluble and associate with one another to form tough structural and/or protective tissues. In the structural protein fibroin, found in silk, the chains of different molecules run antiparallel in a zig-zag fashion, with hydrogen bonds holding them together in a pleated sheet arrangement (Figure 15–4). In hair, each keratin molecule is twisted into a helix, and the molecules are

Figure 15–4
The pleated sheet arrangement of chains of molecules in fibroin, a protein found in silk

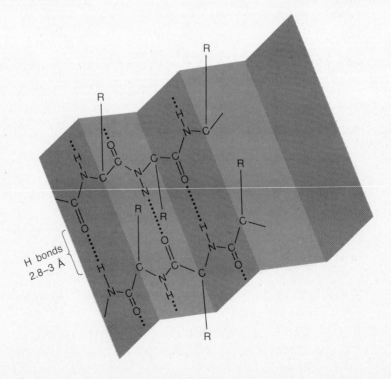

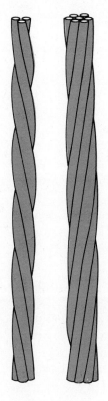

further twisted around one another to form rope-like strands (Figure 15–5).

Globular proteins, in contrast to fibrous proteins, are soluble in water, and the molecules therefore exist separately in solution. The amino acid chain of each molecule is folded and bent back upon itself to form an overall globular or spherical shape called its **conformation**. Every molecule of a given protein is folded into exactly the same shape, even though the molecules may be hundreds of amino acids long. The reason for this is that since the amino acid sequences of two like molecules are identical, the nature of the attractive forces within various parts of the chains must also be identical, and the chains will thus fold up to give the same conformation.

The particular conformation of a given globular protein is absolutely essential for its proper functioning. For example, an enzyme, which is a type of globular protein, must catalyze a reaction involving a certain molecule, called the **substrate**. (Starch is the substrate for amylase.) In order to do this, the substrate molecule must bind to the enzyme molecule in a very specific way. Hence the amino acids of the enzyme must be arranged in just the right manner to permit the proper binding. After the reaction takes place, the products disengage from the enzyme, which is free to bind another substrate molecule. The detailed mechanism by which the reaction itself is carried out is not yet known for any enzyme, although hypothetical mechanisms for particular reactions have been presented.

The conformation of an enzyme is altered, and its catalytic activity destroyed, if optimum conditions of pH and temperature are not maintained. An enzyme that is no longer active because its amino acid chain has become unfolded from its globular shape is said to have been **denatured**. Even moderately high temperatures or small deviations from the proper pH are usually sufficient to denature enzymes.

Figure 15–5
The rope-like formation of helical molecules of keratin, a major component of hair

15.5 Vitamins

The types of molecules that have been considered in the preceding three sections are major constituents of the human body, and therefore the food we eat must contain them in large proportions. Thus carbohydrates, fats (lipids), and amino acids are called **bulk nutrients**; they are the foods that make up the biggest part of our diet. Carbohydrates and fats are used in the body primarily as sources of energy and to a lesser extent as structural components. Amino acids, eaten in the form of animal and plant protein, are the components for the various kinds of proteins synthesized in the body.

In addition to the bulk nutrients there are trace nutrients: chemicals whose presence in the diet in very small amounts is necessary for the maintenance of good health. The trace nutrients are the trace metal ions (page 421) and certain organic molecules called vitamins. These chemicals are needed by the body only in trace quantities because they assist in the catalytic function of enzymes and therefore are not consumed in the reactions that are catalyzed (that is, they are used over and over again).

A properly balanced diet will provide all of the vitamins to the body in the necessary amounts. An unbalanced diet, of course, results in vitamin deficiencies, which are characterized by specific symptoms or diseases. Table 15–3 lists the vitamins, their deficiency symptoms, and their primary food sources. As indicated, the vitamins are often classified according to whether they are fat-soluble (soluble in organic solvents) or water-soluble. The fat-soluble vitamins are considered to be a class of lipids (see Figure 15–2).

Although people who eat a balanced diet consisting of meat and a variety of fruits and vegetables do not develop vitamin deficiencies, many of these people unnecessarily supplement their meals with vitamin pills. It is worth noting, therefore, that vitamins A and D are toxic (poisonous) when taken in excess. It should also be pointed out that strict vegetarians are susceptible to vitamin B_{12} deficiency, since it is not present in any plant foods. However, sufficient amounts of vitamin B_{12} can be obtained merely from eating unwashed vegetables which have soil microorganisms containing the vitamin clinging to them. In all other respects a proper vegetarian diet can provide all of the nourishment necessary for good health. Such a diet should be undertaken only after consulting an authority on nutrition, however.

15.6   Nucleic Acids

Nucleic acids, like carbohydrates and proteins, are high-molecular-weight polymers made up of a specific type of monomer unit. In carbohydrates the building blocks (monomer units) are simple sugars, or monosaccharides, and in proteins they are amino acids. The building blocks in nucleic acids are called nucleotides. Each nucleotide is made up of three parts: a nitrogen-containing base, ribose or deoxyribose (page 424), and phosphate.

The nitrogen bases found in nucleotides are most often one of the following:

Table 15–3

Vitamins

FAT SOLUBLE	DEFICIENCY SYMPTOMS	FOOD SOURCE
Vitamin A	Night blindness, dry eyes, bone thickening, and reduced growth	Plant foods, eggs, milk, and fish-liver oil (toxic in excess)
Vitamin D	Rickets (deficient bone calcification leading to "soft" bones)	Milk and fish-liver oil (toxic in excess)
Vitamin E	Not well defined	Green plants and plant oils
Vitamin K	Slow blood clotting	Green vegetables
WATER SOLUBLE		
Vitamin B_1 (thiamine)	Beriberi (nervous disorders, including sensations in the limbs, paralysis, and heart damage)	Coarse foods, especially whole-grain cereals
Vitamin B_2 (riboflavin)	Painful fissures around the outside of the mouth; dermatitis around tongue, nose, and eyes	Most foods, especially liver, yeast, and milk
Vitamin B_6 (pyridoxine)	Central nervous system disorders; not clearly defined	Most foods, especially liver, yeast, and cereal grains
Vitamin B_{12} (cobalamin)	Pernicious anemia (low red blood cell count, leading to nervous system disorders, including paralysis)	Meats, especially liver
Vitamin C (ascorbic acid)	Scurvy (internal bleeding, bleeding of the gums, defective bones and teeth, and eventual death)	Fruits and vegetables, especially citrus fruits
Niacin	Pellagra (dermatitis, diarrhea, and dementia)	Beef, liver, wheat germ, and yeast
Pantothenic acid	Nonspecific symptoms; deficiency is very rare	Most foods
Biotin	Dermatitis, nausea, and anemia (occurs only because of eating large amounts of egg white, which absorbs biotin from the system)	Most foods, especially yeast and liver
Folic acid	Anemia; deficiency is rare	Most foods, especially green vegetables

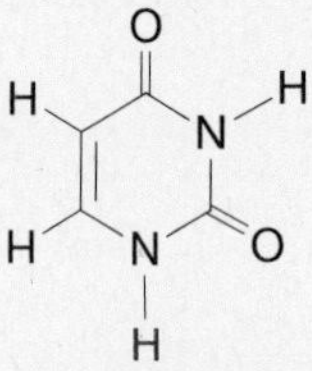

uracil (U) 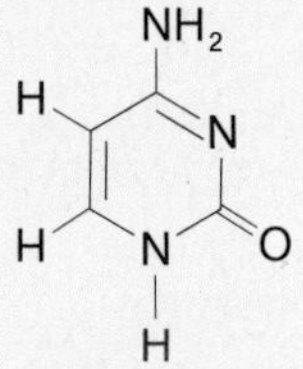   cytosine (C) 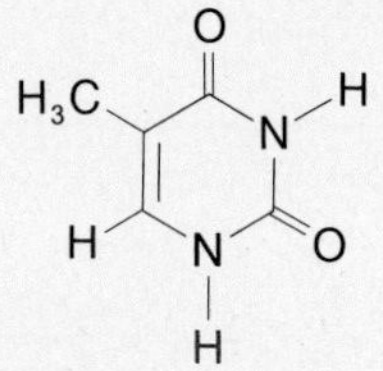   thymine (T)

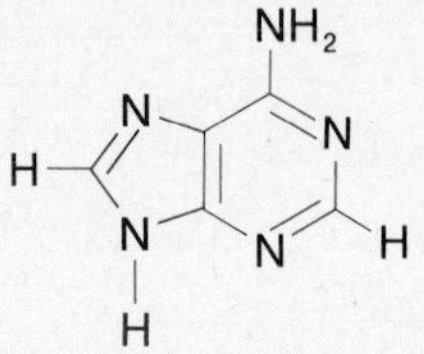

adenine (A) 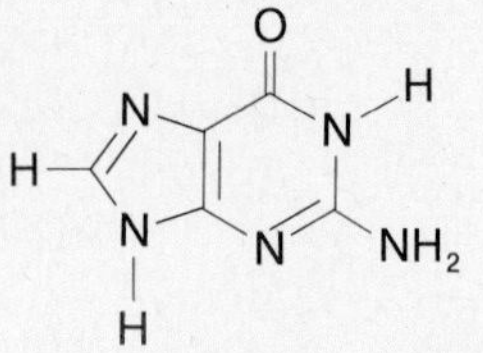   guanine (G)

These molecules are bases because of lone pairs of electrons on the nitrogen atoms (as in NH_3, page 353). Each nitrogen base in a nucleotide is covalently bonded to a ribose or a deoxyribose molecule. The bond is formed in a dehydration reaction involving the H atom indicated in color on the bases and the —OH group on carbon number 1 of the ribose or deoxyribose. For example:

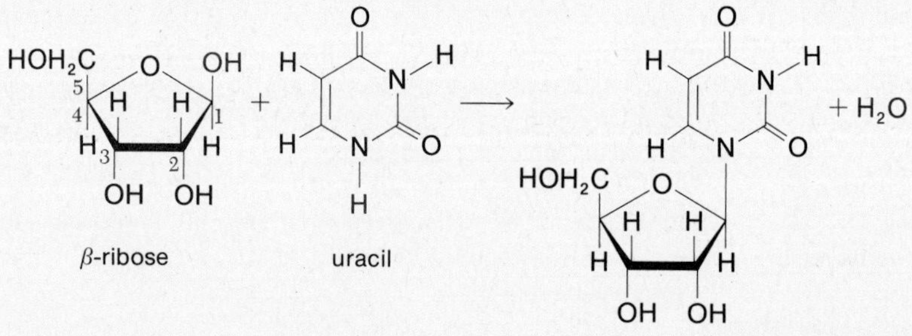

β-ribose   uracil

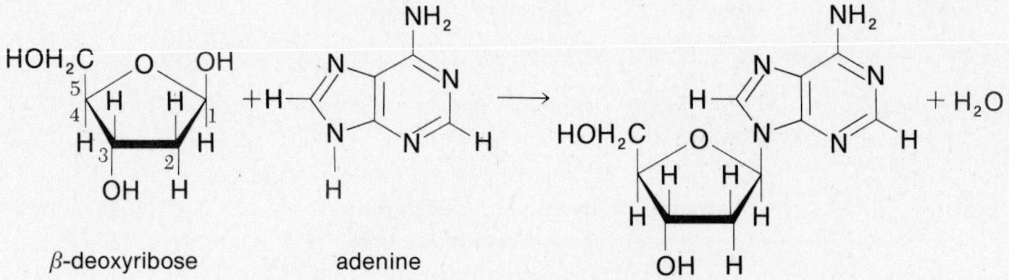

β-deoxyribose   adenine

The formation of the nucleotide is completed when the ribose or deoxyribose joins to phosphate in an ester linkage (page 410) at carbon number 3 or 5.

a ribose with base   a phosphate group   a ribonucleotide

a deoxyribose with base   a phosphate group   a deoxyribonucleotide

These nucleotides are joined together through their phosphate groups to form nucleic acids, as shown in Figure 15–6. The two main types of nucleic acids are the **ribonucleic acids (RNA)** and the **deoxyribonucleic acids (DNA)**. DNA lacks the oxygen atom at carbon number 2 in each sugar unit. The bases found in DNA are A, G, C, and T; in RNA they are primarily A, G, C, and U.

Structure of DNA

Molecules of DNA are the most remarkable molecules known. A few DNA molecules, for example, contain all of the information necessary to guide the development of one cell into an entire human being; that is, DNA contains the **genetic code** for a living organism. (As we shall see, the key to the code is related to the sequence in which the bases appear on the nucleotide units.) Furthermore, DNA can direct the synthesis of exact duplicates of itself, which makes it possible for the genetic code to be passed on from one generation to the next.

The functions of DNA are closely related to its structure. Each DNA molecule is composed of two antiparallel polynucleotide chains which

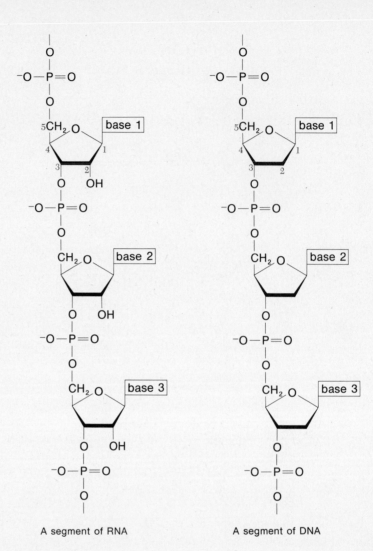

Figure 15–6
The linkage of
nucleotides in RNA
and DNA

A segment of RNA   A segment of DNA

have a particular relationship to each other. For every thymine (T) base on one chain there is an adenine (A) base opposite it on the other chain, and vice versa. Similarly, a cytosine (C) base and a guanine (G) base are always opposite each other. Because of this **base pairing**, the two polynucleotide chains in DNA are said to be **complementary**.

The base pairing of T—A and C—G occurs because of hydrogen bonding (page 178). Each T forms two hydrogen bonds with an A, and each C forms three hydrogen bonds with a G, as diagramed in Figure 15–7. Thus T and A fit together like two pieces of a puzzle, as do C and G.

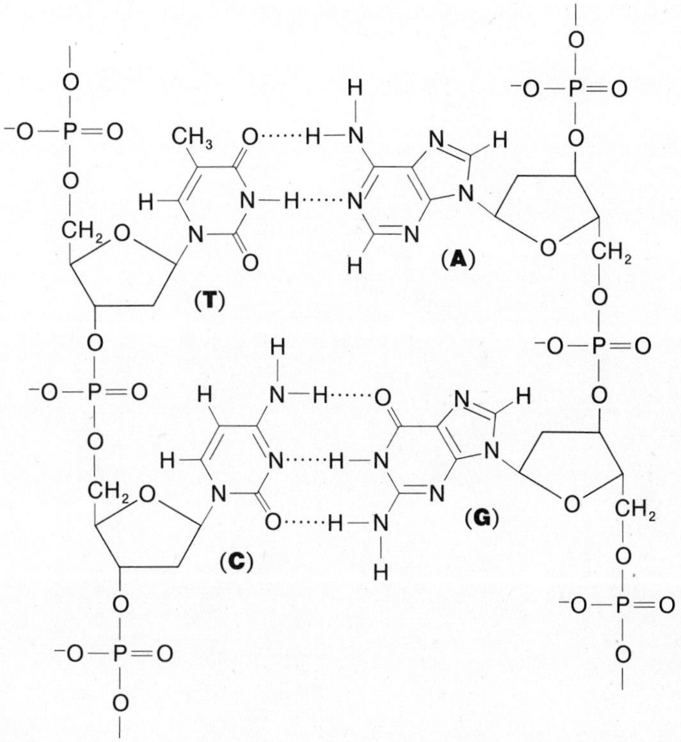

Figure 15–7
Base pairing in
DNA

However, T does not fit with G, nor C with A; therefore, these pairs do not occur.

The two parallel chains of DNA are coiled into a **double helix**, shown schematically in Figure 15–8. The coiled "ribbons," or strands, represent the backbones of the two chains, made up of the alternating sugar (S) and phosphate (P) groups. The base pairs are stacked like plates one on top of another in the center of the coil. This structure for DNA was proposed on the basis of chemical and x-ray crystallographic data by James Watson and Francis Crick in 1953. They later received the Nobel Prize for their work on DNA.

DNA is now recognized to be the ultimate repository of all chemical information in an organism. The three primary processes by which the information is duplicated and expressed are the following:

1. replication
2. transcription
3. translation

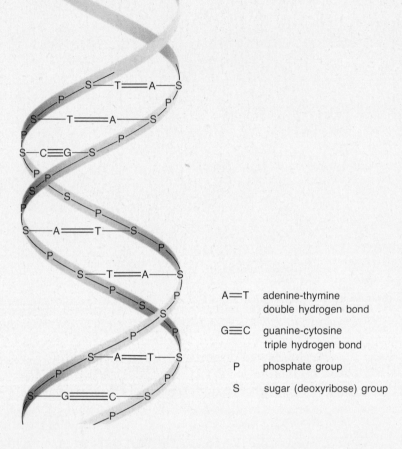

Figure 15—8
The double helix
of DNA

A══T adenine-thymine
      double hydrogen bond

G≡══C guanine-cytosine
      triple hydrogen bond

P   phosphate group

S   sugar (deoxyribose) group

These processes, each of which we will take up in turn, are called the "central dogma" of molecular genetics.

Replication of DNA

All of the enormous amount of genetic information provided to the organism by DNA is stored in the particular sequence of bases on the polynucleotide chains. Thus, it is extremely important that the exact sequence of bases is copied when the molecule is reproduced. This is no small task, since the number of base pairs in the DNA of one human cell, for example, is upwards of five billion. However, the structure of DNA

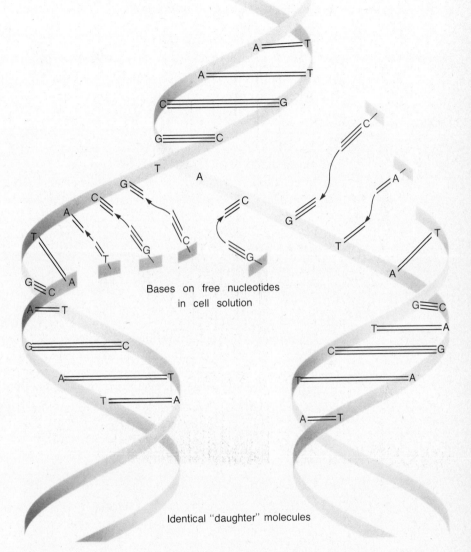

Figure 15–9
The replication
of DNA

suggests an elegant mechanism by which a DNA helix may duplicate
itself.

This process of **replication** is shown in Figure 15–9. The original
DNA molecule unravels, and as it does so, complementary chains are
formed using the separated strands of the original molecule as templates.
In this way two "daughter" molecules are formed with the same sequence
of base pairs as the original.

15.7 Protein Synthesis

The differences among different types of organisms are essentially deter-mined by the differences in the chemical reactions that occur in their biochemical systems. Since the vast majority of chemical reactions that take place in an organism are catalyzed by enzymes, it is the presence or absence of particular enzymes that determines the nature of the organism.

An organism's enzymes, which are made up of specific sequences of amino acids, are coded for in the sequence of bases in its DNA, and we shall now see how this code is translated. The information in DNA is not used directly; first it is transferred to a particular kind of RNA called **messenger RNA (m-RNA)**. An *m*-RNA molecule is synthesized from individual nucleotides using one of the strands of a DNA molecule as a template. During this process of **transcription**, the two strands in part of the DNA molecule probably separate temporarily and then recombine, so that the DNA is left unchanged when transcription is complete. The net result of transcription is a single-stranded *m*-RNA molecule which has a base sequence complementary to that of a DNA strand. That is, if the sequence in DNA were A–T–T–G–C, the sequence in the corresponding *m*-RNA would be U–A–A–C–G. (U occurs instead of T in RNA.) Thus, the information stored in the original DNA is now also stored in the *m*-RNA.

Beginning at one end of the *m*-RNA molecule, each sequence of three bases is called a **codon**. Each codon corresponds to one particular amino acid (found in the cell solution). For example, the triplet GCA is a codon for alanine, AAG is a codon for lysine, and UCA is a codon for serine. The codons on an *m*-RNA molecule are "read" by complex cell particles called **ribosomes**, which synthesize proteins.

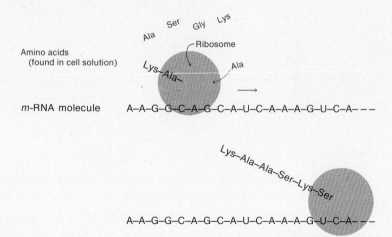

Amino acids
(found in cell solution)

m-RNA molecule

Figure 15–10
Protein synthesis

Biological Effects of Radiation

Both the radiation arising from the decay of certain radioactive nuclei (pages 110–11) and x-rays (page 100) are of high enough energy to interact with electrons in the atoms in the human body. Because the consequence of this interaction is the formation of ions, these types of radiation are called **ionizing radiation**. Recall from Table 4I–1 (page 111) that the different types of radiation have different degrees of penetration into biological tissue. For example, α- and β-rays have a limited penetration into tissue and therefore cause interactions only in or just under the skin. More energetic radiation (γ or x-rays) penetrates into and through animal tissue.

A very high level of radiation causes nausea, vomiting, diarrhea, and eventually death. High radiation doses severely damage the nuclei of living cells and eventually cause cell destruction. Surprisingly, cells that are undergoing very rapid proliferation seem to be more susceptible to radiation damage of this type than normally multiplying cells. It is for this reason that γ-radiation (as well as x-ray radiation) is used in the treatment of cancer, since one of the anomalies of cancerous cells is their continuous rapid division.

Long term exposure to practically any type of radiation can significantly affect organisms. Prolonged exposure to α- and β-radiation, for example, can cause skin cancer. In addition, if a particular α- or β-emitting isotope is ingested, it is quite possible that the isotope will remain in the body long enough to cause a cumulative deleterious effect within the body. For example, strontium 90 (^{90}Sr), a major component in the fallout from atomic tests in the atmosphere, is a β-emitter with a half-life of 28 years. When ^{90}Sr enters the body, it tends to be concentrated in the mineral phase of bone, since it is chemically very similar to calcium, a major elemental component of bone. The β-rays emitted from this rather long-lived isotope attack the bone marrow (which produces red blood cells). The long term effect of ingestion of ^{90}Sr is the development of leukemia, a form of cancer.

One of the more insidious results of radiation exposure is the interaction of ionizing radiation with DNA. This radiation may destroy portions of the DNA molecule, in some cases making it impossible to transmit information to any offspring. Thus, ionizing radiation can cause **genetic mutations**, or alterations within the DNA molecule. These can cause cancer by interrupting the normal processes of cell division and can have long term genetic effects on future generations.

Suppose an m-RNA has the sequence of bases shown in Figure 15–10. The first two codons are AAG and GCA, which correspond to lysine and alanine, respectively. These codons are chemically recognized by a ribosome particle, which joins the two amino acids in a peptide bond (page 430). The ribosome then moves along the m-RNA molecule, and the amino acid alanine corresponding to the next codon (GCA) is joined by a peptide bond to the previous amino acid (also alanine). In this way a protein is synthesized one amino acid at a time according to the sequence of codons on the m-RNA molecule. The process is called **translation** since the genetic code of the m-RNA molecule is being translated into active enzyme catalysts. When the process is complete, the protein spontaneously assumes its characteristic conformation (page 433). Although knowledge of these basic features of protein synthesis has been established, there are many details which have yet to be worked out.

TERMS
AND
CONCEPTS

- Biochemistry
- Trace element
- Biomolecule
- Carbohydrate
- Photosynthesis
- Monosaccharide, disaccharide, and polysaccharide
- Deoxy sugar
- Invert sugar
- Lipid
- Triglyceride
- Phospholipid
- Steroid
- Hormone
- Protein
- Enzyme
- Amino acid
- Peptide bond
- Polypeptide
- Fibrous and globular proteins
- Conformation

- Substrate
- Denaturation
- Bulk and trace nutrients
- Vitamin
- Nucleic acid
- Nucleotide
- Ribonucleic acid (RNA)
- Deoxyribonucleic acid (DNA)
- Genetic code
- Base pairing
- Complementary strands
- Double helix
- Replication, transcription, and translation
- Messenger RNA (m-RNA)
- Codon
- Ribosome
- Ionizing radiation
- Genetic mutation

QUESTIONS

1. What is biochemistry?
2. What are some of the differences between living and inanimate systems?
3. Name the four most abundant elements in the human body and the six most important elements in determining the structure of biological molecules.
4. What is the difference between the α and the β forms of glucose?
5. How does a deoxy sugar differ from a normal sugar?
6. What are disaccharides and how are they formed? Name some examples of common disaccharides.

7. How is cellobiose different from maltose?
8. What are the structural differences among starch, glycogen, and cellulose? What is the function of each?
9. What properties do all lipids have in common? What are the two classes of lipids?
10. Show how a triglyceride is formed from glycerol and fatty acids. What is the function of triglycerides?
11. Draw the structure from which all steroids are derived.
12. What is the function of enzymes? They are in what class of biological molecules?
13. Define an amino acid and write a reaction showing how it can be joined to two other amino acids through peptide bonds.
14. What are proteins? What are the two structural classes of proteins?
15. Explain what the conformation of a protein is and why it is important.
16. What is meant by the substrate for an enzyme?
17. Name the three types of bulk nutrients and explain how they are utilized in the human body.
18. What are the trace nutrients? Why are they needed only in very small amounts?
19. Give examples of several essential vitamins and the food sources that contain them. Which vitamins are toxic in excess quantities?
20. Name the three parts of a nucleotide and draw a structure showing how they are joined together.
21. Explain how nucleotides are joined to form nucleic acids.
22. What is the difference between DNA and RNA?
23. Draw the structure of DNA, labeling all parts of the molecule.
24. Describe the replication process of DNA.
25. What is the relationship of the base sequence in m-RNA to the sequence in the DNA from which it was transcribed?
26. How is the information in DNA expressed in the structure of proteins?
27. Which types of radiation are least penetrating? Which are most penetrating?
28. Why are γ- and x-radiation used in the treatment of cancer?
29. What is the effect of long-term exposure to strontium 90?
30. What is the effect of ionizing radiation on DNA?

Appendix:
Logarithms and pH

In Chapter 12 we defined the term pH, a way of expressing the hydronium ion concentration, $[H_3O^+]$, in a solution:

$$pH = -\log[H_3O^+]$$

In order to calculate pH, we must know how to determine the logarithm (log) of a number.

A logarithm is the power to which 10 must be raised to give a particular number. For example, if we have a number x, we can express it as a power of 10:

$$x = 10^y$$

Since y is the power to which 10 is raised, y is the logarithm of x:

$$\log x = y$$

Notice that if the number x is exactly equal to a power of 10, the $\log x$ is numerically equal to the value of that power:

$$\log 10^3 = 3$$
$$\log 10^{-4} = -4$$
$$\log 10 = 1$$

Furthermore, since $10^0 = 1$:

$$\log 1 = \log 10^0 = 0$$

In general, then, we may say that:

$$\text{if } x > 1, \text{ then } \log x > 0$$
$$\text{if } 0 < x < 1, \text{ then } \log x < 0$$

Numbers less than zero cannot be assigned logarithms since it is impossible to get a negative number by raising 10 to a power.

Table A–1 gives the logarithms to three decimal places for all two-digit numbers between 1 and 10. For example, to find the logarithm of 6.7 (log 6.7), we go down the left-hand column of the table to number 6 and then straight across to the column 0.7; thus the log of 6.7 is found to be 0.826, or 0.83 when rounded off to two significant figures.

To determine the logarithm for a number greater than 10 or less than 1, we first express the number in exponential notation (see pages 5–9) and then proceed as above, remembering that the logarithm of a power of 10 is equal to that power and also noting that the logarithm of two numbers multiplied by each other is equal to the *sum* of the two individual logarithms.

EXAMPLE A.a
Determine the logarithm of 4,200.
We first express 4,200 in exponential notation: 4.2×10^3. Next, we take the logarithm:

$$\log(4.2 \times 10^3) = \log 4.2 + \log 10^3$$

From Table A–1 we can determine log 4.2:

$$\log 4.2 = 0.623$$

We then proceed as follows:

$$\log 4.2 + \log 10^3 = 0.623 + 3.000$$

$$= 3.623$$

$$\log(4.2 \times 10^3) = 3.62$$

Note that the numbers to the left of the decimal in the logarithm help to determine the power of 10 (or the location of the decimal point in the number whose logarithm we are finding) and therefore are *not* considered in determining the number of significant figures.

EXAMPLE A.b
Determine the logarithm of 0.00055.
We first express 0.00055 in exponential notation: 5.5×10^{-4}. We can then take the logarithm:

$$\log(5.5 \times 10^{-4}) = \log 5.5 + \log 10^{-4}$$

$$= 0.740 + (-4.000) = -3.26$$

Antilogarithms The inverse of finding the logarithm of a number is known as finding the antilogarithm—finding the number corresponding to a given logarithm. It is easy to find the antilog that corresponds to a number between 1 and 10. To find the antilog of 0.84, for example, we simply look up this logarithm in the body of the log table and determine the number to which it corresponds: 6.9 in this case.

The task is more complicated when the logarithm which we are looking up does not correspond to a number between 1 and 10. In this case we must rewrite the logarithm in the form of a positive decimal fraction plus or minus a whole number. For example, to find the antilog of 5.74, we separate the number into 0.74 + 5.00. The antilog of 0.74 (from the table) is 5.5 and the antilog of 5.00 is 10^5. Combining these, we have:

$$\text{antilog } 5.74 = \text{antilog } (0.74 + 5.00)$$

$$= \text{antilog } 0.74 \times \text{antilog } 5.00$$

$$= 5.5 \times 10^5$$

As a check, we could take the logarithm of 5.5×10^5, which would give us an answer of 5.74.

EXAMPLE A.c Determine the antilogarithm of -8.62.

We must separate -8.62 into a *positive* decimal fraction and an integer:

$$\text{antilog } (-8.62) = \text{antilog } (+0.38 - 9.00)$$
$$= \text{antilog } 0.38 \times \text{antilog } (-9.00) = 2.4 \times 10^{-9}$$

Table A–1 **A Three-Place Table of Logarithms**

	0.0	0.1	0.2	0.3	0.4	0.5	0.6	0.7	0.8	0.9
1	.000	.041	.079	.114	.146	.176	.204	.230	.255	.279
2	.301	.322	.342	.362	.380	.398	.415	.431	.447	.462
3	.477	.491	.505	.519	.532	.544	.556	.568	.580	.591
4	.602	.613	.623	.634	.644	.653	.663	.672	.681	.690
5	.699	.708	.716	.724	.732	.740	.748	.756	.763	.771
6	.778	.785	.792	.799	.806	.813	.820	.826	.833	.839
7	.845	.851	.857	.863	.869	.875	.881	.887	.892	.898
8	.903	.908	.914	.919	.924	.929	.935	.940	.945	.949
9	.954	.959	.964	.969	.973	.978	.982	.987	.991	.996

Glossary

absolute temperature temperature expressed in units Kelvin. See Kelvin scale.

accuracy an expression of the validity of a measurement, given as the error; that is, how close a measurement is to the true value

acid See Arrhenius acid, Brønsted acid, and Lewis acid.

acid anhydride a nonmetal oxide which reacts with water to form an acid

acidosis a condition resulting in the lowering of the pH of blood

actinides the elements thorium through lawrencium

activated complex (transition state) an intermediate species in the process of going from reactants to products in a chemical reaction

activation energy the minimum energy that must be surpassed in order for a reaction to take place

aerobic process a process that involves oxygen consumption by organisms

alcohol an organic compound of the family R—OH, e.g., ethyl alcohol, C_2H_5OH

aldehyde an organic compound of the family

$$R-\overset{\overset{\displaystyle O}{\|}}{C}-H$$

aliphatic compound an organic compound composed of chains of carbon atoms or nonaromatic rings of carbon atoms

alkali metal an element in Group IA in the periodic table

alkaline earth metal an element in Group IIA in the periodic table

alkalosis a condition resulting in the raising of the pH of blood

alkane a hydrocarbon that contains no double or triple bonds

alkene a hydrocarbon that contains at least one carbon—carbon double bond, but no triple bonds

alkyl group a hydrocarbon minus one hydrogen atom, such as the methyl group, $-CH_3$

alkyl halide a compound composed of an alkyl group and a halide, e.g., methylchloride, CH_3Cl

alkyne a hydrocarbon that contains at least one carbon—carbon triple bond

alpha (α) particle a helium atom from which both electrons have been removed; it is composed of two protons and two neutrons

alpha (α) radiation radiation composed of alpha particles

amide group the functional group $-\overset{\overset{\displaystyle O}{\|}}{C}-NH_2$

amine group the functional group $-NH_2$

amino acid an organic carboxylic acid that also has an amine group $(R-CHNH_2-COOH)$; amino acids are the building blocks of proteins

amorphous solid a permanently supercooled liquid such as a glass

ampere a unit of electric current which has the dimensions coulomb per second (C/sec)

amphoteric having both acidic and basic properties

anaerobic process a process that takes place in the absence of air

analysis determination of the composition of a material

analytical chemistry the branch of chemistry concerned with what something is composed of and in what amounts the components are there

anion a negatively charged ion

anode the electrode at which oxidation takes place in an electrochemical cell

aqueous solution a solution in which water is the solvent

aromatic compound an organic compound having a ring that can be represented by more than one resonant structure

Arrhenius acid a compound that ionizes in aqueous solution to give H^+ ions

Arrhenius base a compound that ionizes in aqueous solution to give OH^- ions

atomic mass the mass of an atom in amu

atomic mass number (A) the number of protons plus the number of neutrons in the nucleus

atomic mass unit (amu) a unit of mass equal to $\frac{1}{12}$ the mass of an atom of ^{12}C, or 1.66053×10^{-24} g

atomic nucleus the positively charged center of an atom that contains protons and neutrons

atomic number (Z) the number of protons in the nucleus of an atom; Z determines the identity of a particular element

atomic radius a measure of the size of an atom when it exists in a lump of the solid element

atomic weight the mass of an atom of an element expressed in atomic mass units

Avogadro's number the number of atoms, molecules, or formula units per gram-atom, gram-molecule, or gram-formula weight, respectively, of any substance; equal to 6.022×10^{23}

Avogadro's Principle the principle of gas behavior that states that equal volumes of different gases at the same temperature and pressure contain equal numbers of molecules

balanced chemical equation a chemical equation that retains conservation of mass and charge; the coefficients in a balanced equation give the relative number of moles of reactants and products

barometer an instrument that measures atmospheric pressure

base See Arrhenius base, Brønsted base, and Lewis base

basic anhydride a metal oxide which reacts with water to form a base

berthollide a nonstoichiometric compound

beta (β) radiation radiation composed of beta particles (electrons)

biochemistry the study of the molecular structure, organization, and interactions of the substances within living matter

biological oxygen demand (BOD) the amount of oxygen consumed during reactions with oxygen-demanding wastes in water

biomolecule a general name for any large molecule found in living systems

boiling point the temperature at which a liquid transforms to a gas, because its vapor pressure is equal to the external pressure

boiling point elevation the increase in the boiling point of a solution over the boiling point of the pure solvent; a colligative property

Boltzman distribution a particular statistical distribution of kinetic energies

Boyle's Law the principle of gas behavior that states that the volume of a given amount of gas at constant temperature is inversely proportional to the pressure.

Brønsted acid a species that donates a proton to another species in a reaction

Brønsted base a species that accepts a proton from another species in a reaction

Brownian motion a continuous random, erratic motion that particles suspended in a gas or liquid undergo

buffer solution a solution containing a weak acid and a salt whose anion is a conjugate base of that acid or a solution containing a weak base and the conjugate acid of that base; buffer solutions are resistant to large changes in pH

calorie (cal) a unit of heat (thermal) energy; one calorie is defined as the amount of heat needed to raise the temperature of one gram of water by 1 °C

carbohydrate a polyhydroxyaldehyde or ketone, including all sugars; carbohydrates constitute one of the bulk nutrients

carboxyl group the functional group
$$-\overset{\overset{\text{O}}{\|}}{\text{C}}-\text{O}-;$$
it is found in carboxylic acids and esters

carboxylic acid an organic compound of the
family $R-\overset{\overset{\text{O}}{\|}}{\text{C}}-\text{O}-\text{H}$

catalyst a material that speeds up or slows down a chemical reaction without being consumed

cathode the electrode at which reduction takes place in an electrochemical cell

cathode rays rays emitted from the negative electrode (the cathode) when a high voltage is passed through a partially evacuated tube; they are composed of electrons (beta radiation)

cation a positively charged ion

cellulose a particular polysaccharide; it is the most abundant structural carbohydrate found in nature

Celsius scale (°C) the temperature scale in which 0 °C is defined by the freezing point of water and 100 °C is defined by the boiling point of water

chalcogen an element in Group VIA in the periodic table

Charles' Law the principle of gas behavior that states that the volume of a given amount of gas at constant pressure is directly proportional to the absolute temperature

chemical equation a chemical shorthand notation that describes a reaction using chemical symbols for the reactants and products. See also balanced chemical equation.

chemical equilibrium a dynamic equilibrium that involves a chemical reaction

chemical formula a shorthand notation that uses chemical symbols to indicate the elemental composition of a compound; the subscripts following each element indicate the atomic ratio of each element in the compound

chemical kinetics the study of equilibria, rates of reaction, and activated complexes

chemical property a property of a substance that may be studied only at the risk of changing the identity of the substance

cleavage a property of a solid such that when it is subjected to a mechanical stress, it separates along specific planes to give fragments with extremely flat surfaces

codon a sequence of three bases on an *m*-RNA molecule; each codon corresponds to one particular amino acid

colligative properties the properties of solutions that result from the presence of a solute but are independent of the specific solute; they include vapor pressure lowering, boiling point elevation, freezing point lowering, and osmotic pressure

colloidal suspension (colloid) a mixture in which the particles of the lesser phase are intermediate in size between those present in homogeneous and heterogeneous mixtures

combined gas law the combination of Boyle's and Charles' Laws

common ion effect the principle of solution chemistry that states that adding to a solution an ion which is common to a salt already in solution will cause the solubility of the salt to decrease drastically; the effect is an example of Le Châtelier's Principle

compound a pure substance that is a chemical combination of elements

condensation point the temperature at which a gas transforms to a liquid

conformation the overall three-dimensional shape that a protein assumes after it folds, coils, and bends back upon itself

conjugate acid-base pair a Brønsted acid (HX) and the base (X^-) formed by the removal of a proton; HX and X^- are conjugate acid-base pairs

conversion factor the ratio of two equivalent quantities used to interconvert different units of measurement or quantities of different substances

cooling curve a plot of temperature versus time when removing heat at a constant rate from a closed system

covalent bond a bond between two atoms formed by sharing a pair of electrons

covalent network solid a solid in which atoms form strong covalent bonds as infinite three-dimensional networks

critical pressure the pressure that will liquefy a gas at its critical temperature

critical temperature the temperature above which thermal motion is so violent that a gas cannot be liquefied

crystalline solid a solid having an ordered internal arrangement

cyclic aliphatic compound an aliphatic compound that has at least one nonaromatic ring

daltonide a stoichiometric compound

Dalton's Law of Partial Pressures the principle of gas behavior that states that in a closed container the total pressure in the container is the sum of the partial pressures of the individual gases

degenerate orbitals electronic orbitals that have the same energy

dehydration reaction a reaction in which two molecules are joined to form a new molecule by the removal of H from one and OH from the other to also form H_2O

denaturation the process of destroying the activity of an enzyme by altering its conformation

denatured alcohol ethyl alcohol sold for laboratory or industrial use; it contains a poisonous additive

density the mass per unit volume (m/V) of a substance

diatomic molecule a molecule composed of two atoms

dimensional (or factor-label) analysis a technique of problem solving that is guided by the use of appropriate conversion factors

dipole-dipole interaction a weak intermolecular interaction between polar molecules

disaccharide a sugar consisting of two monosaccharide units joined by a covalent bond

dissociation the formation of ions in solution by dissolving an ionic compound

Dobereiner triads the result of an early attempt to systematize the elements; it was observed in the early nineteenth century that certain groups of three elements having similar properties had a numerical relationship among their atomic weights

double bond a covalent bond in which two pairs of electrons are shared

dynamic equilibrium the state of a system reached when the rates of forward and reverse processes are equal

elastomer a synthetic rubber polymeric material

electric dipole a separation of positive and negative charge that has both magnitude and direction, as in a polar molecule

electrochemical cell a device in which a redox reaction occurs such that the electrons are transferred through an external circuit

electrodes conductors in an electrochemical cell that make contact with the reactive species

electrode potential the potential (voltage) of one electrode relative to another

electrolysis the passage of an electric current through a solution or a molten salt in order to force a chemical reaction and thus obtain desired products

electrolyte (1) a solute that dissolves to give a conducting solution; (2) a solid or solution that is an ionic conductor

electrolytic cell an electrochemical cell that converts electrical energy into chemical energy

electromagnetic radiation radiation traveling as waves with the speed of light and characterized by a wavelength and a frequency

electron a small particle carrying a negative charge; electrons are found around the nuclei of all atoms

electron affinity the energy emitted in the process of adding an electron to an atom, forming a negative ion

electronegativity the tendency of an atom to attract a shared pair of electrons in a bond

electronic configuration the distribution of electrons among the energy levels and sublevels in an atom

electronic orbital a region in space around a nucleus in which there is a maximum probability of finding an electron

electron-sea model a theory of bonding between metal atoms in which electrons are able to move throughout an ordered three-dimensional array of the atoms; metals are thus viewed as positive ions imbedded in a "sea" of negative electrons

electrostatic attraction the interaction between positively and negatively charged species

element a pure substance that cannot be chemically separated into simpler substances

empirical formula a chemical formula that expresses the relative number of moles of elements in a compound using the smallest possible whole numbers; sometimes called the "simplest formula"

endothermic process   a process in which heat is absorbed by a system from its surroundings

energy level diagram   a figure that shows the electronic orbitals found at different energies

enthalpy (H) a measure of the heat content of, for example, reactants or products

enzyme   a protein catalyst that speeds up a biochemical reaction

equation of state   an equation that describes the physical behavior of a state of matter

equilibrium   See dynamic equilibrium.

equilibrium constant (K) an experimentally determined number that describes the relative concentrations of reactants and products at equilibrium. See K_a, K_b, and K_w.

equilibrium vapor pressure   the pressure exerted by a vapor in equilibrium with a liquid

erg   a unit of energy; 1 erg = 1 g cm²/sec²

ester   an organic compound of the family

$$\begin{array}{c} \text{O} \\ \parallel \\ \text{R}-\text{C}-\text{O}-\text{R}' \end{array}$$

ether   an organic compound of the family R—O—R′

evaporation   the process by which the molecules having the most kinetic energy escape from the surface of a liquid

exothermic process   a process that occurs with heat being released by a system to its surroundings

Fahrenheit scale   the temperature scale in which 32 °F is defined by the freezing point of water and 212 °F is defined by the boiling point of water

Faraday's Law   the law of electrochemistry that relates the amount of material produced and consumed to the amount of charge passed in an electrochemical cell

fatty acid   a carboxylic acid of the family

$$\begin{array}{c} \text{O} \\ \parallel \\ \text{R}-\text{C}-\text{OH} \end{array}$$, where R is an alkyl group

fermentation   the process by which sugar is enzymatically converted to ethyl alcohol

fission   a nuclear process in which a heavier atom is split into lighter fragments, releasing nuclear energy

formula weight   the sum of the masses of the atoms in the chemical formula of a compound

fractional distillation   the process in which the components of a mixture (e.g., petroleum) are separated according to their boiling points

freezing point   the temperature at which a liquid transforms to a solid

freezing point depression   the lowering of the freezing point of a solution below the freezing point of the pure solvent; a colligative property

frequency (ν) the number of waves passing a given point per second (in sec⁻¹)

fuel cell   an electrochemical cell in which a high-energy fuel such as H_2 or natural gas is combined with oxygen to produce electrical energy

functional group   a species attached to a carbon chain in an organic molecule, or a double or triple bond, that is a site of reactivity on the molecule

fusion   a nuclear process in which two lighter atoms are fused or united to form a heavier atom, releasing nuclear energy

galvanic (voltaic) cell   an electrochemical cell that converts chemical energy into electrical energy

gamma (γ) radiation   radiation composed of very high frequency electromagnetic radiation

gas constant (R) the proportionality constant that appears in the ideal gas law; it is equal to 0.0821 L atm/mol K

gaseous state   a totally disordered state of matter in which the molecules move constantly in rapid, random translational motion

geometric isomers   isomers that differ only in the *cis* or *trans* configuration of groups with respect to a double bond or a ring

glass   an amorphous solid, that is, one that does not have an ordered internal arrangement

glycogen   a particular polysaccharide; it is the primary storage form of carbohydrates found in animals

Graham's Law of Diffusion   the principle of gas behavior that states that the rate of diffusion of a gas is inversely proportional to the square root of its molecular weight

gram-atom   the amount of an element that has the same mass in grams as the atomic mass in amu

gram-formula weight   the amount of a compound that has the same mass in grams as the formula mass in amu

group (or family) of elements   a vertical column of elements in the periodic table

habit   the external shape or form of a crystal

half-cell   one-half of an electrochemical cell which may be separated from the other half by a porous barrier

half-life   the time required for one-half of the nuclei of a radioactive isotope to disintegrate

half-reaction   the equation that describes only the oxidation or the reduction process in a redox reaction

halogen   an element in Group VIIA in the periodic table

hard water   water containing relatively high concentrations of Ca^{2+} and Mg^{2+} ions

heat capacity   the amount of heat necessary to raise the temperature of one gram of a material by 1 °C

heating curve   a plot of temperature versus time when adding heat at a constant rate to a closed system

heat of combustion   the amount of heat (enthalpy) evolved in the reaction of a compound with oxygen

heat of fusion (ΔH_f) the amount of heat necessary to convert one mole of a solid into one mole of liquid

heat of vaporization (ΔH_v) the amount of heat needed to convert one mole of a liquid into one mole of gas

Heisenberg's Uncertainty Principle   a fundamental limitation on the measurement of certain pairs of observables, such as position and momentum

Henry's Law   the principle of solution chemistry that states that the solubility of a gas is directly proportional to the partial pressure of the gas over the solution

heterogeneous equilibrium   an equilibrium that involves two or more phases

heterogeneous mixture   a mixture with two or more physically discernible parts

homogeneous mixture   a mixture in which the separate components cannot be seen

hormone   a substance that controls or regulates a specific chemical reaction or process in the body

Hund's Rule   a principle used in constructing the electronic configurations of the elements

hydrate   a compound that contains bonded molecules of water

hydration   interaction in aqueous solutions between the solvent water molecules and the ions in solution through ion–dipole interactions

hydrocarbon   the simplest type of organic compound, which is composed only of carbon and hydrogen atoms

hydrogen bond   an intermolecular force that results from the interaction between an H atom in a molecule and an F, O, or N atom in another molecule

hydronium ion (H_3O^+) a hydrated proton

hydroxyl group   the functional group —OH

ideal gas   a gas that obeys Boyle's Law; in terms of kinetic molecular theory, a gas in which there are no attractive forces between the molecules and in which the molecules are point masses (the volume is negligibly small)

ideal gas law   the principle of gas behavior that states that the volume of an ideal gas is directly proportional to the number of moles and temperature and inversely proportional to the pressure, or $PV = nRT$, where R is a constant equal to 0.0821 L atm/mol K

ideal solution   a solution in which there is negligible interaction between solute molecules

inorganic chemistry   the branch of chemistry concerned with all elements except carbon

insulator   a material that does not conduct heat or electricity

intermolecular force   a force between molecules of molecular substances

International System of Units (SI)   a uniform system of measurement based on the metric system in which there are standard base units and prefixes

intramolecular force a force within a molecule (a chemical bond)

invert sugar an equal mixture of glucose and fructose; it is made by hydrolyzing sucrose

ion an atom or group of atoms that has a positive or negative charge

ionic bond a bond formed between positively and negatively charged ions

ionicity the amount of ionic character in a bond compared to the covalent character

ionic radius a measure of the size of an ion

ionization the process by which a covalent molecule separates into ions when dissolved in a solvent, such as $HCl \rightarrow H^+ + Cl^-$ in water

ionization potential the energy needed to remove an electron from an isolated atom

ionizing radiation radiation that is energetic enough to interact with atoms or molecules to form ions, e.g., α-, β-, γ-, or x-rays

isoelectronic species species that have the same number of electrons

isomers compounds that have the same molecular formula but different molecular structures

isotonic solutions solutions that have the same osmotic pressure

isotopes atoms of a given element that have the same number of protons in the nucleus but different numbers of neutrons; two isotopes of a given element differ only in their atomic masses

K_a the equilibrium constant for an acid

K_b the equilibrium constant for a base

K_w the equilibrium constant for water; it is equal to 1.0×10^{-14} at 25 °C

Kelvin scale the absolute temperature scale in which 0 K (known as "absolute zero") is the lowest possible temperature; 1 K has the same magnitude as 1 °C

ketone an organic compound of the family

$$R - \overset{\displaystyle O}{\underset{\displaystyle \|}{C}} - R'$$

kinetic energy energy associated with motion, given by the equation $KE = \frac{1}{2} mv^2$, where m is mass and v is velocity; the unit of kinetic energy is the erg ($1 \text{ erg} = 1 \text{ g cm}^2/\text{sec}^2$)

kinetic molecular theory a theory that attempts to explain the microscopic behavior of matter

lanthanides (rare earths) the elements cerium through lutetium

Law of Chemical Equilibrium the principle of chemistry that describes the relationships among the concentrations of reactants and products when a system is at chemical equilibrium

Law of Conservation of Energy one of the fundamental laws of chemistry which states that energy is always conserved and can never be created or destroyed in a chemical reaction

Law of Conservation of Mass a fundamental law which states that matter is always conserved and is neither created nor destroyed in a chemical reaction

Law of Constant Proportions the principle of chemistry that states that in every compound, the constituent elements are present in constant proportions by weight

Law of Multiple Proportions the chemical principle that states that when two elements combine to form more than one compound, the masses of one element, which combine with a fixed mass of the other element, are in a ratio of small whole numbers

Le Châtelier's Principle the principle of chemistry that states that when a system at equilibrium is disturbed by a stress, the position of the equilibrium will shift to relieve that stress

Lewis acid a species that accepts a pair of electrons from another species in a reaction

Lewis base a species that donates a pair of electrons to another species in a reaction

Lewis (electron-dot) structure a representation of simple molecules based on the tendency of an atom to attain an octet of electrons

limiting reagent the reactant that disappears first when two or more reactants undergo a reaction

lipids a class of organic biomolecules that are insoluble in water but soluble in nonpolar solvents; they include fats, steroids, and fat-soluble vitamins

liquid state the state of matter intermediate between the gaseous and solid states, characterized by a loose bonding between molecules such that they are free to move around one another but not free to completely fly about at random as in a gas

London force a weak intermolecular interaction between instantaneous dipoles on nonpolar molecules

London smog air pollution composed primarily of soot and SO_2

lone pair of electrons an electron pair not involved in bonding

Los Angeles smog air pollution that is primarily composed of the products of photochemical reactions between primary pollutants

macromolecule a very large molecule; a polymer

manometer a device that measures pressure

Markovnikov's Rule the principle of organic chemistry that states that in the ionic addition of an acid to the carbon–carbon double bond of an alkene, the hydrogen of the acid attaches itself to the carbon atom that already holds the greater number of hydrogens

mass action expression the expression $[C]^p[D]^q$ . . ./$[A]^n[B]^m$ . . . , where C,D, . . . are considered the products in a reaction, A,B, . . . are considered the reactants, and the exponents are the coefficients in the balanced equation; this expression is equal to the equilibrium constant K if the system is at equilibrium

melting point the temperature at which a solid transforms to a liquid

Mendeleev's periodic law a principle that stated that the properties of the elements are periodic functions of their atomic weights (this was later revised to atomic numbers)

metal an element on the left-hand side of the periodic table which is malleable, ductile, conductive, and lustrous

metallic bond a bond between metal atoms packed together in an ordered three-dimensional array in which the electrons are able to move throughout the solid as a whole. See electron-sea model.

metalloid an element that has properties intermediate between those of nonmetals and metals

miscible closely intermixed; used to describe two fluids that mix in all proportions

mixture matter composed of elements or compounds brought together in any proportions

molality (m) a unit of concentration expressed as the number of moles of solute per kilogram of solvent

molar volume of an ideal gas the volume occupied by 1 mole of an ideal gas at STP; equal to 22.4 L/mol

molarity (M) a unit of concentration expressed as the number of moles of solute per liter of solution

mole (mol) a base unit for expressing the amount of a substance; it is equal to Avogadro's number of formula units for any chemical species (atom, molecule, formula unit, etc.)

molecular substance a compound composed of covalently bonded molecules which, in turn, are weakly bonded together in the solid and liquid states

molecular weight the sum of the atomic masses in a molecule of a given compound

monomers single molecules that can be covalently joined to form a polymer

monosaccharides simple sugars that constitute a class of the simplest carbohydrates

net ionic equation an equation that contains only those species that actually take part in a reaction

neutralization the process that takes place when an acid and a base are mixed in such proportions that the resulting solution has no acidic or basic properties

neutron a neutral particle found in atomic nuclei

Newlands' law of octaves the first partially successful systemization of the elements which indicated that elements with similar properties tended to appear at regular intervals of eight when listed in order of increasing atomic weight

noble gas an element in Group VIIIA in the periodic table; the noble gases have the most stable electronic configurations and are therefore relatively unreactive

nonbiodegradable compound a compound that cannot be decomposed by naturally occurring organic processes

nonelectrolyte a solute that dissolves to give a nonconducting solution

nonmetal an element on the right-hand side of the

periodic table which is brittle, dull-appearing, and nonconductive; often a gas at room temperature

nonpolar molecule a molecule that does not have a net electric dipole

normal alkane the isomer of an alkane that has no branches; that is, all the carbon atoms are in one chain

normal boiling point the temperature at which the vapor pressure of a liquid equals one standard atmosphere (760 torr)

nucleic acid a biomolecule composed of polynucleotides which contains genetic information

nucleotides the building blocks of nucleic acids; each nucleotide is composed of a nitrogenous base, ribose or deoxyribose, and phosphate

nucleus the very small, dense, positively charged central portion of an atom which contains most of its mass

octet rule the chemical principle that states that in entering into bonding, many atoms tend to attain a noble gas electronic configuration (ns^2np^6)

olefin an alkene

orbital See electronic orbital.

organic chemistry the branch of chemistry concerned with the element carbon and its compounds

organometallic chemistry the field of chemistry concerned with compounds in which a metal atom is combined with an organic molecule

osmosis the passage of solvent molecules through a semipermeable membrane into a solution of higher concentration

osmotic pressure the external pressure necessary to prevent osmosis

oxidation the loss of electrons by a species in a redox reaction

oxidation-reduction (or redox) reaction a reaction that involves the transfer of electrons from one chemical species to another

oxidation state a positive or negative number assigned to an element according to certain rules

oxidizing agent a species in a redox reaction that is reduced and in the process oxidizes the other species

oxyacid an oxygen-containing acid, such as HNO_3

partial pressure the pressure that one gas exerts in a mixture of gases

parts per million (ppm) a unit used to measure impurities in dilute solutions; 1 ppm = 1 part solute per 10^6 parts solution

peptide bond a covalent bond formed between the carbon of a carboxyl group and the nitrogen of an amino group; peptide bonds join amino acid units to form polypeptides and proteins

percent yield the yield obtained in a reaction expressed as a percentage of the theoretical yield

period a horizontal row in the periodic table

periodic law the fundamental chemical principle that states that properties of the elements are periodic functions of their atomic numbers

periodic table the arrangement of the elements in order of increasing atomic number, illustrating similar electronic configurations and trends in chemical and physical properties

petroleum unrefined crude oil

petroleum ether the lowest-boiling fraction of petroleum, consisting not of ethers but of hydrocarbons

pH a measure of the acidity of a solution; pH $= -\log[H_3O^+]$

phase a state of matter (solid, liquid, or gas)

phase diagram a plot of pressure versus temperature showing the conditions under which a given phase of a substance can exist

phase transition a transformation from one state (phase) into another

phospholipid a lipid that also has a phosphate group in the molecule

photons massless particles that make up electromagnetic radiation; each photon has a packet of energy given by $E = h\nu$, where h is Planck's constant and ν is the frequency of the radiation

photosynthesis the process by which plants produce carbohydrates using energy absorbed from sunlight

physical chemistry the branch of chemistry that deals with the quantitative aspects of the physical properties of substances

physical equilibrium a dynamic equilibrium that involves a physical transformation

physical property a characteristic property of a substance that may be studied without changing the identity of the substance

Planck's constant (h)   the proportionality constant between the frequency and energy of a photon; $h = 6.626 \times 10^{-27}$ erg-sec (g cm²/sec)

plastic   a type of synthetic polymeric material

pnicogen   an element in Group VA in the periodic table

pOH   a measure of the basicity of a solution; $pOH = -\log[OH^-]$

polar bond   a bond in which electrons are shared unequally, thus making one end of the bond negative and the other end positive

polar molecule   a molecule that has a net electric dipole

pollutant   a chemical present where it is not normally found or present in abnormal concentrations

polyester   a synthetic fiber that contains ester linkages in the polymer chains

polymer   a giant molecule composed of covalently bonded segments

polymerization reaction   a reaction in which monomers are covalently bonded to give a polymer

polypeptide   a long molecule composed of several amino acids linked by peptide bonds; polypeptides are subunits of proteins

polysaccharide   a carbohydrate polymer that consists of many monosaccharide units

polyunsaturated fatty acid   a fatty acid that has several double or triple bonds in its hydrocarbon chain

potential energy (PE)   stored energy that results from attractive or repulsive forces acting between objects; it is the energy of relative position

precision   an expression of the validity of a measurement, given as the number of significant figures meaningful to the measurement

pressure (P)   the force exerted per unit of area

primary alkyl halide   an organic compound where the carbon atom to which the halogen is attached is joined to only one other carbon atom

primary cell   an electrochemical cell that may act only as a galvanic cell; that is, it may not be recharged

primary pollutant   a pollutant that is directly produced or released into the atmosphere

proteins   a large class of biomolecules composed of long chains of amino acids joined by peptide bonds

proton   a positively charged particle found in the nucleus of all atoms

quantum   the magnitude of the packet of energy associated with a photon of electromagnetic radiation

quantum numbers   constants that designate the energies and locations of electrons in electronic orbitals

radioactivity   emission of invisible rays by certain materials

Raoult's Law   the principle of solution chemistry that states that the presence of a solute lowers the vapor pressure of the pure solvent in proportion to the solute concentration

rare earths (lanthanides)   the elements cerium through lutetium

redox reaction   See oxidation-reduction reaction.

reducing agent   the species in a redox reaction that is oxidized and in the process reduces the other species

reduction   the gain of electrons by a species in a redox reaction

relative humidity   the water vapor content of air relative to the maximum possible content at a given temperature

replication   the process by which a DNA molecule is duplicated

representative elements   the elements in Groups IA through VIIA in the periodic table

resonance   the property of a molecule such that two or more equivalent Lewis structures can be drawn for it

resonance hybrid   the actual structure of a molecule that is intermediate between the two or more resonant structures that can be drawn

resonant structure   one of the equivalent structures that can be drawn for a single molecule

retrograde soluble   soluble in such a way that the solubility decreases with increasing temperature

ribosome   a complex cell particle which is responsible for synthesizing proteins

salt   an ionic compound

saturated hydrocarbon a hydrocarbon that has no double bonds; that is, the maximum number of hydrogen atoms is attached to the carbon atoms

saturated solution a solution that has dissolved solute in dynamic equilibrium with undissolved solute; it contains the maximum amount of dissolved solute under stable conditions at a particular temperature

scientific method a general approach for acquiring knowledge and developing concepts in which experimental data are used to generate laws about the behavior of something; a theory is then proposed to account for these laws, and predictions are made on the basis of this theory

scientific (or exponential) notation a means of expressing large and small numbers using positive and negative powers of ten

secondary alkyl halide an organic compound where the carbon atom to which the halogen is attached is joined to two other carbon atoms

secondary cell an electrochemical cell that may act as a galvanic cell and as an electrolytic cell; that is, it may be recharged

secondary pollutant a pollutant that is produced in the atmosphere by chemical reactions of primary pollutants

semipermeable membrane a membrane through which only certain ions can move

SI See International System of Units

soap a sodium or potassium salt of a fatty acid

solid state an ordered state of matter; usually the atoms, molecules, or ions making up a solid are in vibrational motion only about an ordered array of positions

solubility the degree to which a compound will dissolve in a solvent

solubility product (K_{sp}) an equilibrium constant that indicates the solubility of a salt

solute the minor component in a binary solution

solution a homogeneous mixture, usually consisting of a substance dissolved in water

solvent the major component in a binary solution

spectator ion an ion that is present but does not participate in a chemical reaction

standard conditions for electrochemical reactions conditions such that the concentration of any solute is 1.00 M, the temperature is 25 °C, and the pressure of any gas present is 1.00 atm

standard hydrogen electrode a half-cell used as a reference electrode in which $[H_3O^+] = 1.00\ M$ and $P_{H_2} = 1.00$ atm

standard oxidation potential the potential (voltage) of a given anodic half-reaction relative to the hydrogen electrode under standard conditions

standard potential $(E°)$ the potential obtained at standard conditions in a redox reaction

standard reduction potential the potential (voltage) of a given cathodic half-reaction relative to the hydrogen electrode under standard conditions

starch a polysaccharide which is the primary storage form of carbohydrates found in plants

steroids a class of lipids which includes cholesterol and some sex hormones

Stock system a systematic method for naming inorganic compounds

stoichiometry the study of weight relationships in chemically equivalent quantities

STP standard temperature and pressure; equal to 273 K and 1 atm for a gas

strong acid an acid that is a strong electrolyte

strong electrolyte a solute that is completely or highly ionized in solution so that the solution is a good electrical conductor

sublimation point the temperature at which a solid transforms directly into a gas

substrate the material upon which an enzyme acts to catalyze a reaction

supercooling the phenomenon of a substance remaining liquid at temperatures below the point where it should have become a solid on being cooled

supersaturated solution an unstable solution that contains more solute than it would in the equilibrium state

surface tension a property exhibited by liquids due to uncompensated forces existing at the liquid/gas interface

synthesis the preparation of chemical compounds

tertiary alkyl halide an organic compound where the carbon atom to which the halogen is attached is joined to three other carbon atoms

tetrahedron a symmetric arrangement of four points about a central point

theoretical yield   the maximum amount of product that can be produced in a given reaction under ideal conditions

thermal pollution   the release of excess heat into an environment

titration   the determination of the quantity or concentration of a substance by adding known amounts of a second substance until a complete reaction occurs, as shown by an observable change in the system

torr   a unit of pressure equal to 1 mm Hg; 760 torr = 1 atm

trace element   an element present in a given system in only a very small concentration

transcription   the process by which an *m*-RNA strand is synthesized from a DNA strand; the two strands have complementary base sequences

transition metals   the elements in Groups IB through VIIIB in the periodic table

translation   the process in which a ribosome "reads" the sequence of codons on an *m*-RNA molecule and synthesizes a protein having the sequence of amino acids coded for

transmutation   the transformation of one element into another in a nuclear reaction

triangular pyramid   a pyramid with a triangular base

triglyceride   an ester of glycerol and fatty acids which functions as an energy storage molecule

triple bond   a covalent bond in which three pairs of electrons are shared

triple point   the temperature and pressure at which there is equilibrium between the solid, liquid, and gas phases of a substance

Tyndall effect   the scattering of light by a colloidal suspension

unsaturated fatty acid   a fatty acid that has double or triple bonds in its hydrocarbon chain

unsaturated hydrocarbon   a hydrocarbon that has double or triple bonds; that is, additional hydrogen atoms could be added to the carbon atoms

unsaturated solution   a solution that contains less than the amount of solute in a saturated solution at a particular temperature

valence electrons   electrons in the electronic configuration of an element outside the noble gas configuration

vapor pressure   the pressure exerted by the vapor over a liquid

vapor pressure lowering   the decrease in the vapor pressure of a solution below the vapor pressure of the pure solvent; a colligative property

vitamins   trace nutrients; vitamin deficiencies result in poor health characterized by specific symptoms

voltaic (galvanic) cell   an electrochemical cell that converts chemical energy into electrical energy

volume percent   a unit of concentration expressed as the volume of solute divided by the volume of solution times 100 percent

wave function (ψ)   a mathematical function describing the behavior of an electron in an atom; the square of the wave function is the probability of locating an electron in a given volume of space

wavelength (λ)   the distance between crests of a wave (in cm)

wave mechanical model   a theory of atomic structure that considers electrons both as waves and as particles

wax   a long-chain ester having from 16 to 30 carbon atoms in its hydrocarbon groups

weak acid   an acid that is a weak electrolyte

weak electrolyte   a solute that is only slightly ionized in solution so that the solution is a weak electrical conductor

weight percent   a unit of concentration expressed as the weight of solute divided by the weight of solution times 100 percent

weight/volume percent   a unit of concentration expressed as the weight of solute divided by the volume of solution times 100 percent

Zintl border   a zigzag line in the periodic table which separates the metals from the nonmetals

Numerical Answers

Chapter 1

3. a. 3.65×10^{-4} b. 6.31×10^2
   c. 7.856×10^3 d. 6.97×10^1
   e. 6.5007×10^1 f. 3.76×10^{-1}
   g. 1.00×10^1 h. 7.0×10^{-5}
   i. 2.1×10^2 j. 2.10×10^2
4. a. 30,000,000,000 cm/sec
   b. 0.0000000000000000000000000000911 g
   c. 25,000 mi
5. a. -12 °C   b. 37.0 °C   c. -26 °F
   d. -54 °F   e. 294 K   f. 295 K
7. a. 13.853   b. 13.8   c. 1.27
   d. 7.8×10^{-3} e. 2.1   f. 0.5   g. 8.5
8. a. 486 yr   b. 1.77×10^5 d
   c. 2.55×10^8 min; Yes (there would be
   1.77×10^5 d or 2.55×10^8 min if the extra
   time for leap year were not included).
9. a. 0.0250 L, 25.0 cm^3 b. 37.5 mg
   c. 3.0 cm, 0.030 m   d. 0.14 cm
   e. 161 km
   f. 1.94×10^3 in^2, 1.25×10^4 cm^2
   g. 3.5×10^{-3} ft^3, 98 cm^3
10. a. 3.4×10^{-2} m/s
    b. 1.86×10^5 mi/s, 6.70×10^8 mi/h
    c. Yes (the piano is 2.95 ft wide).
11. a. 5.0×10^4 lb/in^2 b. 2.8 g/cm^3
12. a. 47.5 cm, 0.475 m
    b. 990 mar^2, 220 m^2, 2.4×10^3 ft^2
    c. 1.5 mar^3
13. a. 1.2 g/cm^3
14. 62.4 lb/ft^3
15. 1.57 g/cm^3
16. 1.88 g/cm^3
17. 32 mL (or 32 cm^3)
18. physical properties: a, b, e, f
    chemical properties: c, d
21. potential energy: a, c, e
    kinetic energy: b, d, f

Chapter 2

3. a. 44.01 g/mol   b. 16.04 g/mol
   c. 181.43 g/mol   d. 119.97 g/mol
4. a. 207.2 g   b. 6.022×10^{23} atoms
   c. 3.441×10^{-22} g
5. a. 3.271×10^{-22} g,

0.00000000000000000000003271 g
   b. 3×10^{17} atoms,
   300,000,000,000,000,000 atoms
6. a. 0.0365 mol   b. 0.575 mol
   c. 0.770 mol   d. 1.53×10^{-3} mol
   e. 2.54×10^{-3} mol
7. a. 0.0417 mol   b. 2.51×10^{22} molecules
   c. 2.51×10^{22} atom Fe; 5.02×10^{22} atom S
8. a. 6.69 g   b. 94.2 g   c. 735 g
   d. 2.48×10^3 g   e. 1.18×10^3 g
   f. 3.01×10^{22} atom Li and atom I;
   4.29×10^{24} atom Ca; 2.86×10^{24} atom P;
   1.14×10^{25} atom O
9. .07 mol; 7 g
10. 2.84×10^{-3} mol, 1.71×10^{21} molecules
11. $C_8H_8O_3$
12. $C_{10}H_{14}O_5NPS$
13. $Na_3C_{20}H_{11}S_3O_9N_3$
14. a. (1) 62.53% C, 8.11% H, 6.63% N, 22.72% O
       (2) 70.90% C, 7.44% H, 13.79% N, 7.87% O
       (3) 74.27% C, 7.79% H, 13.00% N, 4.95% O
       (4) 69.53% C, 8.27% H, 6.76% N, 15.44% O
    b. (1) 64.11% C, 4.71% H, 14.02% N,
          5.34% O, 11.83% Cl
       (2) 49.53% C, 8.31% H, 12.84% N,
          29.32% O
       (3) 67.49% C, 4.60% H, 9.84% N, 5.62% O,
          12.45% Cl
15. b. X: 56.8% As, 43.2% F;
       Y: 44.2% As, 55.8% F
    c. X: AsF_3; Y: AsF_5
16. 37.01% C; 2.22% H; 18.50% N; 42.26% O
17. 41.63% Cl
18. $Na_2B_4O_7 \cdot 4\ H_2O$ (kernite)
19. a. $3\ Mg + N_2 \rightarrow Mg_3N_2$
    b. $P_2O_5 + 3\ H_2O \rightarrow 2\ H_3PO_4$
    c. $Ca_3P_2 + 6\ H_2O \rightarrow 3\ Ca(OH)_2 + 2\ PH_3$
    d. $3\ V_2O_5 + 10\ Al \rightarrow 6\ V + 5\ Al_2O_3$
    e. $2\ Al + 3\ H_2SO_4 \rightarrow Al_2(SO_4)_3 + 3\ H_2$
    f. $2\ MgNH_4PO_4 \rightarrow Mg_2P_2O_7 + 2\ NH_3 + H_2O$
    g. $2\ ZnS + 3\ O_2 \rightarrow 2\ ZnO + 2\ SO_2$
20. 31.5 g $Al_2(SO_4)_3$
21. Si
22. a. 688 kcal   b. 8.4×10^3 g
    c. 3.0×10^4 g
23. a. 38.9 g $CoCO_3$ b. 11.1 g NH_3
24. a. 35.3 g Na_2CO_3 b. 12.0 g H_2O

25. 3.1×10^2 mol O_2, 2.0×10^2 mol CO_2
26. 19 g
27. 174.0 g

Chapter 3

1. a. $C_7H_4NO_3SNa$ b. 7.8×10^{-5} mol
   c. 1.8 mg, 7.8×10^{-5} mol
2. a. 2 mol b. 0.567 g
3. a. P_2O_3, P_2O_5 b. P_4O_6, P_4O_{10}
4. $Sb_4O_5Cl_2$: $4 SbCl_3 + 5 H_2O \rightarrow$
   $10 HCl + Sb_4O_5Cl_2$
5. a. $Al_2O_3(s) + 3 C(s) + 3 Cl_2(g) \rightarrow$
   $2 AlCl_3(s) + 3 CO(g)$
   b. 7.50 mol C, 7.50 mol Cl_2
   c. 5.00 mol $AlCl_3$ d. 11 g C
   e. 43.8 g Cl_2, 54.9 g $AlCl_3$
   f. 262 g $AlCl_3$
6. 1.514 g H_2O
7. a. 34.59–44.97% Al b. 346 kg, 86.7%
8. a. $CS_2(l) + 3 Cl_2(g) \rightarrow S_2Cl_2(l) + CCl_4(l)$
   b. 1.38×10^3 g c. 101 g d. 85.5%
9. a. $4 NaPb(s) + 4 C_2H_5Cl(g) \rightarrow$
   $Pb(C_2H_5)_4(l) + 3 Pb(s) + 4 NaCl(s)$
   b. 188 g
   c. C_2H_5Cl is the limiting reagent, 62.7 g
   d. 95.4% e. 64.07% f. 1.8×10^3
10. a. $2 Ca_3(PO_4)_2(s) + 6 SiO_2(s) \rightarrow$
    $6 CaSiO_3(s) + P_4O_{10}(g)$ *and*
    $P_4O_{10}(g) + 10 C(s) \rightarrow P_4(g) + 10 CO(g)$
    b. 0.200 kg
    c. 0.582 kg SiO_2, 0.194 kg C
    d. 1.08 kg e. 0.8 ton
11. a. 0.154 g b. 59.2%
12. 1.113 g $NiCl_2$
13. C_5H_{12}
14. a. 18.30% H b. C_3H_8 c. 22.53 g CO_2
15. a. 50.52% Ta, 35.04% Ta b. $x = 0.370$
16. a. 32.86% Sr b. $x = 2.78$ c. $x = 0$

Chapter 4

2. a. 8 p, 10 n b. 8 p, 8 n c. 18 p, 22 n
   d. 19 p, 21 n e. 92 p, 146 n
   f. 92 p, 143 n g. 1 p, 0 n
   h. 1 p, 1 n i. 1 p, 2 n
   8, 8, 18, 19, 92, 92, 1, 1, 1
3. a. nucleus/atom $= 10^{-5}$ b. 82 ft
4. 10.81
5. 3×10^{17} photons
6. blue light
7. 5.0×10^2 sec
8. a. 5.09×10^{14} sec^{-1} b. 3.37×10^{-12} erg

14. a. increase b. an outer orbit
17. $n = 1$: 1, 1, 2; $n = 2$: 2, 4, 8;
    $n = 3$: 3, 9, 18; $n = 4$: 4, 16, 32
18. $2s$, 1; $4d$, 5; $3d$, 5; $1p$, no; $3f$, no; $5s$, 1;
    $3p$, 3; $1s$, 1; $2p$, 3; $2d$, no; $1d$, no; $4f$, 7
19. 1, 0, 1, 2, 3, 6, 5, 4, 3, 2, 1, 0, 1, 2, 3, 2, 1, 0
20. a. Li: $1s^22s^1$, Na: [Ne]$3s^1$, K: [Ar]$4s^1$: $1s$ elec-
    tron in outer level
    b. F: $1s^22s^23p^5$, Cl: [Ne]$3s^23p^5$,
    Br: [Ar]$4s^23d^{10}4p^5$: 7 electrons in outer
    level
    c. Ne: $1s^22s^22p^6$, Ar: [Ne]$3s^23p^6$,
    Kr: [Ar]$4s^23d^{10}4p^6$: 8 electrons in outer
    level
    d. all have the same electronic configuration
    as Ne: $1s^22s^22p^6$

Chapter 5

2. Tabulated data for Ge:

atomic mass	72.6
color	grey-white
density	5.32
oxide	GeO_2
oxide density	4.23
chloride	$GeCl_4$
chloride density	1.84
chloride boiling point	84 °C

7. C: $1s^22s^22p^2$, Si: [Ne]$3s^23p^2$,
   Ge: [Ar]$4s^23d^{10}4p^2$, Sn: [Kr]$5s^24d^{10}5p^2$,
   Pb: [Xe]$6s^25d^{10}4f^{14}6p^2$
8. a. decreasing b. increasing
   c. increasing d. decreasing
10. a. $+1$ b. $+4$ c. -1 d. -2
    e. $+3$
13. Se^{-2}, Br^-, Cs^+, Ba^{2+} (listed in order of
    decreasing size)
14. a. O^{2-}, because it has more electrons for the
    same nuclear charge; hence they are less
    tightly bound
    b. Mg, because its outer electrons are in a
    higher major energy level than those of
    Mg^{2+} ($3s^2$ versus $2p^6$)
    c. Fe^{2+} (same reasoning as in a)
    d. Cl^- (same reasoning as in a)
15. a. The outer electrons of Sr are in a higher
    major energy level.
    b. The outer electrons of both atoms are in
    the same energy level, but the Cl electrons
    are held more tightly by added nuclear
    charge.
    c. The extra electron for O must go into a

$2p$ orbital, which already has a single electron. Hence, there is a slight repulsion, making this electron easier to remove even though the nuclear charge is greater.

d. The ions are isoelectronic; the Mg^{2+} has greater nuclear charge, thus pulling the electrons closer to the nucleus.

e. The outer electrons of both atoms are in the same energy level, but the Mg electrons are drawn closer by extra nuclear charge.

Chapter 6

7. decrease in the order listed
8. a. Na_2O b. CaS   c. KI   d. Al_2S_3
   e. Mg_3N_2 f. Li_2Te g. $BaBr_2$ h. AlP
9. Na_2O, $BaBr_2$, Mg_3N_2, KI, CaS, Li_2Te, Al_2S_3, AlP
10. a. $BeCl_2$ b. $MgCl_2$ c. NaBr
    d. LiCl   e. $AlCl_3$ f. CaO   g. CCl_4

11.

$$H : \overset{..}{\underset{H}{S}} :$$

$$\overset{..}{:}Cl : \overset{..}{\underset{:Cl:}{\overset{:\overset{..}{Cl}:}{C}}} : \overset{..}{Cl} :$$

$$:\overset{..}{Cl} : \overset{..}{I} :$$

$$H : \overset{H}{\underset{H}{P}} : H \qquad :C :::O: \qquad :O :: C :: O:$$

$$\overset{:\overset{..}{Cl}:}{:\overset{..}{\underset{:\overset{..}{Cl}:}{As}}:} \qquad \overset{:\overset{..}{Cl}:}{:\overset{..}{\underset{:\overset{..}{Cl}:}{Si}}:\overset{..}{Cl}:} \qquad \overset{H}{\underset{H}{H : C : H}}$$

$$\overset{:\overset{..}{O} :: \overset{..}{N} : \overset{..}{O}:^{-}}{:\overset{..}{O}:} \qquad :\overset{..}{O} :: \overset{..}{S} : \overset{..}{O}: \qquad :\overset{..}{Br} : \overset{..}{Te} : \overset{..}{Br}:$$

12. CH_3NH_2, CH_3NCO, HCN
14. H_2O, NH_3, CH_4
18. a. H_2S bent; CCl_4 tetrahedral; ClI linear; CO, CO_2 linear; $AsCl_3$ trigonal pyramidal; CH_4 tetrahedral; NO_3^- trigonal planar; SO_2 bent; PH_3 trigonal pyramidal; $SiCl_4$ tetrahedral; $TeBr_2$ bent
    b. polar: H_2S, ClI, CO, $AsCl_3$, SO_2, PH_3, $TeBr_2$
    c. NO_3^-, SO_2
21. polar molecules

Chapter 7

1. $+1$, $+2$, $+3$, $+4$, $+5$
2. a. Cu $+1$, Cl -1 b. Sn $+2$, O -2

c. Sn $+4$, O -2 d. Ti $+4$, S -2
e. Ti $+3$, S -2 f. K $+1$, Pt $+4$, Cl -1
g. Li $+1$, P $+5$, F -1 h. Sb $+5$, F -1
i. As $+5$, O -2 j. H $+1$, Cl $+7$, O -2
k. Cl $+3$, O -2 l. H $+1$, Br $+5$, O -2
m. H $+1$, C $+4$, O -2
n. Ca $+2$, S $+6$, O -2
o. H $+1$, N -3, P $+5$, O -2
p. Cl $+3$, F -1

3. a. $+4$ b. $+6$ c. $+6$ d. $+6$
   e. $+6$ f. $+5$ g. $+4$ h. $+4$
   i. $+6$

4. a. lithium nitride   b. potassium cyanide
   c. ammonium nitrate
   d. calcium carbonate   e. sodium bromide
   f. iron(III) fluoride   g. aluminum oxide
   h. mercury(I) nitrate   i. lead(II) chloride
   j. tin(IV) iodide   k. barium perchlorate
   l. sulfur hexafluoride
   m. strontium chloride
   n. iron(II) sulfate   o. iron(III) sulfate
   p. chlorine trifluoride
   q. arsenic trifluoride
   r. arsenic pentafluoride
   s. iodine monochloride
   t. xenon tetrafluoride   u. nickel(II) nitrate
   v. silicon dichloride
   w. sodium hydrogencarbonate
   x. dinitrogen trioxide

5. a. $Hg(NO_3)_2$ b. $BeCl_2$ c. SF_4
   d. MgI_2 e. $CaCO_3$ f. CuOH
   g. CrF_3 h. $KMnO_4$ i. $Ni(NO_3)_2$
   j. $Zn_3(PO_4)_2$ k. CuI   l. MnO_2
   m. BN   n. AlH_3

6. a. $+2$ b. $+3$ c. $+3$, $+5$
   d. $+2$, $+4$ e. Se -2 f. Ga $+3$
   g. -1, $+1$, $+3$

Chapter 8

1. 1.6 atm
2. 0.78 L
3. 1.63 L
4. 34 psi
5. 260 °C
6. a. 491 torr   b. 53%   c. 1.15×10^4 torr
7. a. 1:1   b. 1:1, 1:2
   c. 1:1, impossible to know from the information given
   d. 1:1, 3:2, 2:1
8. 1.68 L
9. 16.5 L

10. 6.08 L
11. 3.92 L
12. a. 19.0 L   b. 36.9 L
13. 4.5 L
14. 5.9×10^3 L
15. 2.04 L
16. 0.754 mol
17. 16.0 g/mol
18. a. CFH_2 b. 66.2 g/mol, $C_2F_2H_4$
19. a. BH_3 b. 27.5 g/mol, B_2H_6
20. $C_2Cl_2F_4$
21. 88.3 g
22. 90.1 g
23. 1.0×10^2 g NH_4NO_3
24. 3.24×10^3 atm
25. 443 g H_2O
26. 120. g/mol; KrF_2 has MW = 122 g/mol
27. a. 9.81 g   b. 0.283 g
28. a. 1.7 L   b. 1.9 L
29. 0.092 L
30. 40.1 mL
31. a. 0.545 L   b. 0.528 L
     c. 0.0243 mol in a, 0.0236 mol in b
32. 1.30 L
33. 2.75 g
34. a. 400 torr; p_{H_2} = 250 torr; p_{N_2} = 150 torr
     b. 600 torr; p_{H_2} = 250 torr; p_{N_2} = 150 torr;
        p_{CH_4} = 200 torr
     c. 3.7 L
     d. 756 torr; p_{H_2} = 315 torr; p_{N_2} = 189 torr;
        p_{CH_4} = 252 torr
35. 1.004/1.000
38. 0.50 L
41. Box B

Chapter 10

7. a. $Ni^{2+}(aq) + S^{2-}(aq) \rightarrow NiS(s)$
    b. $3 Ca^{2+}(aq) + 2 PO_4{}^{3-}(aq) \rightarrow Ca_3(PO_4)_2(s)$
    c. no reaction
    d. $Co^{2+}(aq) + 2 OH^-(aq) \rightarrow Co(OH)_2(s)$
8. a. 0.15 M   b. 0.57 M   c. 0.20 M
    d. 0.042 M   e. 0.0692 M   f. 0.187 M
    g. 0.39 M   h. 0.056 M   i. 0.0893 M
9. 0.792 M
10. 40.2 g
11. 36.3 g
12. 3.19 g
13. a. 0.302 M   b. 6.6×10^{-3} M
     c. 0.050 g
14. 0.105 M
15. 83 mL
16. a. 425 g   b. 0.600 L

17. a. 0.083 L of concentrated acid and dilute to
        1.0 L
    b. 0.20 L of concentrated base and dilute to
       500 mL
    c. 39 mL of concentrated solution and dilute
       to 250 mL
    d. 5.0 mL of concentrated solution and dilute
       to 100 mL
18. a. 0.103 m, 1.82%   b. 0.0917 m, 1.16%
    c. 0.0775 m, 2.59%   d. 0.100 m, 1.21%
    e. 0.213 m, 2.53%   f. 0.147 m, 3.34%
19. 0.343 m, 3.68%
20. 1.71 L
21. 879 mL
22. 0.593 M
23. 0.36 L
24. 95.4 mL
25. 0.844 mol/L
26. 13.7 g
27. 100.333 °C
29. 132 g/mol
30. 360 g/mol
31. a. 14 m   b. 0.78 L/L H_2O
     c. 3.1 qt/gal H_2O

Chapter 11

2. endothermic
3. a. 1.44×10^{-5} b. 3.28×10^{-5}
    c. larger, endothermic
    d. decrease, very small amount of Br
4. b. 0.0165 atm   c. endothermic
5. b. neither   c. 0.560 M   d. no change
6. a. forward   b. reverse   c. neither
    d. 0.330 atm
7. a. 0.425
    b. P_{H_2} = 8.72 atm, P_{H_2S} = 6.56 atm
    c. 0.111 mol H_2, 0.0834 mol H_2S
8. a. 0.025   b. 0.031, larger than K, reverse
9. a. shift to right   b. shift to left
    c. shift to left   d. shift to right
    e. shift to right   f. none
10. a. forward, mass action expression is less
        than K
    b. reverse, mass action expression is greater
       than K
12. $[Ag^+] = [IO_3{}^-] = 0.049$ M; 2.4×10^{-3}
13. 2.80×10^{-7}
14. 6.9×10^{-9}
15. a. 3×10^{-3} M   b. 3×10^{-3} mol
     c. 0.02 g
16. 0.010 g, 3.6×10^{-3} g

17. a. 7.32×10^{-4} M b. 1.46×10^{-3} M
    c. 1.56×10^{-9}
18. 1.3×10^{-24} M, 2.1×10^{-23} g
19. No; no
20. a. shift to right   b. shift to left
    c. shift to left   d. shift to right   e. none
    f. shift to right
21. $K = 0.50$; $K' = 0.71$; $K' = \sqrt{K}$
24. a. 5.9×10^{-15} M
    b. $P_{SO_2} = 1.4 \times 10^{-13}$ atm, $P_{SO_3} = 0.12$ atm
    c. same as without a catalyst, most

Chapter 12

7. 6.5×10^{-5}
8. 1.32
9. 0.23
10. 1.76×10^{-4}
11. 0.623%
12. 4.4×10^{-4}
13. 5.8×10^{-5}
14. 2.29×10^{-5}
15. 6.15
16. a. 2.1×10^{-3} M, 2.68
    b. 1.3×10^{-3} M, 2.89
    c. 1.6×10^{-3} M, 2.80
    d. 2.6×10^{-3} M, 2.59
17. a. 2.44 b. 8.32 c. 7.00 d. 10.22
    e. 1.19 f. -0.30 g. 0.00 h. 2.60
18. a, e, f, g, and h are acid; b and d are basic;
    c is neutral
19. a. 1.0×10^{-4} M b. 1.4×10^{-6} M
    c. 3.9×10^{-12} M d. 0.20 M e. 4.9 M
    f. 1.7×10^{-10} M
20. 0.151 M
21. 0.1012 M
22. 0.106 M
23. 0.213 M
24. 0.155 M
25. 2.4×10^{-4} M, 3.62
27. 3.77 (a change of 0.15 pH units)

Chapter 13

2. a. $3\,Cu + 2\,NO_3^- + 8\,H^+ \rightarrow$
      $3\,Cu^{2+} + 2\,NO + 4\,H_2O$
   b. $Cr_2O_7^{2-} + 3\,U^{4+} + 2\,H^+ \rightarrow$
      $2\,Cr^{3+} + 3\,UO_2^{2+} + H_2O$
   c. $5\,Cl_2 + I_2 + 6\,H_2O \rightarrow$
      $10\,Cl^- + 2\,IO_3^- + 12\,H^+$
   d. $3\,MnO_4^- + 5\,W^{3+} + 8\,H_2O \rightarrow$
      $3\,Mn^{2+} + 5\,WO_4^{2-} + 16\,H^+$

e. $CrO_4^{2-} + 8\,H^+ + 3\,Fe^{2+} \rightarrow$
   $Cr^{3+} + 4\,H_2O + 3\,Fe^{3+}$
f. $VO_3^- + 4\,H^+ + Fe^{2+} \rightarrow$
   $VO^{2+} + Fe^{3+} + 2\,H_2O$
g. $Cr_2O_7^{2-} + 8\,H^+ + 3\,H_2S \rightarrow$
   $2\,Cr^{3+} + 3\,S + 7\,H_2O$
h. $S_2O_3^{2-} + 6\,H^+ + 2\,I^- \rightarrow$
   $2\,S^{2-} + I_2 + 3\,H_2O$
i. $3\,As_2O_3 + 7\,H_2O + 4\,NO_3^- \rightarrow$
   $6\,AsO_4^{3-} + 14\,H^+ + 4\,NO$
j. $2\,NO_3^- + 8\,H^+ + 6\,I^- \rightarrow$
   $2\,NO + 4\,H_2O + 3\,I_2$
k. $CrO_4^{2-} + 4\,H_2O + 3\,Fe(OH)_2 \rightarrow$
   $Cr(OH)_3 + 2\,OH^- + 3\,Fe(OH)_3$
l. $S_3O_6^{2-} + 3\,H_2O + Cl_2 \rightarrow$
   $3\,H_2SO_3 + 2\,Cl^-$
m. $3\,Sn(OH)_4^{2-} + ClO_3^- + 3\,H_2O \rightarrow$
   $3\,Sn(OH)_6^{2-} + Cl^-$
n. $Cu_2SnS_2 + 10\,S_2O_8^{2-} + 26\,OH^- \rightarrow$
   $2\,Cu(OH)_2 + Sn(OH)_6^{2-} + 22\,SO_4^{2-} +$
   $8\,H_2O$
o. $3\,H_2COH + 5\,MnO_4^- \rightarrow$
   $3\,CO_2 + 2\,H_2O + 5\,MnO_2 + 5\,OH^-$
p. $3\,C_2O_4^{2-} + 2\,MnO_4^- + 4\,H_2O \rightarrow$
   $6\,CO_2 + 2\,MnO_2 + 4\,OH^-$
q. $8\,Al + 5\,OH^- + 3\,NO_3^- + 2\,H_2O \rightarrow$
   $8\,AlO_2^- + 3\,NH_3$
r. $2\,Al + 2\,OH^- + 2\,H_2O \rightarrow$
   $2\,AlO_2^- + 3\,H_2$
s. $2\,ClO_2 + 2\,OH^- \rightarrow$
   $ClO_2^- + ClO_3^- + H_2O$
t. $2\,NH_3 + 2\,OCl^- \rightarrow$
   $N_2H_4 + 2\,Cl^- + 2\,OH^-$
9. a. $+1.54$, to the right
   b. -1.61, to the left
   c. $+0.73$, to the right
   d. -1.88, to the left
   e. -2.87, to the left
   f. $+0.44$, to the right
   g. $+0.04$, to the right
   h. -0.77, to the left
   i. $+0.46$, to the right
10. a. $2+$ b. Fe^{2+} will be oxidized to Fe^{3+}
16. a. 720 C   b. 7.46×10^{-3} Faradays
    c. 3.73×10^{-3} mol I_2; 0.947 g I_2
17. 4.7 g Ag
18. a. 3.15 g Ca
    b. 5.58 g Cl_2; 0.0787 mol Cl_2
    c. 1.97 L
19. 0.94 L
20. 1.03 h
21. 11 min
22. 0.34 A

Index

Atomic Numbers and Atomic Weights of the Elements

ELEMENT	SYMBOL	ATOMIC NUMBER	ATOMIC WEIGHT
Aluminum	Al	13	26.98154
Antimony	Sb	51	121.75
Argon	Ar	18	39.948
Arsenic	As	33	74.9216
Barium	Ba	56	137.34
Beryllium	Be	4	9.01218
Bismuth	Bi	83	208.9808
Boron	B	5	10.81
Bromine	Br	35	79.904
Cadmium	Cd	48	112.40
Calcium	Ca	20	40.08
Carbon	C	6	12.011
Cerium	Ce	58	140.12
Cesium	Cs	55	132.9054
Chlorine	Cl	17	35.453
Chromium	Cr	24	51.996
Cobalt	Co	27	58.9332
Copper	Cu	29	63.546
Dysprosium	Dy	66	162.50
Erbium	Er	68	167.26
Europium	Eu	63	151.96
Fluorine	F	9	18.99840
Gadolinium	Gd	64	157.25
Gallium	Ga	31	69.72
Germanium	Ge	32	72.59
Gold	Au	79	196.9665
Hafnium	Hf	72	178.49
Helium	He	2	4.00260
Holmium	Ho	67	164.9304
Hydrogen	H	1	1.0079
Indium	In	49	114.82
Iodine	I	53	126.9045
Iridium	Ir	77	192.22
Iron	Fe	26	55.847
Krypton	Kr	36	83.80
Lanthanum	La	57	138.9055
Lead	Pb	82	207.2
Lithium	Li	3	6.941
Lutetium	Lu	71	174.97
Magnesium	Mg	12	24.305
Manganese	Mn	25	54.9380
Mercury	Hg	80	200.59
Molybdenum	Mo	42	95.94
Neodymium	Nd	60	144.24